D1496466

Direct-current Machinery

McGraw-Hill Electrical and Electronic Engineering Series

FREDERICK EMMONS TERMAN, *Consulting Editor*

W. W. HARMAN and J. G. TRUXAL, *Associate Consulting Editors*

Bailey and Gault · ALTERNATING-CURRENT MACHINERY
Beranek · ACOUSTICS
Bruns and Saunders · ANALYSIS OF FEEDBACK CONTROL SYSTEMS
Cage · THEORY AND APPLICATION OF INDUSTRIAL ELECTRONICS
Cauer · SYNTHESIS OF LINEAR COMMUNICATION NETWORKS, VOLS. I AND II
Cuccia · HARMONICS, SIDEBANDS, AND TRANSIENTS IN COMMUNICATION
    ENGINEERING
Cunningham · INTRODUCTION TO NONLINEAR ANALYSIS
Eastman · FUNDAMENTALS OF VACUUM TUBES
Evans · CONTROL-SYSTEM DYNAMICS
Feinstein · FOUNDATIONS OF INFORMATION THEORY
Fitzgerald and Higginbotham · BASIC ELECTRICAL ENGINEERING
Fitzgerald and Kingsley · ELECTRIC MACHINERY
Geppert · BASIC ELECTRON TUBES
Glasford · FUNDAMENTALS OF TELEVISION ENGINEERING
Happell and Hesselberth · ENGINEERING ELECTRONICS
Harman · FUNDAMENTALS OF ELECTRONIC MOTION
Harrington · INTRODUCTION TO ELECTROMAGNETIC ENGINEERING
Hayt · ENGINEERING ELECTROMAGNETICS
Hessler and Carey · FUNDAMENTALS OF ELECTRICAL ENGINEERING
Hill · ELECTRONICS IN ENGINEERING
Johnson · TRANSMISSION LINES AND NETWORKS
Kraus · ANTENNAS
Kraus · ELECTROMAGNETICS
LePage · ANALYSIS OF ALTERNATING-CURRENT CIRCUITS
LePage and Seely · GENERAL NETWORK ANALYSIS
Millman and Seely · ELECTRONICS
Millman and Taub · PULSE AND DIGITAL CIRCUITS
Rodgers · INTRODUCTION TO ELECTRIC FIELDS
Rüdenberg · TRANSIENT PERFORMANCE OF ELECTRIC POWER SYSTEMS
Ryder · ENGINEERING ELECTRONICS
Seely · ELECTRON-TUBE CIRCUITS
Seely · ELECTRONIC ENGINEERING
Seely · INTRODUCTION TO ELECTROMAGNETIC FIELDS
Seely · RADIO ELECTRONICS
Siskind · DIRECT-CURRENT MACHINERY
Skilling · ELECTRIC TRANSMISSION LINES
Skilling · TRANSIENT ELECTRIC CURRENTS
Spangenberg · FUNDAMENTALS OF ELECTRON DEVICES
Spangenberg · VACUUM TUBES
Stevenson · ELEMENTS OF POWER SYSTEM ANALYSIS
Storer · PASSIVE NETWORK SYNTHESIS
Terman · ELECTRONIC AND RADIO ENGINEERING
Terman and Pettit · ELECTRONIC MEASUREMENTS
Thaler · ELEMENTS OF SERVOMECHANISM THEORY
Thaler and Brown · SERVOMECHANISM ANALYSIS
Thompson · ALTERNATING-CURRENT AND TRANSIENT CIRCUIT ANALYSIS
Truxal · AUTOMATIC FEEDBACK CONTROL SYSTEM SYNTHESIS

DIRECT-CURRENT MACHINERY

Charles S. Siskind, M.S.E.E.

Associate Professor of Electrical Engineering
Purdue University

New York   Toronto   London

McGRAW-HILL BOOK COMPANY, INC.

1952

DIRECT-CURRENT MACHINERY

Library of Congress Catalog Card Number: 52–6002

10 11 12 13 14 – MP – 9 8 7 6
57740

PREFACE

This book, intended for use in the curriculum for electrical-engineering students, is concerned with the principles and practices of *present-day* direct-current generators and motors and their auxiliary equipment. Dealing as it does with a rather complex electromagnetic machine, it represents a coordinated design and construction of properly arranged electric and magnetic circuits; in the carefully planned text, theoretical discussions and numerous practical illustrative examples stress the close interrelation between such electric and magnetic circuits.

The material and its treatment represent the author's experience with direct-current machines, extending over many years, in industry and teaching. The subject is approached from completely general aspects, a real attempt having been made to avoid confusion by simplifying complicated wiring diagrams (note particularly the clarity of all electric and magnetic circuits) and neglecting obsolete arrangements as well as refinements and details of design. Moreover, the great range of topics follow one another in logical sequence, and without gaps, while especially important subjects receive the emphasis of reworded repetition supplemented by the solution of appropriate problems. Simplified graphical constructions have been employed, not only to generalize the operating characteristics of the many types of dynamo, but to show that they yield reasonably good quantitative results; such graphs are frequently used to compare the behavior of different machines, or those whose electric and magnetic circuits are altered or rearranged.

The armature winding, the heart of the direct-current generator and motor, is discussed in an original way (Chap. 2) and, by the use of many easily studied, dissected, and complete diagrams (Figs. 19 to 31), is shown to represent a perfectly symmetrical arrangement of simple coils. A thorough understanding of *modern* winding practice is soon found to be extremely helpful in succeeding discussions of armature reaction, armature reactance, commutation, corrective field windings (interpoles and compensating windings), and the operating performance of these machines. It also aids the student in his study of the important aspects of modern control methods and the rating and applications of electrical machines. A chapter dealing with special machines, circuits, and applications reemphasizes the importance of fundamentals.

Special attention has been given to the many examples that are solved to illustrate discussions and derived equations and to the problems at the

v

end of each chapter. These were carefully selected, for the most part, from actual machine practice; they should, therefore, aid the student to develop a reasonably good sense of judgment with regard to physical dimensions, operating characteristics, and the applications of *up-to-date* direct-current machines. Tables 2 and 3 in Chapter 11 are particularly valuable in this connection because they embody important specifications and design data of several manufacturers of modern types of generators and motors; instructors will find the tables extremely helpful when making up additional problems for home study or tests. A thorough understanding of the book's subject matter will be excellent preparation for advanced study.

The author gratefully acknowledges the courtesies of the various manufacturers who made available the many fine photographs, illustrations, and engineering data used in the preparation of the manuscript.

CHARLES S. SISKIND

WEST LAFAYETTE, IND.
April, 1952

CONTENTS

CHAPTER 1

THE DYNAMO—PRINCIPLES AND CONSTRUCTION

The Dynamo

A *dynamo* is a rotating electrical machine in which an energy transformation takes place. There are two general types of dynamo, namely, the electric *generator* and the electric *motor*. In the generator mechanical energy is converted to electric energy, while in the motor electric energy is converted to mechanical energy. Since generators and motors are fundamentally similar in construction—and this is particularly true of d-c machines—they differ only in the way they are used. When the dynamo is employed as a generator, a prime mover rotates a cylindrical structure that is mounted in a set of bearings; generator action then takes place because there is relative motion between an *existing magnetic field* and conducting wires. A dynamo operates as a motor when it develops torque, *i.e.*, a tendency to produce rotation, if an electric current is passed through conducting wires that occupy proper positions in an *existing magnetic field*. Note especially that the first requirement for both generator action and motor action is the existence of magnets and their accompanying magnetic fields.

The fundamental principles governing generator action and motor action were originally discovered by Michael Faraday in 1831. Applying equally well to the operation of transformers, induction machines, and electromagnetic devices, these initial far-reaching discoveries may properly be regarded as the very beginnings of the great electrical developments that followed, and which have resulted in the tremendous growth of generation and distribution systems and the widespread use of electric energy in industry, office, home, and farm. Briefly summarized, these basic principles may be stated as follows:

1. *Generator action*, involving the development of voltage, may result (a) by moving a conductor in such a manner that it *cuts across* magnetic lines of force, (b) by moving magnetic lines of force in such a manner that they *cut across* a conductor, and (c) by *changing* the number of lines of force that link with a wire or coil of wire.

2. *Motor action*, involving the development of force, results when a current-bearing conductor is placed in a magnetic field so that it is not parallel to the direction of the lines of force.

1

Generator Action

Since an electric generator involves the conversion of mechanical energy into electric energy, it follows that mechanical motion must be imparted to one part of a machine that is made to move with respect to another. In the d-c generator it is the practice to place a large number of properly connected copper wires on a cylindrical laminated steel core and mechanically rotate the structure inside a set of carefully shaped electromagnets

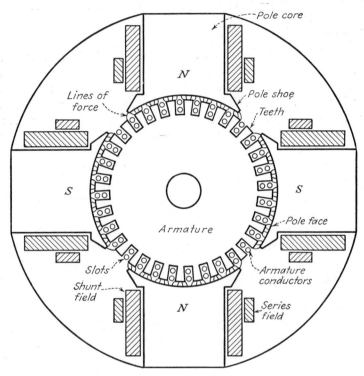

Fig. 1. Sketch illustrating the general arrangement of the field and armature of a d-c generator.

or permanent magnets; the rotating part is called the *armature*, while the stationary set of magnet poles is called the *field*. Since a major portion of the magnetic lines of force leaves the inner pole-face surfaces, crosses the air gap, and passes into the armature core, it should be clear that *the moving copper conductors cut the lines of force* as they are rotated mechanically. This flux-cutting action on the part of the copper conductors results in *generated voltages* in the latter; the entire phenomenon is called *generator action*.

Figure 1 illustrates the general arrangement of the field and armature of a d-c machine and indicates how flux cutting is accomplished. Note particularly that the lines of force enter the armature core almost radially, so that the copper conductors, placed in slots parallel to the shaft, cut perpendicularly through the field as they are rotated; this latter point is important because, for a given speed of rotation, maximum voltage is generated under this condition.

Motor Action

Torque is developed in a motor if the copper conductors that occupy axial positions on the armature core are made to carry electric currents while under the influence of the radial magnetic fields. Obviously, the

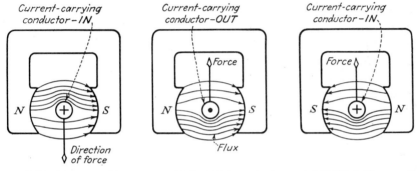

(a)-Field to **right**-current **in**   (b)-Field to **right**-current **out**   (c)-Field to **left**-current **in**

Fig. 2. Sketches showing how force action is produced upon a current-carrying conductor placed in a magnetic field.

forces exerted on the individual wires must be in the same general direction to produce rotation; this is made possible by interconnecting the conductors in such a manner that those occupying positions under *north* poles carry currents in one direction while those occupying positions under *south* poles carry currents in the opposite direction. Of course, the current directions in the individual wires change rapidly as they move successively from pole to pole, but this is readily and effectively accomplished by a commutating mechanism that changes the externally applied direct current to the internal (in the wires) alternating current.

The significant point concerning force action in an electric motor is this: if a wire occupies a position in a *nonuniform* magnetic field so that the flux density on one side of the conductor is less than that on the other side, a force will be experienced by the conductor tending to move it away from the more dense to the less dense field. Moreover, it is immaterial how the nonuniform field is created, although in the actual motor this is accomplished by the interaction of two magnetic fields, one created by a set of stationary magnet poles (the field) and the other produced by currents passing through the very wires that experience the forces. This implies, therefore, that the *magnitude* of the total force that tends to rotate the armature will be determined by the strength of the field and the value of the current in the armature conductors. Referring to Fig. 2, it will be noted that the *direction* of force exerted upon a current-carrying conductor depends upon (1) the magnetic polarity of the field poles and (2) the direction of the current in the conductor.

Arrangement of Generator and Motor Parts

For the purposes of description, electric generators and motors may be divided into two sections, namely, the stationary part and the rotating part; these are generally referred to as the *stator* and *rotor*. The most important function of the stator is to serve as the seat of the magnetic flux that must be made to enter the armature core. Except for permanent-magnet machines, used only in special constructions, the field generally consists of a cylindrical *yoke* or frame to which is bolted a set of electro-magnets. End bells with their *bearings* and *brush rigging* become part of the stator when the machine is assembled. The yoke may have a base with feet or a supporting bracket upon which the entire structure rests. The rotor, which is the real source of the electric (generator) power or the mechanical (motor) power, is built up of a laminated (good magnetic quality) steel core, slotted to receive the insulated armature winding. A shaft through the core center supports the armature winding as well as a commutator, the latter being so located that carbon brushes in the stationary brush rigging, previously referred to, line up and rest on it. Spring tension is applied to the brushes whose rounded contact surfaces make uniform and firm contact with the commutator.

Fig. 3. Laminated main-field pole core. (*General Electric Co.*)

Pole Cores

The earlier machines had solid-steel field-pole cores, but this is no longer true. Modern practice is to construct them of laminations, about 0.045 in. thick per lamination, having good magnetic permeability; each stack of laminations usually has an axial length slightly less than the armature core and is fastened together with several rivets driven through holes in the sheets. The shape of the pole core is extremely important and must be designed to have a smaller cross section around which the copper field winding or windings are placed and a spread-out portion called the *pole shoe* that permits the magnetic flux to spread out over a wide area where the flux enters the air gap and armature core. The upper projecting face of the shoe also provides a ledge upon which the field winding can have mechanical support. This construction has several desirable features among which are (1) reduced cross section where the field coils fit over the core so that a minimum of copper wire may be used, (2) increased area of the pole shoe that is exposed to the armature core so that the reluctance of the air gap is reduced to a minimum and the flux may be spread out over a greater portion of the circumference, and (3) the complete pole core

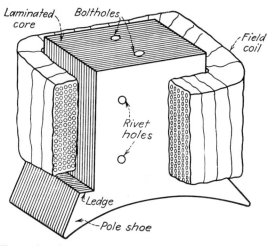

Fig. 4. Sketch illustrating the arrangement of pole core and field coil in a d-c machine.

and its winding or windings may be assembled before it is bolted to the yoke. Figure 3 is a photograph of a bolted stack of laminations and clearly shows the smaller area around which the field winding is placed, the spread-out pole shoe, the ledge that supports the field coil or coils, and the threaded boltholes where the entire assembly is fastened to the yoke. A sketch illustrating how the field winding fits around the core is shown in Fig. 4.

Shunt and Series Windings

Each of the main pole cores may have one of three types of field-winding construction depending upon whether the machine is to be operated as a shunt, series, or compound dynamo. A shunt winding has a comparatively large number of turns of fine wire; its resistance is, therefore, high enough so that it may be connected directly across (*in shunt with*) the full armature voltage or to a separate source of emf of about the same order of magnitude. A series winding has relatively few turns of heavy wire and is connected in such a way that high values of current usually pass through it; its resistance is extremely low so that, even when carrying normal load current, its voltage drop will be small. A compound winding is a combination of shunt and series field.

Figure 5 shows how one shunt-field pole assembly appears before it is bolted to its yoke. Its design and construction involves a careful choice of insulating materials which must have a nominal temperature rise under normal operating conditions. Usually all the field coils (an even number of them) of the machine are joined together in series and, in the final assembly, are connected in series with a control rheostat to the plus and

FIG. 5. Complete core and shunt-field coil assembly. (*Westinghouse Electric Corp.*)

minus brush terminals. It is interesting to note, moreover, that the required number of ampere-turns NI for each field coil, to create the proper air-gap flux density, depends upon the size of wire used, while the temperature rise in the coil is primarily a function of the number of turns of wire. This may be shown as follows:

$$\frac{E_c}{I_f} = R_c = \frac{\rho \times l_c}{\text{CM}} = \frac{\rho \times (N_c \times \text{MLT})}{\text{CM}} \qquad \text{ohms}$$

from which

$$\text{CM} = \frac{\rho \times (N_c I_f) \times \text{MLT}}{E_c} \qquad (1)$$

where E_c = volts per field coil

      I_f = shunt field current

     R_c = resistance per field coil

      ρ = resistivity of the copper

      l_c = length of wire in each coil

   CM = cir-mil area of the wire

     N_c = number of turns per coil

  MLT = mean length of each turn

   $N_c I_f$ = amp-turns per coil

Referring to Eq. (1), it will be seen that any change in the number of turns of *a given size of wire* produces a corresponding change in the resistance and an inverse change in the current; thus the ampere-turns remain essentially unchanged for any number of turns. Furthermore, since the coil heating depends upon $I_f^2 R_c$, the temperature rise will increase as the number of turns is reduced; this follows from the fact that I_f and R_c change by equal percentages in opposite directions as N_c is changed.

EXAMPLE 1. Each shunt-field pole of a 250-volt 6-pole shunt generator requires 4,550 amp-turns per pole. (*a*) If the mean length of each turn (MLT) is 12.1 in., calculate the size of wire in the winding. (*b*) If the field current I_f is to be limited to 1.1 amp, calculate the number of turns in each coil N_c. (Assume $\rho = 11.6$ ohms per mil-ft.)

Solution

(*a*) $\mathrm{CM} = \dfrac{11.6 \times 4,550 \times 12.1/12}{(250/6)} = 1,275$ Use No. 19 wire—1,288 CM

(*b*) $N_c = \dfrac{N_c I_f}{I_f} = \dfrac{4,550}{1.1} = 4,130$ turns

$R_f = \dfrac{11.6 \times (4,130 \times 6 \times 12.1/12)}{1,288} = 227$ ohms

and

$I_f = \dfrac{250}{227} = 1.1$ amp (the correct current)

EXAMPLE 2. If each of the field coils of Example 1 is wound with 3,500 turns, calculate the number of ampere-turns $N_f I_f$ and the field current I_f. Assume ρ and MLT to remain unchanged.

Solution

$$R_f = \frac{11.6 \times (3,500 \times 6 \times 12.1/12)}{1,288} = 192 \text{ ohms}$$

$$I_f = \frac{250}{192} = 1.3 \text{ amp}$$

$$N_c I_f = 3,500 \times 1.3 = 4,550$$

Note in the foregoing example that a decrease in the number of turns has no effect upon the ampere-turns per pole but that the permissible current is exceeded. An increase in the number of turns would likewise produce no change in ampere-turns although the current and heating would be reduced.

There are three important reasons why each coil of the *series field*, whether used in a series or compound machine, must be wound with few

FIG. 6. Three steps in the manufacture of a field coil containing shunt and series windings. (*General Electric Co.*)

turns of heavy wire. These are: (1) the current in this winding is generally quite high, often 15 or more times as much as the shunt-field current, so that the wire size must be selected on this basis; (2) with the high values of series-field current, a comparatively few number of turns are needed to supply the required ampere-turns; and (3) the resistance of this field must be kept as low as possible so that it will incur a minimum voltage drop. In practice it is often desirable to use heavy strap copper of rectangular cross section and to separate the individual turns by air spaces; this construction provides rigidity and permits the coil to remain cool as the air passes through the ducts. In compound machines the series-field coil is generally wound directly over the shunt coil, exposing as much surface area as possible; often a single layer of turns is all that is necessary. Figure 6 depicts three steps in the manufacture of one of the sets of field coils for a small compound generator or motor. The photograph at the left shows the fine-wire shunt coil, while the one at the right indicates how the shunt coil is taped and surrounded by a few turns of very heavy wire representing the series coil. After the field coils are properly wound, they are dipped in an insulating varnish and baked in an oven; this operation adds stiffness, mechanical strength, and good insulating properties to the

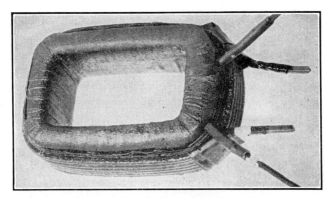

Fig. 7. Main field coil for a d-c motor showing shunt and series windings. (*General Electric Co.*)

winding. Figure 7 shows a complete field assembly, after the dipping and baking operations, ready to be placed over its pole core.

EXAMPLE 3. Each of the series-field coils of a compound motor has 15 turns of No. 4 B & S gage copper wire and carries 36 amp under normal operating conditions. If the resistance of the entire winding is 0.022 ohm, calculate (*a*) the number of ampere-turns per series-field coil; (*b*) the total series-field voltage drop.

Solution

(*a*) $$N_c I_f = 15 \times 36 = 540 \text{ amp-turns}$$

(*b*) $$E_f = 36 \times 0.022 = 0.792 \text{ volt}$$

Interpole Windings

One of the most important developments in the design of d-c machines has been the *interpole*, often called *commutating pole*. When properly employed it provides a component of magnetic flux to the armature in an extremely limited area between the main-field poles so that sparking at the brushes is virtually eliminated under normal, and sometimes abnormal, operating conditions. It is built up of a narrow core of laminations surrounding which is a coil of few turns of heavy wire. Like the series-field this winding is energized by a rather high current, but the flux created by the pole is injected into the armature in a zone where the detrimental effects of the armature-winding currents may be counteracted and pacified.

As will be discussed in some detail later, the currents that flow in the armature winding create mmfs whose magnetic fluxes tend to react adversely with the main-field fluxes to cause objectionable arcing at the brushes. In large machines there are usually as many interpoles as main poles, but in those of the smaller sizes their number is generally one-half the number of main poles. A photograph of a completely assembled com-

FIG. 8. Completely assembled commutating pole.   (*General Electric Co.*)

mutating pole is shown in Fig. 8. Note the long (axially) narrow core, with the tapped hole for bolting to the yoke, and the rather heavy copper winding.

Compensating Windings

In generators and motors of comparatively large sizes, *i.e.*, those in which the values of the armature current are extremely high, the armature mmfs tend to distort the flux-density distributions under the pole faces to such an extent that flashover between brushes is likely to occur. The serious consequences of flashovers, which are, in effect, short circuits, may be completely eliminated by the use of *compensating windings*. These windings are placed in slots or holes in the pole faces and carry, as do the series and interpole windings, very high values of current. Their primary purpose is to counteract the effect of the armature mmf in zones that are outside the influence of the interpoles and, when properly designed, maintain uniform flux-density distributions under the pole faces for all loading and overloading conditions. Compensating windings are expensive to install and generally restrict the free passage of air for cooling purposes. Fortunately, they are not needed for the smaller machines and are, therefore, found only on those of extremely high current ratings. Figure 9 is a photograph of a complete yoke and field assembly for a 3,000-kw 600-volt

360-rpm compound generator in which the pole-face compensating winding is clearly visible; also seen are the series and interpole fields, although the shunt field is obscured by the heavier windings.

FIG. 9. Completely assembled field of a 3,000-kw 600-volt generator, containing shunt, series, interpole, and compensating windings. (*Allis-Chalmers Mfg. Co.*)

Summary of Field Windings

From the foregoing discussions it should be clear that a generator or motor may have as many as four field windings depending upon the type and size of machine and the kind of service the latter is to have. These consist of two *normal exciting fields,* namely, shunt and series, and two *fields that act in a corrective capacity* to combat the detrimental effects of armature reaction, *i.e.,* the commutating and compensating windings. The type of machine, whether shunt, series, or compound, is, however, independent of whether the interpole or compensating field is employed but is determined solely by the kinds and number of normal fields. To emphasize further the relation of the several fields and to show how they are arranged with respect to one another, Fig. 10 has been drawn. No attempt is made here to indicate how and by what electrical circuits they are energized, but this will be fully and appropriately discussed later.

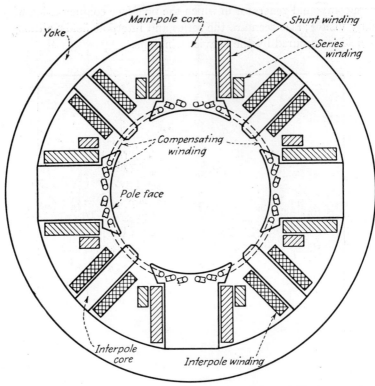

Fig. 10. Sketch illustrating the arrangement of the various fields in a modern d-c machine.

Commutators

The *commutator* is an ingenious device, performing as it does an extremely important function in the d-c machine; in its modern construction it is sturdy and efficient and, when properly installed and serviced, does a remarkably trouble-free job of rectification. Together with the stationary brushes that ride over its rotating surface, it is assigned the duty of changing an internally generated alternating current to an external direct current in the generator and of changing an externally applied direct current to an internal alternating current in the motor. The commutator is a built-up group of hard-drawn copper segments, wedge-shaped in section when viewed on end, and having V-shaped grooves at each end. An exploded view of a typical commutator for a small d-c motor is shown in Fig. 11. The upper row of parts illustrates the outer steel V rings and the inner molded-mica V rings that insulate the copper bars from the shaft. Also seen are a copper and mica segment, the steel cylinder over which the commutator is assembled, the threaded-steel tightening and locking nut,

Fig. 11. Exploded view of a typical commutator.   (*General Electric Co.*)

and the complete assembly. Figure 12 is a photograph depicting a partially completed commutator. This clearly indicates exactly how the mica V rings fit snugly into the V-shaped grooves of the commutator segments to insulate the latter from the shaft, how the mica insulators separate the individual segments from each other, and how the threaded-steel ring tightens the various components together. In the actual d-c armature, a commutator like that shown in Fig. 11 is forced and press-fitted on the shaft to a proper distance from the laminated steel core and to which are connected the many coil ends of the armature winding.

Fig. 12. Partly assembled commutator. (*General Electric Co.*)

Brush Riggings

The brush rigging is a component part of the commutation mechanism and consists of a set of brush holders (usually as many as main poles) that are properly fastened together and bolted to a yoke of strong insulating material. Each brush holder is fitted with a carbon brush of suitable hardness and grade and a stiff spring that presses the former tightly at about 1 to 2 pounds per square inch (psi) against the commutator surface. Figure 13 shows a standard brush rigging for a small 4-pole motor or generator before it is properly fastened to the yoke frame. The brushes must fit snugly in the holders, yet must not bind, must line up carefully with the commutator, and, where contact is made with the commutator, must be accurately curved to fit the cylindrical surface. In large machines

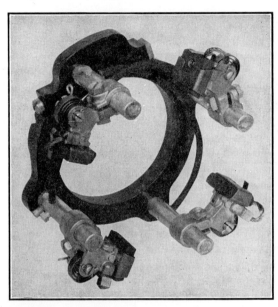

Fig. 13. Brush rigging for a four-pole motor or generator. (*General Electric Co.*)

a brush arm may have several brush holders, into each of which is placed a carbon or copper-graphite brush so that the latter rides freely, without chattering, on the commutator. When more than two brush arms are used, in multipolar machines, alternate sets are electrically connected together because they are at the same potential; thus one of the junctions becomes a positive armature terminal, while the other junction becomes the negative armature terminal. (In a generator, the positive terminal is the one *from which* current is assumed to flow to the load, while in the motor, it is the one *into which* the d-c source is "fed," since it is connected to the positive bus.)

Armature Cores

Like the field core, the *armature* core is a stack of steel laminations, about 0.025 in. thick per lamination, of good permeability, but of circular shape. The outer edge has a uniformly spaced, carefully designed set of slots that hold the armature winding (discussed in Chap. 2); the number of slots are properly chosen in conjunction with the number of commutator segments, on the basis of good design practice. In the case of small-diameter armatures, circular holes are punched in the center of the laminations for the shaft. On large machines it is customary to employ a *spider*, consisting of a hub and projecting arms, so that the annular laminations may be rigidly fastened to the shaft; this construction permits the

FIG. 14. Unwound armature, showing slotted core and commutator. (*General Electric Co.*)

free flow of air between the radial arms to keep the armature ventilated and cooled. Figure 14 illustrates an armature assembly before the winding is installed and shows the laminated core and commutator.

PROBLEMS

1. Calculate the flux density in the air gap of a generator if the air-gap flux per pole is 3.3×10^6 maxwells and the pole face area is 7 by 8 in.

2. The total resistance of the shunt field of a 230-volt motor is 82 ohms, and each pole has 1,450 turns. Determine the number of ampere-turns in each coil.

3. The air-gap flux density in a certain generator is 52,000 lines per sq in. where the pole-face area is 8.25 by 6.5 in. Calculate the flux density in the core body, around which the winding is fitted, if its area is 6.25 by 6.25 in.

4. The series-field ampere-turns per pole of a compound motor operating at full load is 630. If the current passing through the winding under this condition is 78.8 amp, how many turns are there on each pole?

5. The axial length of the pole core of a generator is 14.5 in. If each lamination is 0.045 in. thick and air spaces in the stack make up 8 per cent of the length, calculate the number of laminations in a pole core.

6. A 40-kw generator has an armature-core length of 7 in. with three ⅜-in. ventilating ducts. Assuming that the net iron is 92 per cent of the stacked iron and that the laminations are 0.025 in. thick, determine the number of laminations in the core.

7. What is the cross-sectional area, in square inches, of the series-field copper if it carries 240 amp and the current density in the wire is 1,050 amp per sq in.?

8. Each of the shunt-field coils of a 600-volt 6-pole generator produces 8,360 amp-turns. If the mean length of each turn (MLT) is 32 in., calculate the wire size used. (Assume $\rho = 11.6$.)

9. If the field of Prob. 8 takes 2.5 amp under normal operation, determine the number of turns N_c on each coil.

10. Using the equation $R = \rho \times l/\text{CM}$, calculate the total shunt-field resistance for Probs. 8 and 9.

11. An 8-pole motor has 8 brush arms each of which has ten 1- by 1.25-in. cross-sectional-area carbon brushes. If the total armature current is 2,000 amp, calculate (a) the current per brush arm; (b) the current per brush; (c) the current density in the brushes in amperes per square inch.

12. The field core of a 4-pole d-c motor has an internal diameter of 12 in. and an axial length of 7 in. The pole-face arcs comprise 62 per cent of the circumference. If the air-gap flux per pole is 2.25×10^6 maxwells, calculate the flux density under each pole face.

CHAPTER 2

ARMATURE WINDINGS

Function of the Armature Winding

The armature winding is the heart of the d-c machine; it is where the electric power originates in the generator and where the torque is developed in the motor. Current passes to and from the armature winding across brush contacts—moving contacts; it is here, therefore, that serious arcing may occur to give rise to faulty machine operation. Unlike the shunt-field winding where the direct current is of the order of 2 to 10 per cent of the rated name-plate value, the armature-winding current is comparatively high and always *alternating current*. Moreover, since the armature generally rotates at comparatively high speed, it must be carefully balanced so that smooth, vibrationless operation may result.

Types of Armature Winding

The two types of armature winding used on modern d-c machines are designated *lap* and *wave*. They may be distinguished from each other in two general ways: (1) from the standpoint of construction they differ only by the manner in which the coil ends are connected to the commutator bars; (2) from the standpoint of an electrical circuit they differ in the number of parallel paths between positive and negative brushes. The simplest armature windings are called *simplex, i.e., simplex-lap* and *simplex-wave;* they are, by far, the most widely used winding arrangements in present-day practice. Other modifications of the lap and wave types are called *multiplex, i.e., multiplex-lap* and *multiplex-wave;* these windings differ from those of simplex construction by having more parallel paths between plus and minus brushes.

Simplex-lap windings have as many parallel paths as main poles; simplex-wave windings have two parallel paths regardless of the number of poles. Thus, if the total armature current of a 4-pole machine is 300 amp, each path of a simplex-lap winding will carry 75 amp, while 150 amp will pass through each path of a simplex-wave winding.

The degree of multiplicity of a multiplex winding indicates the relative number of parallel paths with respect to the number in a simplex winding. Thus, a 6-pole *duplex-lap* winding has 12 parallel paths, while an 8-pole *triplex-wave* winding has 6 parallel paths. Hence, designating the multiplicity of a winding by the term *plex*, (1) the number of parallel paths in a lap winding is $P \times$ plex, and (2) the number of parallel paths in a wave winding is $2 \times$ plex, where P is the number of main poles in the machine.

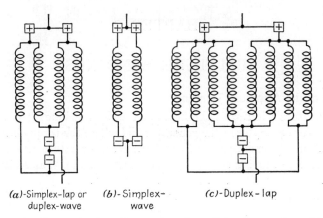

(a)-Simplex-lap or   (b)-Simplex-   (c)-Duplex-lap
    duplex-wave   wave

FIG. 15. Sketches illustrating how the number of parallel paths are formed in *four-pole* armature windings.

Figure 15 illustrates the parallel-path arrangements of 4-pole simplex, duplex, lap, and wave windings.

Coil Constructions

The individual coils of all d-c armature windings are so designed that, when placed in the core slots, they build up two layers of coil sides, one on top of the other; for this reason they are often referred to as *double-layer* windings. The practice is to employ diamond-shaped coils made in

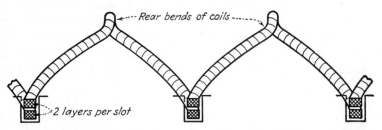

FIG. 16. Sketch illustrating how coils are formed for two-layer windings.

special forming machines. The rear and front bends are constructed so that one coil side is on a circumferentially higher level than the other; this is done in order that the higher side may be placed in the top of a slot and the lower side in the bottom of a slot. Figure 16 indicates the manner in which two such coils are fitted into slots to provide the double-layer arrangement. Note that the left coil side is in the top of the slot and

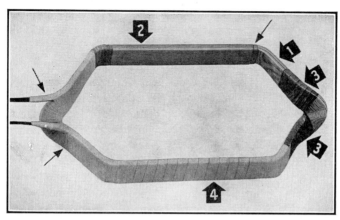

Fig. 17. Lap coil showing details of construction: (1) rectangular insulated conductors; (2) insulating cell; (3) treated cloth; (4) final layer of linen tape. (*Westinghouse Electric Corp.*)

the right coil side is in the bottom of the slot, although it should be stated that the alternate placing of coil sides is equally good.

Coils for lap or wave windings are identically formed. The only difference between them, however, is the manner in which the coil ends are brought out. In lap coils the ends usually emerge midway between the sides so that connections can be readily made to commutator segments that are close together; in wave coils the ends are brought out at the sides so that they may easily be bent outward for connection to commutator bars about 360 electrical degrees apart. Recognizing this simple construction difference, it should, therefore, be clear that (1) a lap winding is one in which the coil ends are connected to commutator segments that are near one another—adjacent in simplex-lap windings, and (2) a wave winding is one in which the coil ends are connected to commutator segments that are some distance from one another—nearly 360 electrical degrees apart. Figure 17 shows a photograph of a lap coil in which the ends are seen to emerge at the middle of the bend. It also clearly depicts the general details of construction. A wave coil is represented by Fig. 18 which indicates how the coil ends

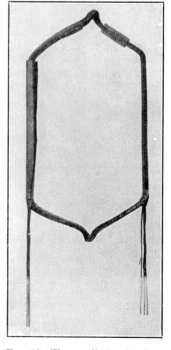

Fig. 18. Wave coil showing how the coil ends are brought out at the sides. (*General Electric Co.*)

are brought out from the coil sides, to be bent outwards for connection to distant segments.

Coil Pitch

The two important aspects of a coil for d-c armature windings are (1) its *coil pitch* and (2) its *commutator pitch*. Coil pitch refers to the distance between the two sides of the individual coils. Measured in terms of slots, *it is determined in exactly the same way for all windings*, whether lap or wave, simplex or multiplex, generator or motor. The fundamental rule that fixes the coil pitch in any given machine is: *the distance between the two sides of a coil must be equal (or very nearly so) to the distance between two adjacent poles.* This is readily understood in view of the following. (1) In a generator the voltage must be directed toward the rear in one coil side at the same instant that the voltage is directed toward the front in the other coil side, if the two voltages are to aid each other; this can only mean that, if one coil side is under the center of a *north* pole, the other coil side must be near the middle of an adjacent *south* pole, about 180 electrical degrees away. (2) In a motor the force exerted on one side of a coil that carries current toward the rear must be in exactly the same direction as the force exerted upon the other coil side that carries current toward the front; this can occur only when one coil side is under the center of a *north* pole at the same instant that the other coil side is near the center of a *south* pole, 180 electrical degrees away.

The foregoing statements may be simplified into an equation, thus:

$$Y_s = \frac{S}{P} - k \qquad (2)$$

where Y_s = coil pitch, slots
S = total number of armature slots
P = number of main poles
k = any part of S/P that is subtracted to make Y_s an integer

EXAMPLE 1. Calculate the coil pitches Y_s, and indicate the slot numbers for the first coil elements, for windings with the following slot and pole combinations: (*a*) $S = 54$, $P = 4$; (*b*) $S = 62$, $P = 4$; (*c*) $S = 66$, $P = 6$; (*d*) $S = 141$, $P = 6$; (*e*) $S = 132$, $P = 8$; (*f*) $S = 180$, $P = 10$.

Solution

(*a*) $Y_s = \dfrac{54}{4} - \dfrac{1}{2} = 13$ Slots 1 to 14

(*b*) $Y_s = \dfrac{62}{4} - \dfrac{1}{2} = 15$ Slots 1 to 16

(c) $\qquad Y_s = \dfrac{66}{6} - 0 = 11 \qquad$ Slots 1 to 12

(d) $\qquad Y_s = \dfrac{141}{6} - \dfrac{1}{2} = 23 \qquad$ Slots 1 to 24

(e) $\qquad Y_s = \dfrac{132}{8} - \dfrac{1}{2} = 16 \qquad$ Slots 1 to 17

(f) $\qquad Y_s = \dfrac{180}{10} - 0 = 18 \qquad$ Slots 1 to 19

Commutator Pitch

Commutator pitch refers to the distance on the commutator between the two ends of a coil element. Measured in terms of commutator segments, its value is determined in a different way for lap and wave windings.

1. *Commutator Pitch for Lap Windings.* Designating the commutator pitch by Y_c, its value is equal merely to the degree of multiplicity—the *plex*—of a lap winding. Thus, Y_c equals 1, 2, 3, 4, etc., for simplex-, duplex-, triplex-, quadruplex-, etc., lap windings, respectively. These numbers indicate that the coil ends are joined to segments 1 and 2, 1 and 3, 1 and 4, 1 and 5, etc., for values of Y_c that are equal to 1, 2, 3, 4, etc., respectively. Figure 19 illustrates the manner in which the first coil ele-

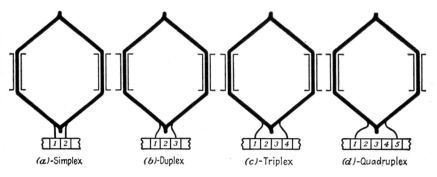

(a)-Simplex   (b)-Duplex   (c)-Triplex   (d)-Quadruplex

FIG. 19. Sketches illustrating how coil-element ends are connected to the commutator for simplex- and multiplex-lap windings.

ments are connected to commutator segments for simplex- and multiplex-lap windings. Since all the coils in a given armature winding are identically constructed, inserted in the core slots, and joined to the commutator, it should now be clear that the first coil element, once correctly established, becomes the pattern for the others.

2. Commutator Pitch for Wave Windings. As previously pointed out, the ends of each coil element of a wave winding are bent outward from the coil sides and are connected to commutator segments nearly 360 electrical degrees apart. The word *nearly* must be taken literally because it is impossible to have a wave winding with a commutator pitch that is exactly

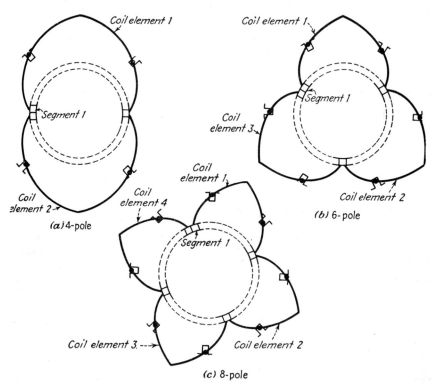

FIG. 20. Sketches illustrating $P/2$ coil elements in simplex-wave windings. Note in each case that start and arrival segments, after one round, are adjacent.

equivalent to 360 electrical degrees. To understand why the foregoing important requirement is essential, consider the following facts concerning simplex-wave windings: (*a*) starting at segment 1 the *complete* winding must be traced from segment to coil side to segment to coil side, etc., before closure occurs, *i.e.*, before the winding reenters; (*b*) if the ends of the coil elements are joined to segments that are exactly 360 electrical degrees apart, every set of $P/2$ coil elements would constitute a complete closure, *i.e.*, a *reentrancy*, because there are 360 electrical degrees in every circumferential span of $P/2$ poles; (*c*) under the condition of the previous statement, therefore, the number of reentrancies would be equal to *seg-*

ments/pairs of poles instead of *one; (d)* moreover, since all alternate sets of brushes are exactly 360 electrical degrees apart and are joined together, they would always short-circuit at least $P/2$ coil elements, depending upon the brush widths.

For a simplex-wave winding to have one degree of reentrancy, the number of commutator segments must be selected with relation to the number of pairs of poles so that the commutator pitch Y_c results in a value that is equivalent to a circumferential span slightly *more* or *less* than 360 electrical degrees. The value of Y_c must, in fact, be such that, after tracing the winding once around the commutator, the last coil-element end must arrive one segment behind or one segment ahead of the starting segment; under this condition, therefore, repeated tracings around the commutator cause the arrival segment to continue to drop back or fall forward one segment at a time *until the complete winding closes on the starting segment.* To illustrate how this is accomplished in the first round of coil elements, Fig. 20 has been drawn. Without attempting to show how the values of Y_c were determined, it should be noted that in each case the arrival segment, after one trip around the commutator, is always one removed from the starting segment.

From the foregoing analysis it is possible to make the following general statement: *a simplex-wave winding is NOT possible if segments* ÷ *P/2 is an integer.* However, *a simplex-wave winding IS possible if the following equation results in an integer:*

$$Y_c = \frac{C \pm 1}{P/2} \qquad (3)$$

where Y_c = commutator pitch
C = total number of commutator segments
P = number of poles

Equation (3) can be made entirely general for all wave windings having any multiplicity if the 1 in the numerator is replaced by m whose value is the *plex* of the winding, *e.g.*, 2 for duplex-wave, 3 for triplex-wave, 4 for quadruplex-wave, etc. Thus

$$Y_c = \frac{C \pm m}{P/2} \qquad (4)$$

EXAMPLE 2. Calculate the commutator pitches Y_c, and indicate the commutator-segment numbers for the first coil elements, for simplex-wave windings with the following segment and pole combinations: (*a*) $C = 69$, $P = 4$; (*b*) $C = 145$, $P = 4$; (*c*) $C = 227$, $P = 6$; (*d*) $C = 269$, $P = 8$; (*e*) $C = 326$, $P = 10$.

Solution

(a) $Y_c = \dfrac{69 \pm 1}{2} = 34 \text{ or } 35$ Segments 1 to 35 or 1 to 36

(b) $Y_c = \dfrac{145 \pm 1}{2} = 72 \text{ or } 73$ Segments 1 to 73 or 1 to 74

(c) $Y_c = \dfrac{227 + 1}{3} = 76$ Segments 1 to 77

(d) $Y_c = \dfrac{269 - 1}{4} = 67$ Segments 1 to 68

(e) $Y_c = \dfrac{326 - 1}{5} = 65$ Segments 1 to 66

EXAMPLE 3. Calculate the commutator pitches Y_c, and indicate the commutator-segment numbers for the first coil elements, for multiplex-wave windings with the following segment and pole combinations: (a) $C = 98$, $P = 4$, $m = 2$; (b) $C = 144$, $P = 6$, $m = 3$; (c) $C = 162$, $P = 8$, $m = 2$; (d) $C = 213$, $P = 12$, $m = 3$; (e) $C = 570$, $P = 14$, $m = 4$.

Solution

(a) $Y_c = \dfrac{98 \pm 2}{2} = 48 \text{ or } 50$ Segments 1 to 49 or 1 to 51

(b) $Y_c = \dfrac{144 - 3}{3} = 47$ Segments 1 to 48

(c) $Y_c = \dfrac{162 + 2}{4} = 41$ Segments 1 to 42

(d) $Y_c = \dfrac{213 - 3}{6} = 35$ Segments 1 to 36

(e) $Y_c = \dfrac{570 + 4}{7} = 82$ Segments 1 to 83

After determining the commutator pitch for a given winding, it is desirable to test its value. This may be done by tracing segments once around the commutator to see if arrival is made m segments from the starting point. Thus, in Example 2(d): 1-68-135-202-269, note that segment 269 is *one* behind segment 1. Also, in Example 3(c): 1-42-83-124-165 (or segment 3), note that segment 3 is *two* ahead of segment 1 for duplex-wave.

Reentrancy

As previously pointed out, all d-c armatures have closed-circuit windings; this implies that they may be traced completely from any point through all or part of the winding, and such tracing will *always* lead back to the starting point. In the case of simplex windings, lap or wave, it is necessary to trace the *entire* winding from a commutator segment before returning to the starting point; such windings are, therefore, said to be *singly reentrant.* A duplex winding, on the other hand, may have one or two degrees of reentrancy; it is singly reentrant if, after tracing the entire winding, the starting point is reached; it is *doubly reentrant* if the entire winding is divided into two independent insulated sections. A triplex winding may be singly or *triply reentrant,* never doubly reentrant. A quadruplex winding may be singly, doubly, or *quadruply reentrant,* never triply reentrant.

Although the degree of reentrancy has, in general, no effect upon machine operation, it is necessary to know what it is when tests are performed upon armature windings to locate faults. This is easily determined by applying the following rule: *the degree of reentrancy is that number which is the highest common factor* (HCF) *between the number of commutator segments and the commutator pitch* Y_c.

Referring to Example 3, the degrees of reentrancy thus became (*a*) equals 2, (*b*) equals 1, (*c*) equals 1, (*d*) equals 1, (*e*) equals 2.

Armatures with More Segments than Slots

Modern armatures are generally constructed with more commutator segments than slots for the following reasons. (1) As the number of segments is increased, the voltage between those that are adjacent to each other decreases. For a given terminal voltage, therefore, this also de-

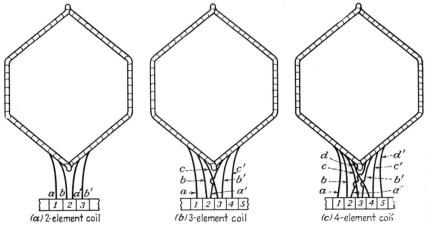

Fig. 21. Sketches illustrating multielement lap coils connected to the commutator.

creases the number of turns of wire in the coil or coils connected to adjacent segments. The result is that, from a performance standpoint, commutation is improved; this is because the objectionable reactance voltage, which is a function of the square of the number of turns, is thereby

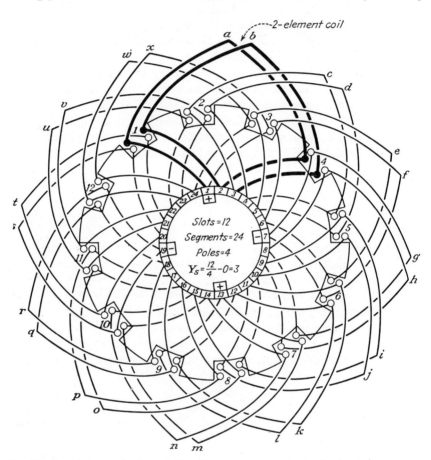

Fig. 22. Complete simplex-lap winding diagram for an armature having twice as many segments as slots. Single-turn coils are shown for convenience.

reduced. (2) As the number of core slots is reduced, the teeth become mechanically stronger, and this results in less damage to laminations and coils when these are handled in manufacture. (3) Assuming that a comparatively large number of segments has been selected for good commutation, the choice of an armature core with one-half, one-third, one-fourth, etc., as many slots means that fewer coils will be constructed; this reduces the manufacturing cost.

When there are n times as many segments as slots, each complete formed coil must have n coil elements. Thus, if the ratio of segments to slots is 2, 3, 4, etc., the individual coils will have 2, 3, 4, etc., elements. This is illustrated by Fig. 21 for simplex-lap coils that are also shown

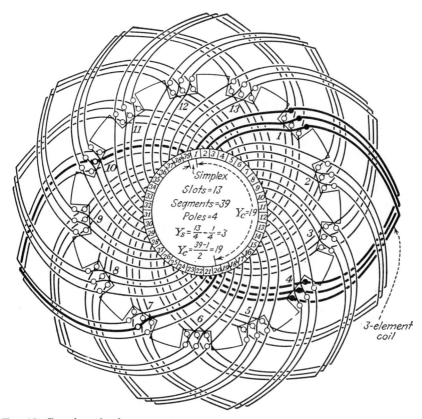

Simplex
Slots = 13
Segments = 39
Poles = 4

$Y_c = 19$

$Y_s = \dfrac{13}{4} - \dfrac{1}{4} = 3$

$Y_c = \dfrac{39-1}{2} = 19$

3-element
coil

Fig. 23. Complete simplex-wave winding diagram for an armature having three times as many segments as slots.

connected to the commutator. It should be thoroughly understood that the coil and commutator pitches Y_s and Y_c are independent of the ratio of segments to slots and that calculations are made in exactly the same way as in the previous illustrative examples; obviously, the commutator pitch applies to each coil element. Figure 18 also shows a 3-element coil for a wave winding whose armature has three times as many segments as slots.

To emphasize further the practical importance of windings having multi-element coils, as well as the systematic arrangement of the coils and their commutator connections, two complete diagrams are given. Figure 22 illustrates a 24-segment 12-slot 4-pole simplex-lap winding in which single-turn elements are drawn for convenience.

An armature such as this would, of course, be used in a rather small machine, but its counterpart, having many more segments and slots, is frequently found in large generators and motors. Of particular significance is the fact that, once the first 2-element coil is properly inserted and connected to the commutator, the others follow with complete regularity into succeeding slots and segments. Another complete diagram is given in Fig. 23 for a 39-segment 13-slot 4-pole simplex-wave winding. Note especially that each coil has three elements because the segment-to-slot ratio is 3. Another point to observe is that, starting at segment 1, the winding is traced to segment 39 after one trip around the commutator; successive tracings result in a dropping back of one segment at a time until the winding reenters segment 1. Many large machines having a similar type of winding, although more segments and slots, are wound in exactly this way.

Dummy Elements in Wave Windings

Four-pole machines with ratings up to 75 kw for generators and 100 hp for motors are manufactured and used in considerable numbers. These are generally simplex-wave wound when the voltage is high enough to limit the current to about 250 amp per armature-winding path. Furthermore, the design of many armatures in the foregoing ranges makes it desirable to employ a segment-to-slot ratio of 2. Now then, since 4-pole simplex-wave-wound armatures must have *an odd number of commutator segments* [apply Eq. (3)], the number of slots cannot be exactly half that many, because an odd number divided by two always yields an integer plus one-half. To solve the dilemma, the designer, having selected the proper *odd* number of segments for the 4-pole simplex-wave winding, must use one-half slot more than required. Thus, a 39-segment commutator will require a 20-slot core; other practical combinations are 73 segments and 37 slots, 89 segments and 45 slots, 93 segments and 47 slots. The result is, of course, that the core has a one-half slot excess or the equivalent of one coil element. In practice this excess is compromised by clipping off the ends of one complete coil element so that it has no electrical function; this implies that the core contains the proper number of electrically active coils and one-half coil that is a "dummy element." The latter is generally taped at the ends so that it is open-circuited; it remains on the armature to maintain mechanical balance only.

Armatures with three times as many segments as slots (approximately) are also used for 4-pole simplex-wave armatures. Practical examples are the following: 95 segments and 32 slots, 119 segments and 40 slots. 227

segments and 76 slots. In each of these a dummy element must be employed because the core has a one-third slot excess.

Dummy elements must be employed in all windings that are placed on armatures whose segment-to-slot ratios are not integers. This rule generally applies to 4- and 6-pole simplex-wave windings because of design

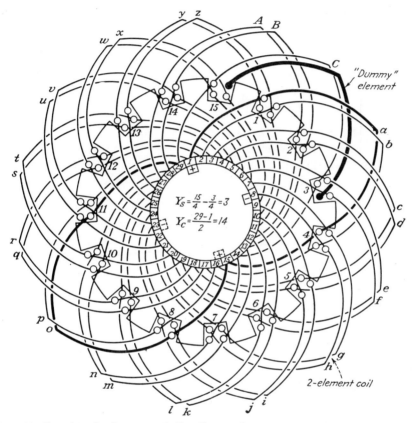

$$Y_s = \frac{15}{4} - \frac{3}{4} = 3$$

$$Y_c = \frac{29-1}{2} = 14$$

Fig. 24. Complete simplex-wave winding diagram for a 29-segment 15-slot 4-pole armature showing a dummy element.

and manufacturing requirements. However, in some unusual cases where, for example, it is found desirable to use an available armature for a special purpose, or where an armature must be redesigned to fulfill a different set of specifications, dummy-element coils may sometimes be found on lap- as well as wave-wound machines having almost any number of poles; infrequently they may be seen on multiplex windings.

Figure 24 illustrates a complete diagram for a 4-pole simplex-wave winding in which the dummy element is represented by one of the elements of a 2-element coil.

Parallel Paths in Armature Windings

It was previously pointed out that simplex-lap and -wave windings differ from each other by the number of parallel paths through which the total current passes; simplex-lap windings have as many parallel paths as poles, while simplex-wave windings have two paths regardless of the number of poles. Since wave-wound machines operate more satisfactorily than those having lap windings (commutation is better), they are the preferred type; they can, however, be employed only when the total current is no greater than about 500 amp, because, for good commutation, it has been found

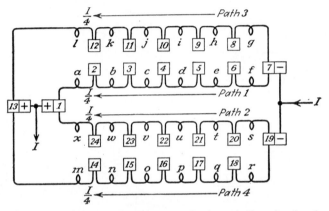

FIG. 25. Schematic diagram of a four-pole simplex-lap winding showing four parallel paths. (Refer to Fig. 22 for complete winding diagram.)

practicable to limit the current to approximately 250 amp per path. For larger values of current the lap winding must be used for the reason that the current through each path is readily limited to acceptable ratings. However, in such cases it is necessary to install equalizers, not needed on wave windings, to eliminate objectionable circulating currents. (The latter is discussed in the next article.)

In order to emphasize the importance of this difference in the number of parallel paths in the two types of winding, simplified schematic sketches have been drawn. These represent the complete winding diagrams in a dissected form that can be readily traced from positive to negative brushes and clearly show how the paths are arranged. Figure 25 illustrates such a sketch for the 4-pole simplex-lap winding shown in its complete arrangement in Fig. 22. Note particularly the coil and commutator connections and how the total current I divides into four $I/4$ parts through the four parallel paths. Figure 26 is a dissected sketch of the complete winding diagram of Fig. 24 and shows how two parallel paths are formed. Of special interest is the fact that the machine requires only two brushes instead of the customary four; however, four may be used if, from the standpoint of current-carrying capacity, this seems desirable. The latter point is of special significance in machines that are mounted in such a manner as to make brush replacement difficult; the two-brush rigging is suitable under such conditions.

Similar analyses of other multipolar and multiplex armature windings would indicate that (1) the number of parallel paths in a lap winding is

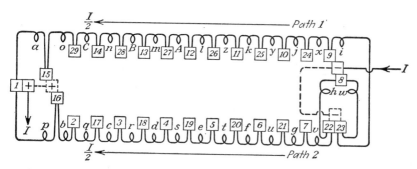

FIG. 26. Schematic diagram of a four-pole, simplex-wave winding showing two parallel paths. (Refer to Fig. 24 for complete winding diagram.)

equal to P × plex, and (2) the number of parallel paths in a wave winding is equal to 2 × plex.

Equalizer Connections for Lap Windings

The voltages generated in the various paths of lap-wound armatures are rarely, if ever, the same. This situation arises in the practical machine because the air gaps under all the poles are not always alike, due to some degree of misalignment, and because the reluctances of the several iron magnetic circuits are unequal. As a result of such voltage inequalities, circulating currents flow in the armature winding and tend to heat the armature to temperatures well above those caused by the normal load current. Moreover, these undesirable currents pass across the brush contacts as they circulate from one path to another, and this produces an unusual amount of arcing and burning at the commutator; in fact, if the situation becomes serious—and this may happen under conditions of heavy load and a roughened commutator—a flashover between positive and negative brushes is likely to occur, a situation that represents a direct short circuit across the supply lines.

To understand why nonuniform flux distributions in the several magnetic circuits will result in circulating currents in lap windings—not in wave windings—it is necessary to recognize two important facts: (1) the conductors of each path of a lap winding occupy positions under *two adjacent poles only,* and this means that the generated voltage in each path will be determined, for the most part, by the given flux distributions; (2) the conductors of each of the two paths of a wave winding occupy positions under *all* the poles simultaneously so that variations in the flux distributions affect both paths similarly. These statements can be verified by referring to Figs. 25 and 26; in the lap-winding sketch of Fig. 25 note that each path is made up of a succession of coils such as *a* to *f*, *g* to *l*, *m* to *r*, and *s* to *x*; in the wave-winding sketch of Fig. 26 each of the two paths consists of coils that are spread completely around the armature.

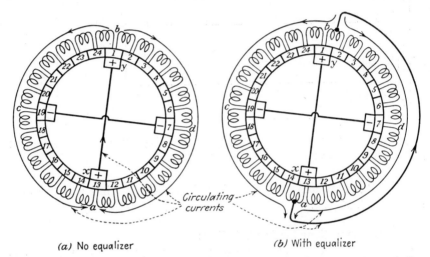

(a) No equalizer   (b) With equalizer

FIG. 27. Sketches illustrating how circulating currents flow in an armature winding without and with an equalizer connection.

To overcome the objectionable effects of the circulating currents, it is customary to employ *equalizer connections* in all lap-wound armatures. These are extremely low-resistance copper wires that connect together points on the armature winding that are exactly 360 electrical degrees apart; these points should, under ideal conditions, be at the same potential at all times but because of electrical, magnetic, and mechanical differences, are not. Such equalizer connections perform two important functions: (1) they relieve the brushes of existing circulating currents by providing paths of low resistance that by-pass the brush contacts; (2) they create electromagnetic effects that tend to equalize the flux distributions under all the poles, strengthening the weaker ones and weakening the stronger ones.

Figure 27 illustrates rather simply how the circulating current is made to avoid the brush contacts when an equalizer connection is used. In the schematic 4-pole lap winding, assume that point *a* is at a higher potential than point *b* and that points *c* and *d* are at the same potential. (Under ideal conditions all points on the armature winding that are 360 electrical degrees apart would be at exactly the same potential.) In Fig. 27a, where *no* equalizer connection is employed, the circulating current is seen to pass across brush contacts *x* and *y* and through the winding as indicated. *With*

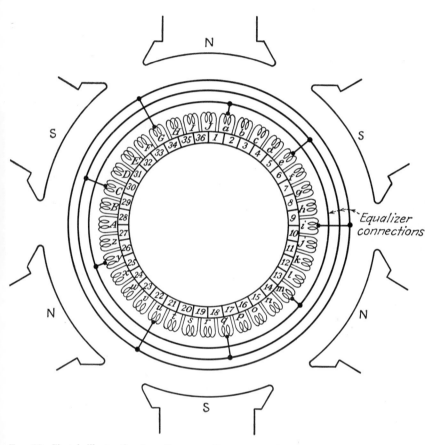

FIG. 28. Sketch illustrating how three equalizer connections are made in a six-pole lap-wound armature. This winding is 25 per cent equalized.

an equalizer connection, however, as in Fig. 27b, the circulating-current paths by-pass brush contacts *x* and *y*; this improves the operating performance of the machine.

Moreover, since the circulating currents that flow through the armature winding and the equalizer connections are alternating currents, they are subject to the laws that govern such circuits. This means that the currents will lag behind the generated voltages in the coils by nearly 90 electrical degrees, *i.e.,* one-half the distance between adjacent poles, because the circuits are highly inductive. As a result of this action an interesting and helpful phenomenon takes place that strengthens the weak poles and weakens the strong poles. Thus, the installation of equalizer connections has the effect of making the circulating currents correct the very unbalanced magnetic distributions that are originally responsible for the trouble.

When equalizer connections are installed in lap-wound armatures, and this is done as a matter of course in nearly all cases, the number of coil elements must be a multiple of the number of pairs of poles $P/2$; this is necessary because exact 360-electrical-degree points on the armature are available only in this way. Then, if all the coil elements are properly joined by equalizers, the winding is said to be 100 per cent equalized; if one-half or one-third the coil elements are so connected, the winding is said to be equalized 50 and 33⅓ per cent, respectively. Figure 28 illustrates a schematic sketch of a 6-pole lap-wound armature with three equalizer connections; this winding is, therefore, 25 per cent equalized. For complete 100 per cent equalization, nine additional connectors would have to be added involving the following coil elements: b-n-z; c-o-A; d-p-B; f-r-D; g-s-E; h-t-F; j-v-H; k-w-I; l-x-J.

Equalizers are often used to connect together commutator segments instead of coil elements. When this is done involute-type connectors are applied and soldered to the segments before the armature winding is installed, and often before the completed commutator is pressed on the shaft.

EXAMPLE 4. A 6-pole lap-wound armature has 54 slots and 162 commutator segments and is equalized 100 per cent at the commutator. Make a table showing the segments that are joined to each of the connectors.

Solution

Number of equalizers for 100 per cent equalization $= \dfrac{162}{6/2} = 54$

Equalizer connections:

1-55-109	10-64-118	19-73-127	28-82-136	37-91-145	46-100-154
2-56-110	11-65-119	20-74-128	29-83-137	38-92-146	47-101-155
3-57-111	12-66-120	21-75-129	30-84-138	39-93-147	48-102-156
4-58-112	13-67-121	22-76-130	31-85-139	40-94-148	49-103-157
5-59-113	14-68-122	23-77-131	32-86-140	41-95-149	50-104-158
6-60-114	15-69-123	24-78-132	33-87-141	42-96-150	51-105-159
7-61-115	16-70-124	25-79-133	34-88-142	43-97-151	52-106-160
8-62-116	17-71-125	26-80-134	35-89-143	44-98-152	53-107-161
9-63-117	18-72-126	27-81-135	36-90-144	45-99-153	54-108-162

Frog-leg Windings

Wave windings are cheaper to install than equalized lap windings; also, they are easier to service when repairs must be made. However, since a simplex-wave winding has only two parallel paths, each of which is practically restricted to a maximum current capacity of about 250 amp, 500-amp machines seem to represent the upper limit for this type of winding; for higher current values equalized lap windings are generally employed. Multiplex-wave windings having 2 × plex parallel paths were attempted by the designers of early machines, but it was soon discovered that commutation was not much better than unequalized lap windings; blackening

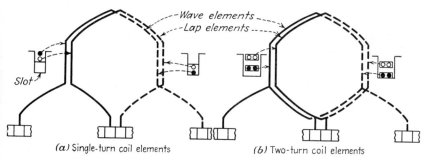

(a) Single-turn coil elements   (b) Two-turn coil elements

FIG. 29. Sketches illustrating two arrangements of frog-leg coils.

and burning of the commutator resulted unless all the simplex sections of the multiplex winding were completely balanced, a condition that was extremely difficult to attain.

Since recognition of the fact that equalizer connections on lap windings represent an addition of material without a gain in voltage-generating current-carrying copper, attempts have frequently been made to develop a winding that would require no equalizers, be self-equalizing, and have many parallel paths. This was accomplished by the engineers of the Allis-Chalmers Manufacturing Company who developed the so-called *frog-leg* winding. Actually a combination of a simplex-lap and a multiplex-wave winding, the latter has a plex that provides it with the same number of parallel paths as in the lap winding. Thus, an 8-pole frog-leg winding would be designed to have a simplex-lap section with 8 paths and a quadruplex-wave section also having 8 paths; the total number of parallel paths would then be 16. In general, therefore, these windings have 2 × P parallel paths, which is equivalent to the number in a duplex-lap winding.

The unique feature of the frog-leg winding is that each finished coil is made up of a lap and wave section; the lap section has its ends brought *in* for connection to adjacent segments, while the wave section has its ends bent *outward* for connection to segments about 360 electrical degrees apart. Figure 29 illustrates the arrangement indicated for single-turn and two-turn coils.

To make the winding 100 per cent self-equalizing, *every pair of lap and wave coil elements that are connected in series must be joined to commutator segments exactly 360 electrical degrees apart.* Such a connection then permits every series lap-wave combination to act as an equalizer connection as well as voltage-generating current-carrying copper; this is true because, like an equalizer connection, it joins together two points on the commutator that are separated by exactly 360 electrical degrees. Figure 30 illustrates the procedure followed for two single-turn frog-leg coils. The important fact to note in this diagram is that the series combination of the wave coil w_1 and the lap coil l_1 are joined to segments 360 degrees apart; this also applies to lap coil l_2 and wave coil w_2.

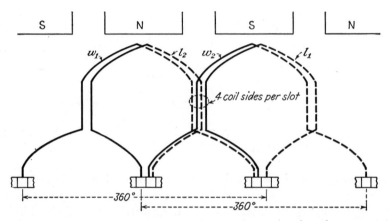

Fig. 30. Sketch illustrating two frog-leg coils properly connected to the commutator. Note: coils w_1 and l_1 are in series between segments 360 degrees apart; also l_2 and w_2 are in series between segments 360 degrees apart.

To emphasize further the important points concerning this combination simplex-lap multiplex-wave winding—the frog-leg winding—a problem will be solved and a simplified sketch made for a fictitious armature with a comparatively few slots and segments. The latter will be employed to clarify the significant parts of the solution; it should be understood, however, that practical armatures have many slots and commutator bars.

EXAMPLE 5. Calculate the coil and commutator pitches Y_s and Y_c for a 4-pole 32-slot 32-segment frog-leg winding. Make a simplified sketch showing several frog-leg coils to clarify the solution, indicating the following:

(a) that the wave section is duplex-wave; (b) that the lap section is simplex-lap; (c) that a series wave-lap combination of coil elements is connected to segments 360 electrical degrees apart; (d) that the coil sides are arranged in the slots in four layers.

Solution

$$Y_s = \frac{32}{4} - 0 = 8 \qquad \text{Coil span is slot 1 to slot 9 for lap and wave sections}$$

$$Y_c = 1 \qquad \text{For the lap section}$$

$$Y_c = \frac{32 - 2}{2} = 15 \qquad \text{For the wave section}$$

This winding will have eight parallel paths—the simplex-lap section provides four paths and the duplex-wave section contributes four paths. Figure 31 is a sketch showing the coil arrangement and commutator con-

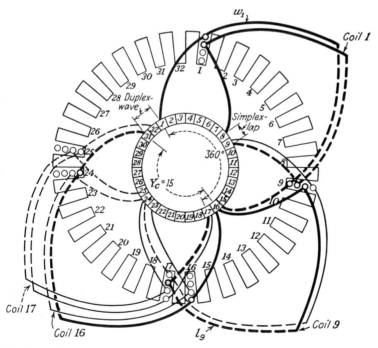

FIG. 31. Part of a frog-leg winding showing four coils properly inserted in slots and connected to the commutator. (See Example 5.)

nections. Note particularly that wave element w_1 and lap element l_9 are connected in series to segments 1 and 17, 360 electrical degrees apart.

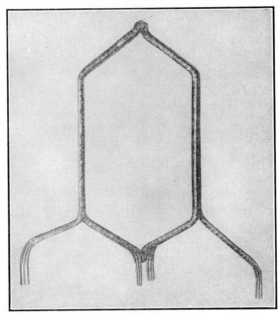

Fig. 32. Frog-leg coil showing lap and wave sections.   (*Allis-Chalmers Mfg. Co.*)

A photograph of a two-turn frog-leg coil is shown in Fig. 32. Clearly visible are the three-element lap and wave sections; the armature for this winding has three times as many segments as slots.

PROBLEMS

1. How many parallel paths are there in (*a*) a 10-pole simplex-lap winding? (*b*) a 6-pole simplex-wave wi ding? (*c*) an 8-pole triplex-wave winding? (*d*) a 4-pole duplex-lap winding?

2. Calculate the armature current per path of a 4-pole 50-kw 250-volt generator if the winding is (*a*) simplex-wave; (*b*) simplex-lap. (Neglect the shunt-field current.)

3. Determine the coil pitches Y_s for the following slot and pole combinations: (*a*) $S = 52$, $P = 6$; (*b*) $S = 69$, $P = 8$; (*c*) $S = 130$, $P = 8$; (*d*) $S = 234$, $P = 10$; (*e*) $S = 286$, $P = 16$.

4. What are the commutator pitches for simplex-, duplex-, triplex-, and quadruplex-lap windings?

5. Calculate the commutator pitches for wave windings with the following combinations of segments, poles, and plex: (*a*) $C = 53$, $P = 4$,

$m = 1$; (b) $C = 86$, $P = 6$, $m = 1$; (c) $C = 287$, $P = 6$, $m = 2$; (d) $C = 423$, $P = 6$, $m = 3$; (e) $C = 396$, $P = 8$, $m = 4$.

6. Determine the degree of reentrancy for the following windings: (a) simplex-lap, $C = 54$; (b) duplex-lap, $C = 54$; (c) duplex-lap, $C = 53$; (d) triplex-lap, $C = 92$; (e) triplex-lap, $C = 93$.

7. Determine the degree of reentrancy for each of the combinations listed in Prob. 5.

8. Make a sketch, similar to that of Fig. 21, showing a five-element coil connected to a commutator, for a simplex-lap winding.

9. Make a sketch, similar to that of Fig. 21, showing a three-element coil connected to a commutator, for a duplex-lap winding.

10. Make a complete winding diagram, similar to that of Fig. 22, showing a simplex-lap winding for a 28-segment 14-slot 4-pole armature.

11. Make a complete winding diagram, similar to that of Fig. 23, showing a simplex-wave winding for a 38-segment 19-slot 6-pole armature.

12. Make a complete winding diagram, similar to that of Fig. 24, showing a simplex-wave winding for a 31-segment 16-slot 4-pole armature. Clearly indicate the "dummy" element.

13. Using Fig. 25 as a guide, make a diagram showing that the winding of Prob. 10 has four parallel paths.

14. Using Fig. 26 as a guide, make a diagram showing that the winding of Prob. 11 has two parallel paths.

15. How many points on the armature winding must be connected to each equalizer connection for lap windings with the following numbers of poles: (a) four? (b) six? (c) eight? (d) ten? (e) twelve?

16. A 6-pole lap-wound armature has 48 segments with involute-type connectors at the commutator to equalize the winding. Make tables listing the interconnected segments for (a) 25 per cent equalization; (b) 50 per cent equalization; (c) 100 per cent equalization.

17. An 8-pole armature has a frog-leg winding. (a) What is the multiplicity of the wave section? (b) How many parallel paths does this winding have?

18. A 6-pole armature has 288 segments and 72 slots and a frog-leg winding. Determine the coil and commutator pitches Y_s and Y_c for (a) the lap section; (b) the wave section.

CHAPTER 3

GENERATOR PRINCIPLES

Generator Action

The generation of voltage in a d-c machine requires the cutting of magnetic flux by moving conductors. The *magnitude* of the emf will, however, depend upon the *rate* at which this action occurs, while its *direction* will be determined by both the magnetic polarity and the direction of rotation of the armature. If a single conductor moves at a constant speed across a magnetic field of uniform flux density, 1 *volt will be generated for every* 10^8 *maxwells cut per second.* Where the field is nonuniform, the instantaneous voltage per conductor will be

$$e_c = \frac{d\phi}{dt} \times 10^{-8} \tag{5}$$

and the average value as it rotates at a speed of rpm/60 revolutions per sec to cut ϕ maxwells under each pole will be

$$E_c = \frac{P \times \phi \times \text{rpm}}{60} \times 10^{-8} \tag{6}$$

Since the actual armature has a total of Z conductors divided into a parallel paths, each path will have Z/a conductors in series. Thus, the total generated voltage—the average value—will be

$$E = \frac{P \times \phi \times Z \times \text{rpm}}{a \times 60} \times 10^{-8} \tag{7}$$

EXAMPLE 1. Calculate the voltage that will be generated by the armature of a d-c generator, given the following particulars: $P = 4$, $\phi = 2.08 \times 10^6$ maxwells per pole, slots = 33; conductors per slot = 6, rpm = 1,750, winding = wave.

Solution

$$E = \frac{4 \times (2.08 \times 10^6) \times (33 \times 6) \times 1,750}{2 \times 60} \times 10^{-8} = 240 \text{ volts}$$

Figure 33 represents a simple analysis—the so-called *"rubber-band"* analysis—that effectively shows how voltage is generated and indicates its direction. In the two-pole single-turn coil arrangement, flux is assumed to pass from left to right from *north* to *south* pole. In Fig. 33a the coil is in a vertical plane so that the conductors *ab* and *cd* are cutting no flux; no voltage is generated at this instant. In Fig. 33b the coil has just moved to a slightly oblique position in a clockwise direction; conductor *ab* moves *down* against the flux lines under the *south* pole and is assumed to bend them as though they were "stretched rubber bands"; at the same time

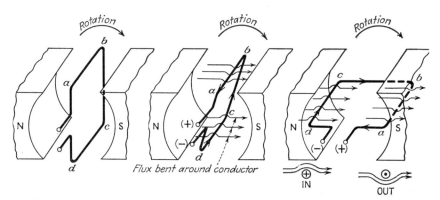

(a) No flux cutting-no voltage   (b) Voltage just increasing   (c) Maximum flux cutting-maximum voltage

FIG. 33. Sketches illustrating the "rubber-band" analysis of voltage generation and how its direction is determined.

conductor *cd* moves *up* against the flux lines under the *north* pole. Note that the flux partially encircles conductor *ab* in a counterclockwise direction and partially encircles conductor *cd* in a clockwise direction. Applying the well-known right-hand rule, it is seen that the generated voltages are directed from *b* to *a* and from *d* to *c*. The voltage is, of course, just increasing from zero in this position because the *rate* of flux cutting is low. In Fig. 33c the coil has reached a horizontal plane so that maximum flux cutting and maximum voltage are attained, with the same directions as indicated for the previous position.

As the coil continues to rotate, the voltage diminishes to zero as it again approaches a vertical plane, but with the same directions as before. Thus, during a one-half revolution, *a* is positive and *d* is negative. During the next half revolution, however, conductor *ab* cuts flux under a *north* pole and conductor *cd* cuts flux under a *south* pole. This implies that the electric polarity reverses, *i.e.*, *d* is positive and *a* is negative.

Still another analysis makes use of *Lenz's law* which states that *the direction of the generated voltage in a coil is such that it tends to produce a current flow opposing a change of flux in the coil.* Referring first to Fig. 33a, it is noted that maximum flux passes through the coil. As the coil rotates clockwise, the flux through the coil tends to diminish until the flux linkages are zero in the horizontal plane; during the period, therefore, the generated emf must be so directed that a current that might flow would tend to maintain the original flux through the coil. Applying the right-hand rule again, this can only mean that the direction of the generated emf must be as indicated by Fig. 33b. As the coil continues to rotate clockwise from the horizontal position, the flux linkages tend to increase. Again by Lenz's law the direction of the generated voltage in the coil must tend to produce a current flow that opposes an increase in flux linkages; thus the generated voltage will be as indicated by Fig. 33c.

Since the magnitude of the generated voltage depends upon the *rate* at which the flux changes through the coil—the rate of change of flux linkages—minimum voltage will be developed in Fig. 33b and maximum voltage produced in Fig. 33c.

Commutation

From the foregoing discussion it should be clear that the generated voltage, as well as the current, in a d-c armature winding is *alternating.* Since the frequency f in cycles per second is proportional to both the speed in revolutions per second, rpm/60, and the number of pairs of poles, $P/2$,

$$f = \frac{P}{2} \times \frac{\text{rpm}}{60} = \frac{P \times \text{rpm}}{120} \tag{8}$$

EXAMPLE 2. What is the frequency of the alternating emf in the armature winding of a 14-pole generator that operates at a speed of 375 rpm?

Solution

$$f = \frac{14 \times 375}{120} = 43.7 \text{ cps}$$

Figure 34 illustrates graphically how the number of cycles per revolution is affected by the number of poles. It is true, of course, that nothing can be done in the modern generator to develop an internal d-c emf; what can be done, however, is to rectify the internal alternating current so that the brush voltage—the external voltage—is direct current. The mechanism for doing this consists of the *commutator* and its *brushes,* previously described. In its simplest form it may be represented by a split ring to which are connected the two ends of one of the armature coils; this is shown in Fig. 35. Comparing the latter with Fig. 33c, it will be seen

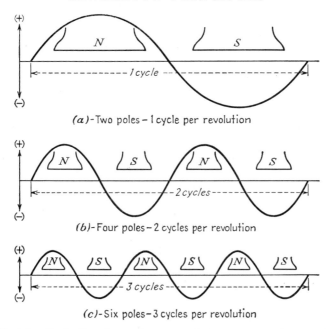

(+)

(−)

(a)-Two poles – 1 cycle per revolution

(+)

(−)

(b)-Four poles – 2 cycles per revolution

(+)

(−)

(c)-Six poles – 3 cycles per revolution

Fig. 34. Sketches illustrating that cycles per revolution are proportional to the number of poles.

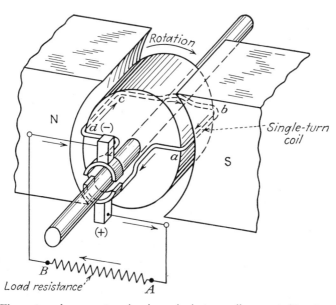

Fig. 35. Elementary d-c generator, showing a single-turn coil connected to a two-segment commutator.

that the coil ends are connected to the two-segment commutator so that, for the instant shown, current flows to the load resistance in a direction from b to a to A to B to d to c. When the plane of the coil is vertical, it will be short-circuited by the brushes at the instant when the generated emf is zero and the current in the coil is *about* to reverse. Continued rotation with coil side ab under the *north* pole and coil side cd under the *south* pole causes the generated voltage in the coil to reverse, *but the direc-*

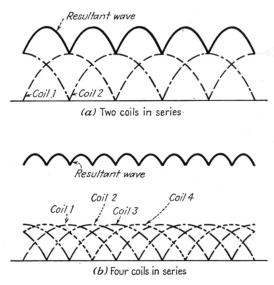

(a) Two coils in series

(b) Four coils in series

FIG. 36. Sketches illustrating how the generated voltage wave becomes smoother as the number of armature coils increases.

tion of the current in the external circuit will remain the same. Thus, current flows during this half revolution from c to d to A to B to a to b. Note particularly that the electrical polarity of the brushes remains unaltered even though the coil current reverses.

In practice, many coils are properly joined together at a multisegment commutator so that (1) a rather large voltage may be developed at the brushes and (2) the voltage pulsations may be greatly subdued. Figure 36 illustrates the effect upon the magnitude and the wave form when the number of coils is increased. Clearly, when an armature has a great many coils and commutator segments, the resultant wave tends to approach a smooth, unvarying form corresponding to that of a storage battery; strictly speaking, however, a d-c generator can never deliver a *pure* direct current.

The Magnetization Curve

In a given machine the generated voltage will be directly proportional to the air-gap flux if the machine is operated at constant speed; this is in accordance with Eq. (7) where the terms $(P \times Z \times \text{rpm})/(a \times 60 \times 10^8)$ may be replaced by a constant k, so that $E = k\phi$. However, the flux ϕ results from an mmf that must act not only upon an air gap but also upon iron whose magnetic permeability varies considerably with flux density. This implies, then, that for varying values of field current, where

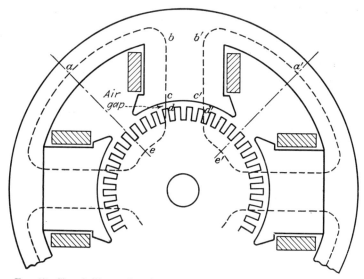

Fig. 37. Sketch illustrating the magnetic flux paths in a d-c generator.

mmf $= 0.4\pi N I_f$, the generated voltage will, in general, not be proportional to the magnetizing current I_f. If a test is, therefore, performed upon a constant-speed generator, whereby the field current is varied over a considerable range, the plotted results of E vs. I_f will not yield a straight line.

Figure 37 represents a section through part of a four-pole generator and shows, in particular, the magnetic circuits that are acted upon by the field mmf. Note that each field coil must magnetize one-half of each of *two magnetic circuits in parallel*. One of these is made up of the iron consisting of yoke ab, pole core bc, and armature core de, while the other has similar iron portions indicated by yoke $a'b'$, pole core $b'c'$, and armature core $d'e'$; both have air gaps cd and $c'd'$, respectively.

Since the total magnetomotive force per pole must be sufficient to magnetize all parts of one series magnetic circuit, the number of ampere-turns equals

$$NI_f = (NI)_y + (NI)_p + (NI)_a + (NI)_g \qquad (9)$$

where N = total turns on each field coil

I_f = field current

$(NI)_y$, $(NI)_p$, $(NI)_a$, and $(NI)_g$ are the required amp-turns for the yoke, pole core, armature core, and air gap, respectively.

Under normal operating conditions the air-gap ampere-turns will usually be about 65 to 85 per cent of the total field NI_f even though the effective length of the air gap is considerably less than the iron portions of the magnetic circuit; its value may be calculated by the equation

$$(NI)_g = 0.313 \times B_g \times \delta_e \qquad (10)$$

where B_g = air-gap flux density, lines per sq in.

δ_e = equivalent air-gap length, in.

EXAMPLE 3. How many turns are there in each of the field coils of a d-c generator given the following particulars: B_g = 54,000, δ_e = 0.23 in., $(NI)_g = 0.75 \times NI_f$, I_f = 3 amp.

Solution

$$(NI)_g = 0.313 \times 54{,}000 \times 0.23 = 3{,}880 \text{ amp-turns}$$

$$NI_f = \frac{3{,}880}{0.75} = 5{,}170 \text{ amp-turns}$$

$$N = \frac{5{,}170}{3} = 1{,}725 \text{ turns}$$

To obtain data for the so-called *magnetization curve*, a d-c generator is driven at a constant speed. Then, with the field excited separately, and varied over a considerable range, E and I_f values are recorded as the latter is increased *progressively* from zero to a point well above that which gives rated voltage E_0. The data are then plotted with the generated voltage E as ordinate (dependent variable) vs. I_f or NI_f as the abscissas (independent variable). Curves such as this are extremely important for the purpose of analyzing, predicting, and comparing the operating performance of the various types of generator. Figure 38 shows a typical magnetization curve, as well as a circuit diagram for the experimental work. Note particularly that the curve is virtually a straight line up to the so-called "knee"; this is true because, in this region, the iron portions of the magnetic circuit are unsaturated and require a comparatively low per cent of the total mmf.

With increasing values of flux density the iron saturates, the magnetic permeability drops, and a greater per cent of the field ampere-turns are required for the iron. It should also be observed that the initial voltage is not zero at zero field current; its value E_r, usually low, is due to residual magnetism.

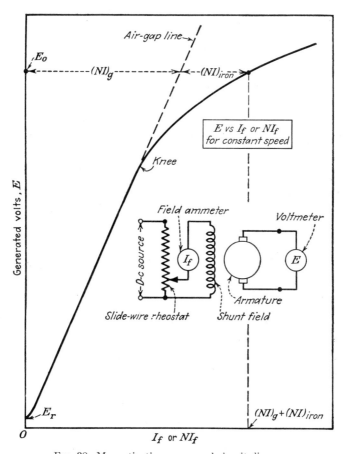

FIG. 38. Magnetization curve and circuit diagram.

After data have been obtained for increasing values of field current, the experimental work may be immediately continued as the magnetization is gradually and progressively reduced to zero. The descending curve, when plotted, will be found to lie slightly above the ascending curve; this is due to the hysteresis property of the iron which tends to produce a lag of the magnetization with respect to the magnetizing force. Figure 39 illustrates the relative position of the two curves.

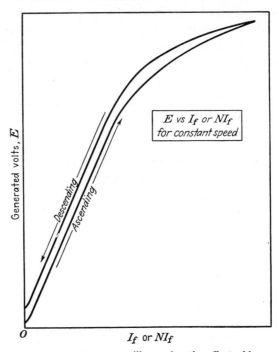

FIG. 39. Magnetization curves illustrating the effect of hysteresis.

Effect of Speed upon Voltage

Referring again to Eq. (7), it should be obvious that the generated voltage E will be directly proportional to the speed if the magnetization is kept constant, that is, $E = k \times$ rpm in a given machine if the value of ϕ remains unchanged, because $(P \times Z \times \phi)/(a \times 60 \times 10^8)$ may be replaced by the constant term k. Thus, using a circuit diagram similar to that of Fig. 38, experimental data may be obtained for plotting a straight-line relation between E and rpm. It is, in fact, possible to perform a set of tests using several constant values of field current so that a family of straight lines may be drawn as shown in Fig. 40. Note that these lines converge at the origin, as they should, although the actual testing range lies within reasonable values of E and rpm.

The family of E vs. rpm curves may be used to yield a family of magnetization curves, each one of which represents the E vs. I_f relationship for a constant speed. To do this it is necessary only to draw a set of vertical lines on Fig. 40 at desired values of speed; the intersections on each vertical line will then provide the E vs. I_f values for the magnetization curve at the particular speed. Figure 41 illustrates such a family of curves, restricted to limited operating ranges, that was derived from Fig. 40.

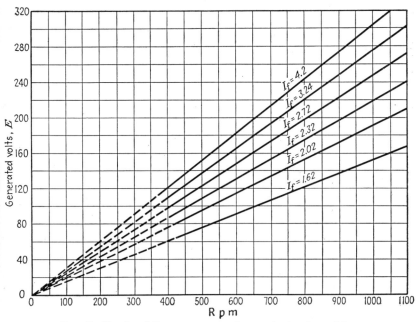

FIG. 40. Family of E vs. rpm curves for constant values of I_f.

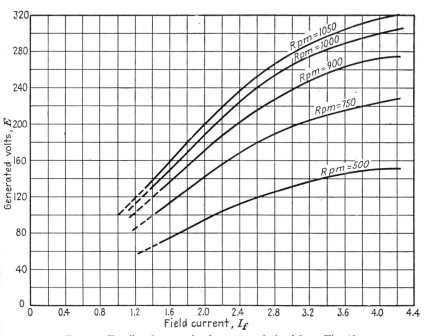

FIG. 41. Family of magnetization curves derived from Fig. 40.

Leakage Flux

All the magnetic flux that is created by each main pole does not enter the armature core through the air gap; some flux actually escapes from the lateral surfaces of the pole core and pole shoe, passes across the extremely long air spaces, and enters similar surfaces of adjacent poles. For most well-designed machines this so-called *leakage flux* represents about 10 to 20 per cent of the flux that is useful in the voltage-generating process; it is called the *leakage flux* and is symbolized by ϕ_l.

Since the pole-core area must be determined on the basis of *actual* values of flux and allowable flux densities, a *leakage-factor term*, *lf*, is helpful in making such calculations. It is defined as the ratio of the total pole flux to the armature useful flux and is given by the equation

$$\text{lf} = \frac{\phi + \phi_l}{\phi} \tag{11}$$

EXAMPLE 4. A 250-volt 6-pole 1,200-rpm generator has a lap-wound armature with a total of 300 conductors. If the leakage factor is 1.15, calculate the leakage flux per pole.

Solution

$$\phi = \frac{250 \times 6 \times 60 \times 10^8}{6 \times 300 \times 1,200} = 4.17 \times 10^6 \text{ maxwells}$$

$$\phi_l = (\text{lf} \times \phi) - \phi = \phi(\text{lf} - 1) = 4.17 \times 10^6 \times 0.15$$

$$= 0.625 \times 10^6 \text{ maxwells}$$

EXAMPLE 5. In Example 4 the net pole-core and pole-shoe areas are 56 and 72 sq in., respectively. Calculate (*a*) the maximum pole-core flux density (near the yoke); (*b*) the air-gap flux density.

Solution

$$B_c = \frac{(4.17 + 0.625) \times 10^6}{56} = 85,500 \text{ lines/sq in.}$$

$$B_g = \frac{4.17 \times 10^6}{72} = 57,800 \text{ lines/sq in.}$$

To indicate, in a general way, the paths of the useful flux, and a major portion of the leakage flux between the pole-core surfaces, Fig. 42 is given. Of special significance is the fact that the pole-core flux density is a maxi-

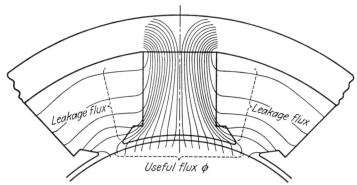

FIG. 42. Sketch illustrating the paths of the useful flux and a major portion of the leakage flux in a d-c generator.

mum near the top and a minimum at the pole face; this is true because the *total flux* passes through the upper section while *useful flux* enters the armature from an enlarged pole face.

Magnetization-curve Calculations

In the design of d-c generators it is necessary to *calculate* points for, and plot, the magnetization curve. This can readily be done if information is available concerning the pole-core, armature-core, and yoke dimensions, the lengths of the various parts of the magnetic circuit, and the leakage factor. Such calculations are treated in detail in texts dealing with the design of d-c machines, and it is therefore felt that the solution of an actual problem is beyond the scope of this book. However, since a study of the general method does serve to clarify important magnetic-circuit relations, it will be outlined in the following procedure.

1. *The equivalent air gap* δ_e. This is generally about 20 per cent greater than the actual air gap under the center of the pole, *i.e.*, δ_e is assumed to be about $1.2 \times \delta$ because of the presence of an irregular tooth-slot armature surface.

2. *The pole-face area* A_g. This is determined by multiplying the pole arc by the axial length of the pole.

3. *The pole-core area* A_p. This is determined by multiplying the pole-core width at the winding space by the *net* axial iron length; the latter is usually about 92 per cent of the axial-core length because of the presence of air spaces between laminations.

4. *The yoke area A_y.* This is determined by multiplying the radial depth by the *net* axial iron length, allowances being made for rounded corners and other irregularities.

5. *The armature-core area A_a.* This is determined by multiplying the radial depth of the armature core below the bottoms of the slots by the *net* axial iron length; the latter must take into account the ventilation ducts as well as air spaces between laminations.

6. *The armature-teeth area A_t.* First determine the width of one tooth one-third of the distance from the bottom of the slot; then multiply this

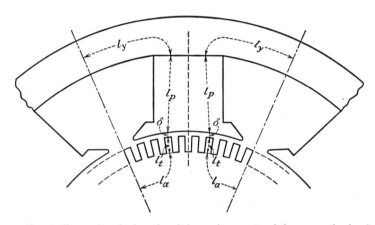

FIG. 43. Sketch illustrating the lengths of the various parts of the magnetic circuit in a d-c generator. Note two parallel circuits.

width by the number of teeth in the pole arc. The latter calculation is finally multiplied by the *net* axial iron length of the armature core, as in item 5.

7. *The magnetic-circuit lengths l_p, l_y, l_a, and l_t.* These lengths must be scaled from an actual drawing of the magnetic circuit, as shown in Fig. 43.

8. *The table of calculations.* Using a table similar to that shown herewith, assume several values of generated voltage. Then proceed to make calculations for the corresponding values of ϕ and flux densities in the various parts of the magnetic circuit. From suitable available *B-H* curves for the irons used in the machine, determine the values of H (amperes turns per inch) for the various parts of the magnetic circuit at their corresponding flux densities. Next calculate the number of ampere-turn required for each magnetic-circuit part by multiplying $H \times l$. Finally sum up the ampere-turn columns, under each assumed value of E. The magnetization curve may now be drawn.

TABLE FOR MAGNETIZATION-CURVE CALCULATIONS

Assumed values of voltage		E_1	E_2	E_3	E_4	E_5
$\phi = \left(\dfrac{60 \times a \times 10^8}{P \times Z \times \text{rpm}}\right) \times E$						
Flux densities	$B_y = \dfrac{\phi \times \text{lf}}{2 \times A_y}$					
	$B_p = \dfrac{\phi \times \text{lf}}{A_p}$					
	$B_a = \dfrac{\phi}{2 \times A_a}$					
	$B_t = \dfrac{\phi}{A_t}$					
	$B_g = \dfrac{\phi}{A_g}$					
Ampere-turns	$(NI)_y = H_y \times l_y$					
	$(NI)_p = H_p \times l_p$					
	$(NI)_a = H_a \times l_a$					
	$(NI)_t = H_t \times l_t$					
	$(NI)_g = 0.313 \times \delta_e \times B_g$					
Total ampere-turns						

Separately and Self-excited Generators

There are two general classifications of d-c generators. They are (1) *separately excited generators*, whose fields are energized by a source of direct current external to the machine, and (2) *self-excited* generators, whose fields are energized by their own armatures. Whether the machine is separately or self-excited will, of course, depend upon the kind of service and the conditions of operation, but the following practical points should be noted in this connection: (1) separately excited generators are used infrequently; (2) in the case of a separately excited compound generator, only the shunt field is energized by an outside source of direct current, under which condition the machine may be said to be *dual-excited;* (3) the series field of a compound generator may be placed in series with the armature or in series in one of the lines "feeding" the load.

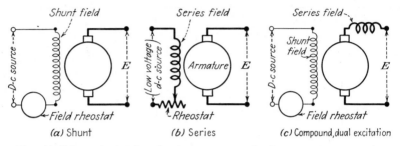

(a) Shunt   (b) Series   (c) Compound, dual excitation

Fig. 44. Schematic sketches showing separate-excitation generator connections.

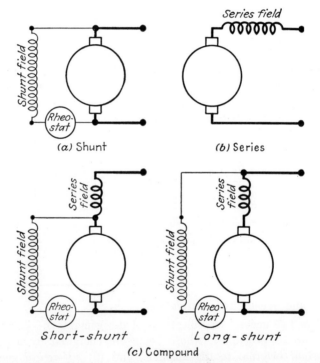

(a) Shunt   (b) Series

Short-shunt   Long-shunt

(c) Compound

Fig. 45. Schematic sketches showing self-excitation generator connections.

Figure 44 shows how the three types of generators are connected for separate excitation, with the addition of rheostats for voltage control. It should be borne in mind that the shunt-field resistance is comparatively high and is connected to a normal-voltage source; the shunt-field current is usually less than 5 per cent of the rated armature current. The series-field resistance, on the other hand, is extremely low; its field, therefore, carries high values of current and must be excited from a low-voltage source.

Connection diagrams for the commonly employed self-excited types of generator are shown in Fig. 45. Note that (1) the field of the shunt machine is excited from the normal *armature-voltage* source, (2) the normal *armature current* excites the field in the series machine, and (3) the armature voltage and armature *or* line current excites the shunt and series fields, respectively, in the compound machine.

Voltage Build-up of a Self-excited Shunt Generator

Consider Fig. 46, which illustrates a self-excited shunt generator, assuming that it is operating at normal speed with the field switch open;

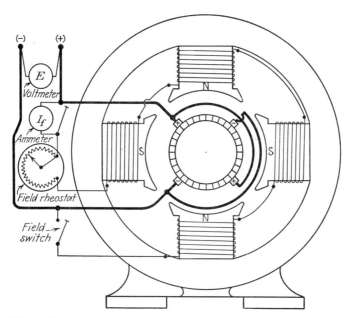

Fig. 46. Sketch illustrating the wiring connections for a self-excited shunt generator.

under this condition—$I_f = 0$—the voltmeter will register a residual voltage E_r as indicated on Fig. 38. Now then, if the field switch is closed *and all the conditions for building up are fulfilled*, the voltage will quickly rise to a value that is much higher than E_r; a desired open-circuit voltage can be obtained by making the necessary adjustments with the field rheostat. Moreover, if the generator has functioned properly in the past, it will generally build up to rated value, or nearly so, merely by bringing the machine up to speed and closing the field switch; after that, load current can be delivered in the usual way, as explained in a subsequent chapter.

What are the conditions under which a self-excited generator *will* build up, and what will determine the value of the generated voltage? Briefly, four conditions must be fulfilled for build-up. These are as follows: (1) the machine must develop a small voltage resulting from residual magnetism; (2) the total field resistance must be less than a so-called *critical resistance;* (3) the speed of the armature must be above a so-called *critical speed;* (4) there must be a proper relation between the direction of rotation and the connections of the field to the armature terminals. Finally, the *value* of the voltage to which the machine will build up will be determined by the shape of the magnetization curve and the total resistance of the field circuit.

1. *Residual Magnetism.* The voltage of a self-excited shunt generator will not rise much above an extremely low residual value if the residual flux is insufficient; generators that are expected to operate at voltages up to 250 should have residual values of flux so that about 4 to 10 residual volts are developed. Assuming then that all other conditions are correct for build-up, the initial voltage E_r causes a small current to flow through the exciting coils as soon as the field switch is closed. The small increment of mmf thus produced aids the residual field to strengthen it; the slightly strengthened field results in a little higher voltage which, in turn, acts to add another small increment of mmf and an accompanying field that is still stronger. This cumulative process will continue until a point of equilibrium is reached, the latter being determined by the shape of the magnetization curve and the total resistance of the field.

The foregoing is made clear by considering Fig. 47. Assume first that data for the upper magnetization curve is obtained by experiment when the residual voltage is $E_r = 8$. If the total resistance of the field circuit is 70 ohms, where the field winding and field rheostat resistances are 50 and 20 ohms, respectively, the generator will build up to 210 volts. To understand why this is so, it is necessary to draw a so-called excitation line—an *Ohm's law* line—which represents the relation between E and I for the given field resistance of 70 ohms; thus a field voltage of 210 volts implies a field current of 3 amp. Now then, *the build-up point is always indicated by the intersection of the magnetization curve and the excitation line.* Thus, at a point below the intersection the generated emf is greater than that required by the field; the difference, represented by the vertical distance between the magnetization curve and the excitation line, is an *accelerating voltage* that results in a further increase in the terminal emf. For example, when the generated voltage is 200, the field current is 2.6 amp; the field-voltage drop is, therefore, $2.6 \times 70 = 182$ volts. An accelerating emf of $200 - 182 = 18$ volts then causes the build-up to continue further until, at 210 volts, when the field current is exactly 3 amp, the field-voltage drop of $3 \times 70 = 210$ volts just matches the developed value.

Consider next the lower magnetization curve obtained experimentally when the machine is operated at a lower speed and the residual voltage

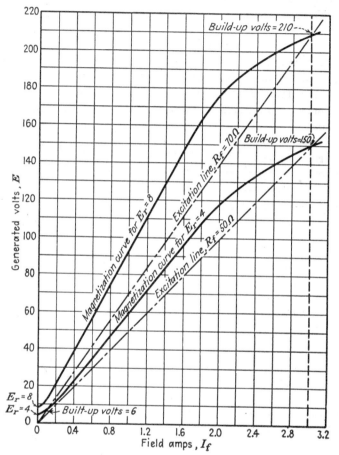

Fig. 47. Magnetization curves and excitation lines illustrating build-up of a shunt generator.

$E_r = 4$. For a field resistance of 70 ohms the intersection of the magnetization curve and the excitation line indicates a build-up value of only 6 volts, *i.e.*, the generator is said *not* to build up. However, if the field-rheostat resistance of 20 ohms is cut out so that the new field resistance is only 50 ohms, the machine will build up to 150 volts as indicated.

2. *Total Field Resistance.* The foregoing discussion should make it clear that the total value of the field-circuit resistance determines the

slope of the excitation line and, therefore, its intersection with the magnetization curve. For higher values of field-circuit resistance the slope increases so that the build-up voltage drops; vice versa, with low values of field resistance the slope decreases and the point of intersection with the magnetization moves higher up. Obviously then, the highest voltage to which a given generator will build up occurs when the field rheostat is short-circuited and the brushes are making good contact with the commutator. On the other hand, a generator will fail to build up if the slope of the excitation line is about equal to, or greater than, the straight-line portion of the magnetization; in fact, a generator will not build up if the total field resistance is greater than the so-called *critical value*, the latter being defined as the resistance below which a machine will build up and above which it will not.

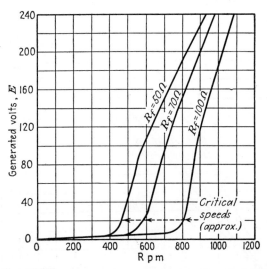

FIG. 48. Curves illustrating how the critical speeds of a self-excited shunt generator are determined.

3. *Armature Speed.* It was previously shown (Fig. 41) that the relative positions of the magnetization curves are influenced by the speeds at which the machine is operated. This implies that a given excitation line will intersect a family of magnetization curves at progressively lower values of voltage with diminishing speeds of rotation. A generator will, in fact, fail to build up if, *for a given field resistance*, the speed is below the so-called *critical speed*, the latter being defined as the speed above which build-up will occur and below which it will not. The critical speed may be determined experimentally if, starting from rest, the armature speed is gradually increased; the critical speed will be indicated by a *sudden* rapid rise in

GENERATOR PRINCIPLES 59

voltage. Figure 48 illustrates experimental curves obtained for three values of shunt-field resistance. Note particularly that, in the regions just below the critical speeds, the voltages seem to be on the verge of increasing abruptly.

As a matter of practical significance, it is well to remember, however, that generators are usually designed to operate at definite speeds fixed by the manufacturer, and that substantial departures from name-plate values are not recommended. If a generator fails to build up, therefore, causes other than low speed must be investigated, assuming that the name-plate specifications are followed.

4. *Direction of Rotation and Connections.* A generator will not build up if the initial field current, at the instant the field switch is closed, is in such a direction that the residual flux is opposed; under this condition the machine will build *down*, not up. This means that there must be a definite relation between the direction of rotation and the connections of the field terminals with respect to the armature terminals. Thus, if a generator fails to build up, and other conditions have been fulfilled, the difficulty may be corrected (a) by reversing the direction of rotation or (b) by interchanging the field terminals with respect to the armature terminals. However, if the rotation is reversed, the electrical polarity of the brushes will change. Another point to remember is that the magnetic polarity of the residual magnetism has absolutely no effect upon whether or not a generator builds up; it merely determines the electrical polarity of the brushes.

PROBLEMS

1. Calculate the generated voltage in a 6-pole 1,200-rpm machine if its lap-wound armature has 8 conductors in each of its 126 slots and a flux density of 57,000 lines per sq in. exists over each pole face of 52.2 sq in.

2. Calculate the number of turns in each of the coil elements of a wave-wound armature of a generator, given the following information: $E = 500$, $P = 4$, slots $= 45$, segments $= 135$, $\phi = 1.85 \times 10^6$, rpm $= 1,500$.

3. A 250-volt 8-pole 750-rpm generator has a frog-leg armature winding with a total of 480 conductors. If each pole face has an area of 140 sq in., calculate the air-gap flux density.

4. Determine the frequency in cycles per second in the armatures of the following generators: (a) $P = 6$, rpm $= 870$; (b) $P = 8$, rpm $= 750$; (c) $P = 10$, rpm $= 900$; (d) $P = 12$, rpm $= 600$.

5. The equivalent air gap of a d-c generator is 0.26 in. where the flux density is 52,000 lines per sq in. If each shunt-field coil has 2,400 turns, calculate the field current, assuming that $(NI)_g = 0.70\ NI_f$.

6. The generator of Prob. 3 has an equivalent air gap of 0.3 in., and the shunt field takes 8.3 amp when rated voltage is developed. Determine the number of ampere-turns needed by each field coil of 905 turns to magnetize its iron portions of the magnetic circuit.

7. If the leakage factor in Prob. 3 is 1.2, calculate the flux density at the top of the pole core (where it joins the yoke) if the area is 118 sq in.

8. The flux in the yoke of a certain generator is 1.3×10^6 maxwells. If the flux entering the air gap from the pole face is 2.3×10^6 maxwells, calculate the leakage factor.

9. The following information is given in connection with a d-c generator: $\phi = 2.6 \times 10^6$, lf $= 1.15$, $A_y = 16.3$, $A_p = 36.6$, $A_a = 16.4$, $A_t = 23.1$, $A_g = 49.5$. Calculate, in lines per sq in., (a) B_y; (b) B_p; (c) B_a; (d) B_t; (e) B_g.

10. Using the upper magnetization curve of Fig. 47, determine the voltage to which the generator will build up if the total shunt-field resistance is 77 ohms.

11. What must be the resistance of the field rheostat if the generator of Fig. 47 (upper magnetization curve) is to build up to 190 volts?

12. Each of the shunt-field coils of a d-c generator has 2,000 turns and takes 2 amp to develop rated voltage. If the equivalent air gap is 0.19 in. and $(NI)_g = 0.72\, NI_f$, calculate the air-gap flux density.

13. Each pole of a compound generator has 1,260 shunt-field turns and 18 series-field turns. If rated voltage is developed when the shunt field alone is separately excited, under which condition it takes 3.7 amp, how much current would it be necessary to supply to the separately excited series field for the same generated emf?

14. A separately excited d-c generator develops 230 volts when it is driven at 1,200 rpm and the shunt-field current is adjusted to 2.6 amp. What emf will be generated if the field current is maintained at the same value and the speed is changed to (a) 1,400 rpm? (b) 1,000 rpm?

15. A self-excited shunt generator builds up with the wrong polarity. What two methods may be employed to make the machine build up with the proper polarity?

CHAPTER 4

MOTOR PRINCIPLES

Motor Action

The primary function of a motor is to develop torque, *i.e.*, a tendency to produce rotation. This is accomplished by the armature when its *current-carrying winding* is acted upon by properly oriented, *stationary magnetic fields*. In the d-c machine a d-c source, applied to the brushes, is changed to a-c by commutation so that groups of conductors under successive poles carry currents in opposite directions; this implies that the direction of the current in the individual conductors reverses as they pass from the influence of one pole to that of its adjacent neighbor of the opposite polarity. As a result all the conductors exert forces *in the same direction* tending to rotate the armature.

The foregoing may be interpreted to mean that force action in a given machine, and the accompanying motor action, depends upon two factors, namely, the strength of the air-gap flux and the magnitude of the armature current. Starting from fundamental concepts this statement is given concrete mathematical form by the following analysis. Remembering that a force of 1 dyne will be exerted upon a conductor 1 cm long if it carries unit cgs current, *i.e.*, 1 *abampere*, and is placed perpendicular to a magnetic field whose density is 1 *gauss* (1 line per sq cm), the total force acting upon a conductor 1 cm long placed θ degrees with respect to a field of B gauss will be

$$F = B \times I_{ab} \times l \times \sin \theta \quad \text{dynes} \quad (12)$$

and since $I_{ab} = I/10$

$$F = \frac{B \times I \times l}{10} \sin \theta \quad \text{dynes} \quad (12a)$$

where the relation between the various terms are indicated by Fig. 49; with the direction of the field and current as shown, the conductor will tend to move away from the observer.

EXAMPLE 1. Referring to Fig. 49, what force in pounds will be exerted upon a conductor 8 in. long if it carries 250 amp and is placed 60° with respect to a field whose flux density is 59,000 lines per sq in.?

Solution

$$F = \frac{(59{,}000/6.45) \times 250 \times (8 \times 2.54)}{10 \times 980 \times 454} \times \sin 60° = 9.03 \text{ lb}$$

Considering next the modern d-c motor, it is permissible to assume that the magnetic field is radial and perpendicular to the axial armature conductors; thus, the sine term in Eq. (12a) becomes unity. Furthermore,

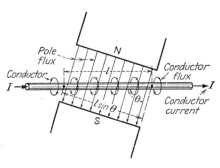

FIG. 49. Sketch illustrating how force action is produced on a current-carrying conductor when placed in a magnetic field.

the armature winding has Z conductors located an average distance r cms from the center of rotation; also each conductor carries I_A/a amp, where I_A is the total armature current. Combining these facts with Eq. (12a), the motor torque becomes

$$T = \frac{ZBI_A lr}{10a} \quad \text{dyne-cm} \tag{13}$$

EXAMPLE 2. Calculate the torque, in dyne-centimeters and pound-feet, developed by an armature, given the following particulars: $Z = 552$, $I_A = 39.5$; $B = 6{,}500$ gauss ($= 41{,}900$ lines/sq in.), $l = 8.9$ cm ($= 3.5$ in.), $r = 7.62$ cm ($= 3$ in.), winding = wave.

Solution

$$T = \frac{552 \times 6{,}500 \times 39.5 \times 8.9 \times 7.62}{10 \times 2} = 4.8 \times 10^8 \text{ dyne-cm}$$

$$T = \frac{4.8 \times 10^8}{980 \times 454 \times 2.54 \times 12} = 35.4 \text{ lb-ft}$$

Motor Counter Electromotive Force (Counter EMF)

As was previously pointed out, the armature of a motor carries current when it is rotating. In doing so it produces a magnetic field of its own that is displaced 90 electrical degrees with respect to the main magnetic field. The armature field ϕ_A, like the main-pole field ϕ_P, is stationary in

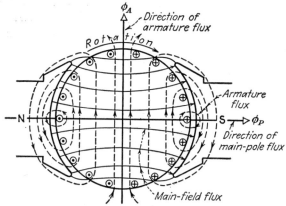

(a) Main poles and armature flux distributions

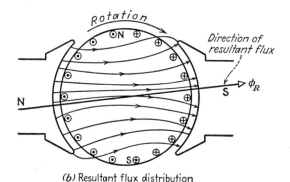

(b) Resultant flux distribution

Fig. 50. Sketches illustrating flux distribution in a d-c motor in operation.

space even though it results from mmfs of rotating conductors; this is true because the alternating currents in the armature conductors always flow in the same direction as they pass under main-field poles of the same polarity. The existence of two magnetic fields in quadrature with each other is, of course, absolutely essential for motor action since the resultant field, somewhat distorted, causes the magnetic density on one side of each of the conductors to be greater than it is on the other. Or, viewing the machine in another way, the armature may be considered as building up its own magnetic poles with axes displaced with respect to the main poles, under which condition force action between two sets of magnetic poles tends to rotate the armature.

The foregoing discussion may be illustrated by simplified sketches representing the two-pole motor. Figure 50a shows the two magnetic fields ϕ_P and ϕ_A superimposed on each other with the quadrature relation between them. Figure 50b indicates how the resultant field is established and how its axis is oriented with respect to the main poles. Note particularly that force actions of repulsion will result between main and armature poles of the same polarity.

Assuming next that the armature is rotating due to motor action, the armature conductors continually cut through the resultant stationary mag-

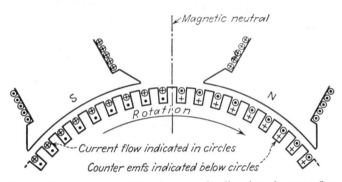

FIG. 51. Sketch illustrating the relation between the direction of current flow and the direction of the counter emfs in a d-c motor.

netic field, and because of such flux cutting, *voltages are generated* in the very same wires that experience the force action. This implies, therefore, that while a motor is rotating, and only then, it is simultaneously functioning as a generator. Obviously, motor action is stronger than generator action because the direction of the current in the armature winding is determined by the electrical polarity of the source. The generated emf does, however, oppose the impressed voltage to the extent that the current in the armature conductors is limited to exactly the value that is required for the power requirements of the motor.

It is extremely important to understand that the *generated voltage* in the armature winding of a motor *directly opposes* the impressed emf, and in doing so has a limiting effect upon the armature current. This opposing generated voltage, properly called a *counter emf*, is, in fact, the primary cause of the automatic control of the speed and torque relations of a motor as the latter operates under varying load conditions. Consider Fig. 51 which represents a portion—two poles—of a d-c motor. For clockwise rotation of the armature, the *current directions* in the armature conductors must be as indicated by the crosses and dots in the circles for the given field polarities. Now then, as rotation proceeds, *voltages are generated* in the very same conductors as the latter cut the magnetic flux that is originally responsible for the motor action; the crosses and dots under the circles represent the *voltage directions*. Being counter emfs, therefore, the armature current I_A must be a function of the difference between the impressed armature voltage V_A and the counter emf E_c. Thus, by *Ohm's law*,

$$I_A = \frac{V_A - E_c}{R_A} \tag{14}$$

where R_A is the resistance of the armature winding. In practice the counter emf will usually be about 80 to 97 per cent of the terminal voltage, the larger values applying to machines of higher kilowatt ratings.

EXAMPLE 3. The armature of a 230-volt shunt motor has a resistance of 0.37 ohm. Assuming a drop across the brush contacts of 3 volts and a counter emf of 207 volts, calculate the armature current.

Solution

$$I_A = \frac{(230 - 3) - 207}{0.37} = 54 \text{ amp}$$

EXAMPLE 4. The armature of a 550-volt compound motor has a resistance of 0.038 ohm and takes 605 amp when delivering normal load. Assuming a brush-contact drop of 5 volts, calculate the counter emf.

Solution

$$E_c = (550 - 5) - (605 \times 0.038) = 522 \text{ volts}$$

It is significant that motors that are designed so that the counter emf is a comparatively high percentage of the impressed voltage operate more efficiently than do machines where E_c is small compared with V_A. The reason for this is that the difference between V_A and E_c is a measure of the armature copper loss $I_A{}^2 R_A$ so that the latter becomes less as the value of E_c increases. Thus, from Eq. (14)

$$V_A - E_c = I_A R_A \tag{14a}$$

Multiplying Eq. (14a) by I_A

$$V_A I_A - E_c I_A = I_A{}^2 R_A$$

and

$$E_c I_A = V_A I_A - I_A{}^2 R_A \tag{15}$$

Equation (15), therefore, indicates that the *power developed* by the motor P_d, in watts, is equal to $E_c I_A$ because it is represented by the difference between the *impressed armature power* $V_A I_A$ and the *armature copper loss* $I_A{}^2 R_A$; it follows then that the larger the value of E_c, for a given armature current, the greater will be the power output. In practice this generally means that a designer attempts to keep the armature resistance as low as possible.

EXAMPLE 5. Calculate the power developed, in kilowatts and horsepower, by the motor of Example 4. (1 hp = 746 watts.)

Solution

$$P_d = \frac{522 \times 605}{1,000} = 316 \text{ kw}$$

$$= \frac{522 \times 605}{746} = 423 \text{ hp}$$

Motor-torque Relations

The power developed by a motor must be sufficient to drive the mechanical load and take care of its own mechanical (friction and windage) losses. This, as was previously shown, is equal to

$$P_d = E_c \times I_A \qquad \text{watts}$$

But

$$E_c = \frac{P \times \phi \times Z \times \text{rpm}}{a \times 60 \times 10^8} \qquad \text{volts} \qquad \text{[by Eq. (7)]}$$

therefore

$$P_d = \frac{P \times \phi \times Z \times \text{rpm}}{a \times 60 \times 10^8} \times I_A \qquad \text{watts}$$

Also

$$\text{hp} = \frac{2\pi \times \text{rpm} \times T}{33,000} = \frac{\text{rpm} \times T}{5,250} \tag{16}$$

where T = lb-ft so that

$$P_d = \frac{\text{rpm} \times T}{5,250} \times 746 \text{ watts} \tag{17}$$

Equating the two values of P_d

$$\frac{P \times \phi \times Z \times \text{rpm}}{a \times 60 \times 10^8} \times I_A = \frac{\text{rpm} \times T}{5,250} \times 746$$

$$T = \left(\frac{5,250}{60 \times 746 \times 10^8}\right)\left(\frac{P \times Z}{a}\right) \times \phi \times I_A \quad \text{lb-ft}$$

$$= \left(\frac{0.1173}{10^8}\right)\left(\frac{P \times Z}{a}\right) \times \phi \times I_A \quad \text{lb-ft} \quad (18)$$

EXAMPLE 6. A 50-hp 4-pole 1,750-rpm compound motor has a wave-wound armature with a total of 232 conductors. The area of each pole face is 30.5 sq in. where the average flux density is 54,500 lines per sq in. Calculate the torque developed by the armature for an armature current of 176 amp.

Solution

$$T = \left(\frac{0.1173}{10^8}\right) \times \left(\frac{4 \times 232}{2}\right) \times (54,500 \times 30.5) \times 176 = 159 \text{ lb-ft}$$

For the purposes of comparison it is desirable to know how the torque of a motor changes under varying conditions of loading. Moreover, it is well to recognize the differences between the characteristic *torque* vs. *load* curves for the three general types of d-c motor, namely, shunt, series, and compound, so that machines may be properly selected on the basis

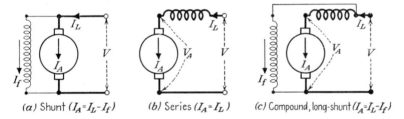

(a) Shunt ($I_A = I_L - I_f$)   (b) Series ($I_A = I_L$)   (c) Compound, long-shunt ($I_A = I_L - I_f$)

FIG. 52. Schematic sketches showing three types of motor.

of actual industrial requirements. Such special and general torque variations can readily be determined or studied by simplifying Eq. (18) to the form

$$T = k\phi I_A \quad (18a)$$

where, for a given motor, the proportionality constant k replaces all constant terms, that is, $k = 0.1173 \ PZ/a \times 10^8$. Observe that, in a given machine, the torque can change only if ϕ or I_A, or both ϕ and I_A, change. In the shunt and compound types of motor (Figs. 52a and 52c), the shunt-field current I_f is practically constant for all conditions of loading and is fixed only by the shunt-field resistance and the terminal voltage V; this implies that the shunt-field flux remains substantially the same for all values of load current I_A. However, in series and compound motors (Figs. 52b and 52c), the series-field current does change with changes in load, so that load variations affect both ϕ and I_A in these two types. The foregoing statements lead to the following general conclusions concerning the manner in which the torque developed by a motor varies with the load, and therefore the armature current I_A:

1. The torque of a shunt motor varies directly with the armature current I_A, assuming that the shunt-field current I_f is not altered either by line-voltage changes or field-rheostat adjustments. Thus, a *torque* vs. *armature-current* graph will be a straight line.

2. The torque developed by a series motor varies with changes in both **the** armature current *and* the flux because the series-field ampere-turns, which influence the magnitude of ϕ, are directly proportional to the load current I_A. At light loads, when the iron in the magnetic circuit is not saturated, ϕ is directly proportional to I_A; under this condition $T = k \times (k_1 I_A) \times I_A = k_2 I_A^2$, the equation of a parabola. At heavy loads, when the magnetic-circuit iron is saturated, the flux will change very little or not at all with variations in I_A; under this condition $T = k I_A$, so that the graph tends to become a straight line. Thus, a complete curve of T vs. I_A for a series motor will be parabolic at light loads and approach a straight line as the load increases.

3. The *torque* vs. *load* characteristic of a compound motor, where the series-field and shunt-field ampere turns aid each other (cumulative compound), is a composite of the shunt and series motors, and the extent to which the curve departs from that exhibited by the shunt machine depends upon the strength of the series field with respect to the shunt field. As the mechanical load on the motor increases, I_A, which passes through the series field, creates flux that adds to the constant shunt-field flux. The increasing resulting flux thus tends to give the motor a rising torque curve under light-load conditions when the iron portions of the magnetic circuit are not greatly saturated. When the iron becomes saturated at heavy loads, however, the series-field ampere-turns can add little to the total flux so that the graph tends to become a straight line.

Characteristic curves illustrating the foregoing discussion, for motors having the same torque at a given value of I_A, are shown in Fig. 53. Note particularly that between no load and full load the shunt motor develops the most torque while the series-motor torque is the least. In the overload region the reverse is true; the compound-motor characteristic lies between the other two. Also observe that the differences between the motors show up quite prominently at overloads where the curves tend to depart greatly from one another; this significant fact indicates, in part, why compound and series motors are usually employed in installations where extremely high values of overload torque must be developed. It is true, of course, that a torque increase is always accompanied by a drop in speed; but whereas the series motor will slow down considerably under heavy overloads, the shunt motor will usually be unable to exert sufficient torque and will stall. The subject of *speed* vs. *torque* will be discussed subsequently.

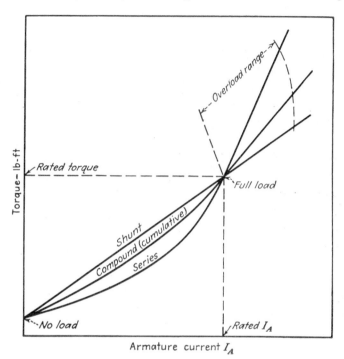

Fig. 53. Characteristic *torque* vs. *armature-current* curves for three types of motor.

EXAMPLE 7. A compound motor develops a torque of 271 lb-ft when it is operating at 1,200 rpm, under which condition its armature current I_A is 215 amp. (a) What horsepower does it develop? (b) What will be the torque and hp of the motor if the load is increased so that it slows down to 1,120 rpm in which case I_A changes to 238 amp and the total flux increases by 8 per cent?

Solution

(a) $\quad \text{hp}_1 = \dfrac{271 \times 1,200}{5,250} = 61.8$

(b) $\quad T_2 = T_1 \times \dfrac{I_2 \times \phi_2}{I_1 \times \phi_1} = 271 \times \dfrac{238}{215} \times \dfrac{1.08\phi_1}{\phi_1} = 324$ lb-ft

$\quad \text{hp}_2 = \dfrac{324 \times 1,120}{5,250} = 69.1$

EXAMPLE 8.   A series motor develops 15 hp at a speed of 1,630 rpm, when it takes a current of 65 amp. (a) What torque is developed? (b) If the developed horsepower increases to 21.5 at 1,450 rpm, under which condition the flux is 31 per cent greater than in (a), calculate the line current.

Solution

(a)
$$T_1 = \frac{15 \times 5,250}{1,630} = 48.3 \text{ lb-ft}$$

(b)
$$T_2 = \frac{21.5 \times 5,250}{1,450} = 77.9 \text{ lb-ft}$$

$$I_2 = 65 \times \frac{77.9}{48.3} \times \frac{\phi_1}{1.31\phi_1} = 80 \text{ amp}$$

Motor-speed Relations

Motors are generally designed and manufactured to deliver specified horsepower outputs *when they operate at certain speeds;* such ratings are always indicated on the name plates. For conventional-type motors, *i.e.,* shunt, series, and cumulative compound, the speed will be greater or less than the name-plate value if the mechanical loads are, respectively, below or above the rated horsepower output. In shunt-type motors the speed change between rated horsepower output (rated load) and no load is about 2 to 8 per cent of the name-plate designation, while in cumulative-compound machines it may be as much as 10 to 25 per cent. The speed rise of a series motor is extremely rapid as load is removed and at light loads tends to race dangerously; for this reason this type of motor must drive *some* load if a "runaway" tendency is to be avoided.

When the speed of a motor rises or falls because of a load change, it is always accompanied by an inherent tendency on the part of the armature current I_A to decrease or increase, respectively. On the other hand, the motor speed will be affected if, for any reason, there is a change in the flux ϕ or the armature voltage V_A. The way in which the three terms I_A, ϕ, and V_A are responsible for the actual speed of a motor can best be studied if they are related to each other mathematically. From Eq. (14)

$$E_c = V_A - I_A R_A$$

and for a given motor

$$E_c = \frac{P \times \phi \times Z \times \text{rpm}}{a \times 60 \times 10^8} = k \times \phi \times \text{rpm}$$

therefore

$$k \times \phi \times \text{rpm} = V_A - I_A R_A$$

and

$$\text{rpm} = \frac{V_A - I_A R_A}{k\phi} \tag{19}$$

Equation (19), therefore, indicates that the speed of a motor is directly proportional to the counter emf $(V_A - I_A R_A)$ and is inversely proportional to the flux ϕ. Furthermore, since load changes affect the values of I_A and ϕ in different ways in shunt-, series-, and compound-type motors, their *speed* vs. *load* characteristics will be dissimilar.

1. *The Shunt Motor.* Assuming a constant voltage V_A, and this is usually the case, the flux ϕ will remain substantially constant over the normal operating-load range for this type of motor. Remembering that R_A is extremely low, the armature-voltage drop $I_A R_A$ will generally be small when compared with V_A; the counter emf $(V_A - I_A R_A)$ will, therefore, change very little between full load and no load. Hence, shunt motors operate over limited speed ranges (variations of 2 to 8 per cent) in most applications.

If a rheostat is used in the shunt-field circuit, the motor speed may be *controlled* by altering the flux ϕ. An increase in field resistance will reduce the flux ϕ and raise the speed; vice versa, a decrease in field resistance will increase ϕ and lower the speed. Obviously, the motor speed will be a minimum when the field-rheostat resistance is zero. Also, the accidental opening of the shunt-field circuit will cause the motor to "race" dangerously, although this operation will tend to increase the value of I_A to limit the speed of small motors or open the circuit breaker in the larger sizes.

2. *The Compound Motor.* Referring to Fig. 52c and assuming a constant applied potential V, the shunt-field flux will remain practically constant for the normal-load operation of the motor. However, as load increases, the series-field ampere-turns does likewise, since the value of I_A becomes greater; this means that the *total flux* rises and, therefore, tends to lower the speed. Moreover, an increased armature current I_A causes the counter emf $(V_A - I_A R_A)$ to drop for two reasons: (a) because V_A is lessened as a result of the increased series-field voltage drop and (b) because the armature-resistance drop $I_A R_A$ rises. All these factors thus tend to give the *speed* vs. *load* curve a drooping characteristic so that the speed of this type of motor will vary about 10 to 25 per cent between full load and no load.

As in the shunt motor the speed may be controlled by adjusting the shunt-field rheostat resistance. Furthermore, a compound motor will operate at practically the same speed as a shunt machine at *no load* if the only difference between them is the addition of a series field in the former.

3. *The Series Motor.* The speed of the series motor varies considerably with changes in load because, unlike the shunt or compound motor, there is no constant strong flux—shunt-field flux—that is independent of the

load. This implies that the armature current I_A, which is a function of the load, determines the strength of the field and in this respect has a major influence upon the actual speed. Assuming that the impressed emf V is constant with the motor operating with normal load at rated speed, a reduction in load (a lower value of I_A) will result in the following three changes that will tend to increase the speed: (a) the voltage V_A will

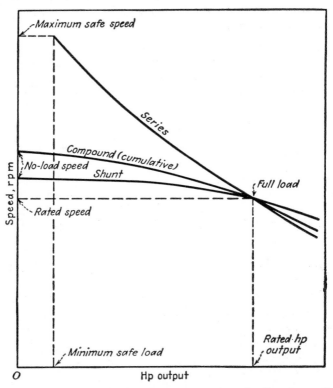

FIG. 54. Characteristic *speed* vs. *horsepower-output* curves for three types of motor.

rise because the series-field voltage drop will decrease; (b) the armature resistance drop $I_A R_A$ will fall; (c) the flux will be diminished. In fact, if the load on a series motor is reduced below a recognized "safe" value, the speed may become excessive. It is for this reason that series motors, except in the case of the extremely small sizes, must not be permitted to "lose" their loads; such applications are generally coupled or geared, never belted.

Figure 54 illustrates typical *speed* vs. *horsepower-output* curves for the three common types of d-c motor. For purposes of comparison the three motors are assumed to have identical name-plate values of horsepower and speed. (Per cent speed vs. per cent full-load horsepower would yield similar curves.) Note particularly that the shunt and compound motors have definite no-load speeds, while the series motor must not be unloaded below a certain value that is indicated by its maximum safe speed.

EXAMPLE 9. A 230-volt shunt motor operates at full load at a speed of 1,750 rpm, under which condition its armature current is 257 amp. The brush drop is assumed to be 3 volts, and the armature resistance was found to be 0.042 ohm. At what speed will the motor operate at no load, if the armature current is then 11.9 amp and the brush drop is 1.5 volts? Assume that the flux remains constant.

Solution

$$\text{rpm}_1 = 1{,}750 = \frac{(230 - 3) - (257 \times 0.042)}{k\phi} = \frac{216.2}{k\phi}$$

$$\text{rpm}_2 = \frac{(230 - 1.5) - (11.9 \times 0.042)}{k\phi} = \frac{228}{k\phi}$$

$$\frac{\text{rpm}_2}{1{,}750} = \frac{228}{216.2}$$

Therefore,

$$\text{rpm}_2 = 1{,}750 \times \frac{228}{216.2} = 1{,}845$$

EXAMPLE 10. The following information is given in connection with a 550-volt 1,160-rpm compound motor: full-load line current = 15.6 amp, shunt-field resistance = 916 ohms, series-field resistance = 0.3 ohm, armature resistance = 2.7 ohms. Calculate the speed of the motor for a load that raises the line current to 19.4 amp, under which condition the increased series-field ampere-turns raises the flux by 8 per cent. Assume a long-shunt connection (Fig. 52c) and a brush drop of 5 volts.

Solution

$$I_f = \frac{550}{916} = 0.6 \text{ amp}$$

$$I_{A_1} = 15.6 - 0.6 = 15 \text{ amp} \qquad I_{A_2} = 19.4 - 0.6 = 18.8 \text{ amp}$$

$$\frac{\text{rpm}_2}{1{,}160} = \frac{\dfrac{(550 - 5) - (18.8 \times 3)}{1.08\phi_1}}{\dfrac{(550 - 5) - (15 \times 3)}{\phi_1}} = \frac{488.6}{500 \times 1.08}$$

$$\text{rpm}_2 = 1{,}160 \times \frac{488.6}{540} = 1{,}050 \text{ rpm}$$

EXAMPLE 11. A 115-volt 1,700-rpm series motor takes 39 amp when delivering rated load. It has an armature resistance of 0.28 ohm and a series-field resistance of 0.16 ohm. When the load is reduced until the maximum safe speed of 3,450 rpm is reached, under which condition the line current is 5 amp, calculate the per cent reduction in flux. Assume brush drops of 2 volts and 1 volt, respectively, at full load and light load.

Solution

$$1{,}700 = \frac{(115 - 2) - (39 \times 0.44)}{k\phi_1} \qquad k\phi_1 = \frac{95.8}{1{,}700} = 0.0563$$

$$3{,}450 = \frac{(115 - 1) - (5 \times 0.44)}{k\phi_2} \qquad k\phi_2 = \frac{111.8}{3{,}450} = 0.0324$$

$$\text{Per cent flux change} = \frac{0.0563 - 0.0324}{0.0563} \times 100 = 42.5$$

Acceleration of D-C Motors

When a d-c motor is operating normally, the armature current I_A is limited by the counter emf [Eq. (14)]; the *difference* between V_A and E_c always adjusts itself to a value that permits the armature, whose resistance is R_A, to take just sufficient current to develop the required torque. At the instant of starting, however, E_c is zero because the armature is not revolving; this means that some external resistance must be inserted in series with the low armature-winding resistance to offset the lack of counter emf, if excessive values of armature current are to be avoided. As the motor accelerates the so-called *starting resistance* may be cut out gradually, because E_c rises, until the entire external resistance is ultimately cut out (or short-circuited), under which condition the motor is connected across the line and running at full speed.

In practice the starting resistance is generally cut out (or short-circuited) in several steps and is chosen so that the maximum current or torque peaks during acceleration are adjusted on the basis of good commutation and torque limitations of the driven mechanical load. Moreover, the value of the external resistance is generally selected to permit the armature to take about 150 per cent of rated current so that the motor will be capable of starting under load.

EXAMPLE 12. The armature of a 230-volt shunt motor has a resistance of 0.82 ohm and takes 28.2 amp when operating at full load. (a) If the value of I_A is not to exceed 150 per cent of the rated current at the instant of starting, calculate the starting resistance. (b) Determine the armature current if no resistance is inserted in the armature circuit. (Assume a 3-volt drop at the brushes.)

Solution

(a) $\quad 1.5 \times 28.2 = \dfrac{(230 - 3) - 0}{0.82 + R} \qquad R = \dfrac{227}{42.3} - 0.82 = 4.55$ ohms

(b) $\qquad I_A = \dfrac{230 - 3}{0.82} = 277$ amp (an excessive value)

Figure 55a represents a schematic sketch of a shunt motor with a starting resistance in the armature circuit that is supposedly designed to

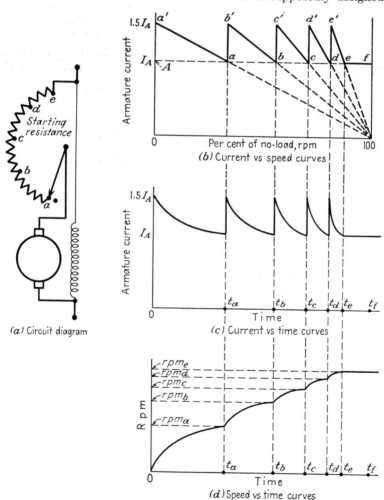

(a) Circuit diagram

(b) Current vs speed curves

(c) Current vs time curves

(d) Speed vs time curves

Fɪɢ. 55. Shunt-motor acceleration.

limit the armature current to $1.5I_A$, where I_A is the rated value; this would be designated a five-step starter, which is one more than the number of accelerating resistors. Assuming a mechanical load that will eventually result in an armature current of I_A, Fig. 55b is a step diagram indicating the current-speed variations as the motor is accelerated. When the starter arm is moved to point a, the initial inrush of current is $1.5I_A$. The motor then accelerates along line $a'a$ and would continue to 100 per cent speed if the mechanical load were zero. However, when the current reaches I_A at point a, the arm is moved to point b on the starter; the armature current again rises to $1.5I_A$ and the motor accelerates along line $b'b$. At point b when the current drops to I_A, the arm is moved to point c with a repetition of the acceleration along line $c'c$. Finally, when the arm has reached point e, the motor is operating normally with the armature connected directly across the line. While the current-speed changes are taking place as explained, the current-time variations follow the step pattern of Fig. 55c, whereas the speed increases with time in accordance with Fig. 55d. Note particularly that, for each step on the starting resistance, the armature current tends to level off at I_A (Fig. 55c), and the speed attempts to reach a steady value that is determined by the *total* armature resistance.

If the graph of Fig. 55b is accurately drawn to scale, the magnitudes of the resistances between points a and b, b and c, c and d, and d and e may be determined. Remembering that rpm $= (V_A - I_A R_A)/k\phi$ [Eq. (19)], it should be clear that, for a shunt motor, the speed is proportional to the counter emf, that is, rpm $= kE_c = k[V_A - I_A(R - R_A)]$. This implies that the distance along the abscissas is a *measure* of the counter emf. At no load, I_A is theoretically zero; $I_A(R + R_A) = 0$; the speed is 100 per cent; and $Af = kV_A$. At point a the speed is Aa per cent, and $Aa = k[V_A - I_A(R + R_A)]$. Therefore,

$$af = Af - Aa = kI_A(R + R_A)$$

and for a constant value of I_A

$$af = k_1(R + R_A)$$

This shows that the distance af is a measure of the *total armature circuit resistance*, consisting of the starting resistance R and the armature winding resistance R_A.

At point e, when the starting resistance is completely cut out, the speed is Ae per cent. Therefore,

$$ef = Af - Ae = k_1 R_A$$

This shows that the distance ef is a measure of the *armature-winding resistance* R_A. Hence

$$ae = af - ef = k_1 R$$

so that ae is a measure of the *starting resistance R*.

Similar reasoning leads to the conclusion that the distances ab, bc, cd, and de are *measures* of the ohmic values between corresponding markings on Fig. 55a.

Making use of the foregoing analysis, it is merely necessary to know the value of R_A to determine the total starting resistance, because $R = (ae/ef)R_A$. Similarly $R_{ab} = (ab/ef)R_A$; $R_{bc} = (bc/ef)R_A$; $R_{cd} = (cd/ef)R_A$; $R_{de} = (de/ef)R_A$.

The ohmic values between contact points of a starting resistance can be determined *analytically* as can the speed to which the motor will accelerate as the arm is moved to each of the studs in succession. The procedure for doing this is given in the following illustrative example.

EXAMPLE 13. Using the data of Example 12 calculate the values of the resistances between contact points for a six-step starter (Fig. 55a), and determine the speed to which the motor will accelerate at each stud.

Solution

$$R_{ae} = \frac{(230 - 3) - 0}{1.5 \times 28.2} - 0.82 = \frac{227}{42.3} - 0.82 = 5.37 - 0.82 = 4.55 \text{ ohms}$$

$$E_{c_a} = 227 - (28.2 \times 5.37) = 227 - 151.5 = 75.5 \text{ volts}$$

$$\text{rpm}_a = 1,800 \times \frac{75.5}{227 - (28.2 \times 0.82)} = \frac{1,800}{203.9} \times 75.5 = 667$$

$$R_{be} = \frac{227 - 75.5}{42.3} - 0.82 = 3.58 - 0.82 = 2.76 \text{ ohms}$$

$$R_{ab} = 4.55 - 2.76 = 1.79 \text{ ohms}$$

$$E_{c_b} = 227 - (28.2 \times 3.58) = 227 - 101 = 126 \text{ volts}$$

$$\text{rpm}_b = \frac{1,800}{203.9} \times 126 = 1,110$$

$$R_{ce} = \frac{227 - 126}{42.3} - 0.82 = 2.39 - 0.82 = 1.57 \text{ ohms}$$

$$R_{bc} = 2.76 - 1.57 = 1.19 \text{ ohms}$$

$$E_{c_c} = 227 - (28.2 \times 2.39) = 227 - 67.3 = 159.7 \text{ volts}$$

$$\text{rpm}_c = \frac{1,800}{203.9} \times 159.7 = 1,410$$

$$R_{de} = \frac{227 - 159.7}{42.3} - 0.82 = 1.59 - 0.82 = 0.77 \text{ ohm}$$

$$R_{cd} = 1.57 - 0.77 = 0.80 \text{ ohm}$$

$$E_{c_d} = 227 - (28.2 \times 1.59) = 227 - 44.8 = 182.2 \text{ volts}$$

$$\text{rpm}_d = \frac{1,800}{203.9} \times 182.2 = 1,610$$

$$\text{rpm}_e = 1,800$$

Compound and series motors are started in essentially the same way as are shunt machines, *i.e.*, a starting resistance must be inserted in the armature circuit and cut out in steps as the acceleration proceeds. Furthermore, calculations may be made in a manner similar to those made for the shunt motor to determine starting-resistance values and speeds; however, because of the presence of the series field, flux changes must be taken into account with the varying values of field ampere-turns.

When an application requires a higher accelerating torque than that developed by armature currents of the order of $1.5I_A$, it is necessary to reduce the starting resistance and thereby increase the maximum current surges as the arm is moved from contact to contact. When this is done the starter will generally have fewer steps.

PROBLEMS

1. Calculate the force in pounds exerted upon a conductor 12 in. long if it carries a current of 140 amp and is placed in a field whose density is 9,000 gauss, with the conductor and field (*a*) at right angles to each other; (*b*) parallel to each other; (*c*) at an angle of 45° with respect to each other.

2. The following information is given in connection with a certain motor: $Z = 116$, $I_A = 348$, $B = 56,000$ lines per sq in., $l = 5.75$ in., $r = 7.25$ in., armature winding = wave. Calculate the torque developed in pound-feet.

3. A certain motor develops 50 hp at a speed of 1,750 rpm. Calculate the air-gap flux density if the following particulars are known: effective number of armature conductors = 162, $I_A = 178$, $l = 5$ in., $r = 5.5$ in., armature winding = wave.

4. The motor of Prob. 2 develops 100 hp. At what speed does it operate?

5. The armature of a motor has 740 conductors, 30 per cent of which lie in the interpolar spaces where no force is experienced, *i.e.*, there are 518 effective conductors. Calculate the developed horsepower for a speed of 1,160 rpm if the air-gap density is 47,200 lines per sq in., the armature current is 26.2 amp, the winding is wave, and the armature length and average conductor radius are 3.5 and 2.75 in., respectively.

6. The armature of a 550-volt motor takes 88 amp when operating at full load. Assuming that the counter emf is 92 per cent of the impressed voltage and the brush drop is 5 volts, calculate the approximate armature resistance.

7. What horsepower is developed by the motor of Prob. 6?

8. A 4-pole 1,500-rpm shunt motor has a lap-wound armature with 432 conductors. If the air-gap flux per pole is 2.06×10^6 maxwells, what horsepower is developed for a normal armature current of 345 amp?

9. What torque is developed by the motor of Prob. 8 for a current of 250 amp? (Assume no flux change.)

10. What starting current must the armature of the motor of Prob. 8 take if the starting torque must be 50 per cent greater than that calculated for the normal load?

11. A compound motor develops 16.5 hp when operating at 1,600 rpm, under which condition the armature current is 63 amp. Calculate the developed torque and horsepower when an increased load lowers the speed to 1,500 rpm, raises the armature current to 75 amp, and increases the flux by 6 per cent.

12. A series motor takes 285 amp and develops 153 lb-ft torque when operating at 1,200-rpm. Calculate the torque and horsepower for a speed of 1,700 rpm, under which condition the current drops to 210 amp and the flux is decreased by 18 per cent.

13. A 230-volt shunt motor has an armature resistance of 0.28 ohm and a field resistance of 115 ohms. At no load the line current is 8 amp and the speed 2,300 rpm. What is the speed when the line current is 52 amp? Assume brush drops of 1 volt and 3 volts, respectively, for the no-load and load conditions, and that the flux remains constant.

14. A 550-volt long-shunt compound motor has an armature resistance of 0.75 ohms and a series-field resistance of 0.15 ohm. The full-load speed is 1,800 rpm when the armature current is 20 amp. At what speed will the motor operate at no load if the armature current drops to 3 amp with a corresponding drop in flux to 90 per cent of the full-load value? (Assume brush drops of 5 volts and 2 volts at full load and no load, respectively.)

15. A 250-volt series motor has an armature resistance of 0.52 ohm and a series-field resistance of 0.18 ohm. If the speed is 600 rpm when the current is 32 amp, what will be the motor speed when the load is reduced so that the current is 18 amp, under which condition the per cent flux change is 50 per cent of the per cent current change. (Assume a 3-volt brush drop.)

16. The armature and shunt-field resistances of a 230-volt shunt motor are 0.28 and 153.5 ohms, respectively. If the starting resistance is 3.22 ohms, calculate the total line current at the instant of starting. (Assume a 3-volt brush drop.)

17. What would be the total line current in Prob. 16 if no starting resistance were used?

18. The motor of Prob. 16 has a *normal* speed of 1,500 rpm when the armature "takes" its rated current of 42 amp. Calculate the speed to which the motor will accelerate on the first stud of the starting resistance when the armature-circuit current reaches the 42-amp value.

CHAPTER 5

ARMATURE REACTION

Magnetic Action of Armature

It was previously shown (Fig. 50) that the armature mmf sets up a magnetic field in quadrature with the main magnetic field. Unlike the shunt-field flux whose magnitude is essentially constant, the armature flux varies with the current in the armature conductors which, in turn, depends upon the electrical load of the generator or the mechanical load on the motor. The resulting magnetic action of the armature then tends to distort and alter the direction of the uniformly distributed main field and create a slight demagnetizing effect. Since the latter are, in general, detrimental to good dynamo operation, particularly commutation, modern machines are usually equipped with additional magnetic poles and windings—*interpoles* and *compensating windings*—that oppose and neutralize the effects of *armature reaction*.

For similar main magnetic polarities and the same direction of rotation the armature currents are oppositely directed with respect to each other

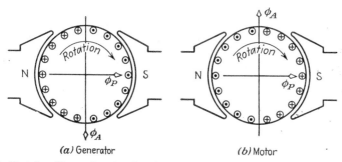

(a) Generator   (b) Motor

Fig. 56. Sketches illustrating the directions of the armature fluxes with respect to the main-pole flux for generator and motor.

in the generator and motor; this is illustrated in Fig. 56. This means that the armature flux will tend to distort the main field in different ways in the two types of machine and, as will presently be shown, the "twisting action" will be in the same direction as that of rotation in the generator and opposite to that of rotation in the motor. It should be pointed out, of course, that the armature flux does not exist independently of the

81

main-field flux but combines with the latter to create a resultant field; however, the quadrature-field analysis is extremely useful and straightforward in the study of dynamo operation.

Field Distortion

One of the most important functions of the d-c machine is to commutate the armature currents properly; this requires the changing of a generated alternating current to an external direct current in the generator, or the changing of an impressed direct current to an internal (armature-winding)

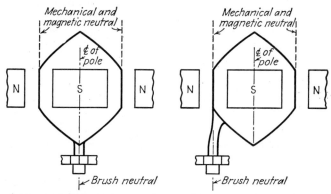

(a) Symmetrical commutator connection   (b) Unsymmetrical commutator connection

Fig. 57. Sketches illustrating the brush positions for armature coils that are connected symmetrically and unsymmetrically to the commutator. Negligible armature reaction.

alternating current in the motor. Commutation for each individual coil element always involves a succession of extremely short periods during which it is short-circuited; before the short circuit, current flows in one direction, while after the short circuit, the current flow is reversed. For successful commutation, coil elements must be short-circuited (theoretically) when the coil sides are cutting no flux. This implies that *the brushes must be located so that the coil sides are in magnetic neutral zones during the short-circuit periods;* it does not necessarily mean that the brushes line up exactly on the mechanical neutral (midway between pole tips). Figure 57 illustrates how the brushes and coil sides are located with respect to each other when the effect of armature reaction is negligible and the magnetic neutral is in line with the mechanical neutral. Note that in one sketch (Fig. 57a), where the coil ends connect to segments midway between the coil sides, the brush neutral lines up with the center of the pole; in Fig. 57b, where the coil ends connect to segments in line with one side of a coil, the brush neutral lines up with the magnetic neutral. Furthermore, if the effect of armature reaction is to shift the neutral ahead for a generator or behind for a motor, the brushes must likewise be shifted as shown in Fig. 58.

Referring again to Fig. 50a, it will be observed that the main field acting alone creates a perfectly symmetrical pattern of flux lines between the *north* and *south* poles, and that the flux-density distribution is practically uniform over the pole-face area; the flux and flux density in the interpolar zones drop to low values because of the high magnetic reluctance of these regions. Moreover, the armature field acting alone also creates

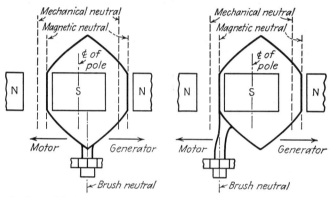

(a) Symmetrical commutator connection   (b) Unsymmetrical commutator connection

Fig. 58. Sketches illustrating the brush positions for armature coils that are connected symmetrically and unsymmetrically to the commutator. Armature reaction shifts magnetic neutral with respect to the mechanical neutral.

a perfectly symmetrical pattern of flux lines that are mostly centered about the pole faces. However—and this is extremely important—the combined effect of both symmetrical patterns of flux and flux-density distributions is *not symmetrical* but badly twisted out of shape, *i.e.*, distorted. The distortion comes about (Fig. 50b) because the cross-magnetizing action of the armature mmf has an additive influence on one-half of each pole and a subtractive influence on the other half of each pole. Furthermore, the presence of iron in the magnetic circuit—saturated iron—means that the net demagnetizing influence of the armature mmf is greater than the net magnetizing influence so that the resultant flux is actually diminished; the latter is small, however, and is about 1 to 4 per cent.

A very useful kind of diagram that emphasizes the effect of the cross-magnetizing ampere-turns is shown in Fig. 59. It is divided into three parts, illustrating the mmf and flux-density distributions of the main poles and armature separately (Figs. 59a and b) and the badly distorted resultant effect (Fig. 59c). Note particularly that the two component flux-density distributions combine to yield an unsymmetrical pattern, with the left sides of the poles weakened and the right sides strengthened. Also, since the area under the flux-density curve is a *measure* of the total flux $\left(\phi = \int_0^\pi Blr\, d\alpha\right)$, it may be shown that the main-pole and armature fluxes

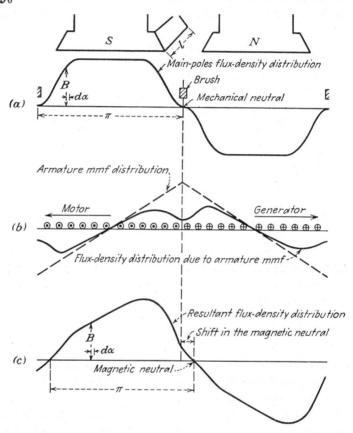

Fig. 59. Sketches illustrating how the armature mmf distorts the main-pole flux and shifts the position of the neutral.

interact to create a slightly weaker field than was produced by the main poles alone. Still another point to observe is the shift in the magnetic neutral; this is in the direction of rotation for the generator and against the direction of rotation for the motor.

Demagnetizing Effect of Cross-magnetizing Armature Reaction

The extent to which the cross-magnetizing armature reaction affects the main field may be determined by the following analysis in connection with

Fig. 60. The armature has Z/P conductors under each pole and each one carries I_A/a amp. The total number of ampere-conductors per pole will, therefore, be ZI_A/aP. But only those conductors that are directly under the pole faces have a measurable magnetizing or demagnetizing effect upon the main poles, because the conductors between the pole tips, in the interpolar zones, act upon high-reluctance magnetic circuits. If τ represents

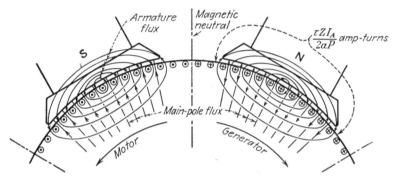

FIG. 60. Sketch illustrating the cross-magnetizing armature-reaction effect.

the ratio *pole arc/pole pitch*, the maximum effective ampere-conductors per pole will be $\tau ZI_A/aP$. And since two conductors are the equivalent of one turn, it follows that one-half of each pole is effectively magnetized and the other half effectively demagnetized by

$$\text{Cross-magnetizing amp-turns/pole} = \tau ZI_A/2aP \qquad (20)$$

In practice the magnetic-circuit iron is usually saturated before armature reaction adds or subtracts its ampere-turns, and this means that it is more difficult to increase the degree of magnetization than it is to decrease it. Thus, the half of the pole that is strengthened gains less flux than the half that loses flux; the net result is a reduction in flux. Figure 61 illustrates graphically how each pole is affected when a machine is operating at point p on the magnetization curve. Note especially that the flux density (1) is unchanged at the center of the pole, (2) is increased gradually and slightly on the upper portion of the magnetization curve, (3) is decreased sharply and somewhat more on the lower portion of the curve, (4) is affected most, up or down, at the *tips* of the poles.

EXAMPLE 1. The lap-wound armature of a 6-pole d-c generator has a total of 378 conductors and carries 800 amp at full load. If the pole arc is 6.75 in. and the armature diameter is 20 in., calculate the maximum

cross-magnetizing ampere-turns per pole that has a magnetizing or demagnetizing effect on each pole tip.

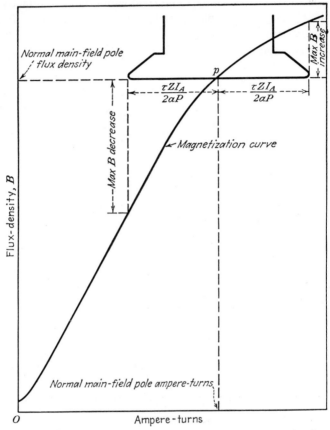

Fig. 61. Sketch illustrating how the cross-magnetizing armature reaction decreases the
main-pole flux.

Solution

$$\tau = \frac{6.75}{\pi \times {}^{20}\!/_{6}} = 0.645$$

$$\text{Cross-magnetizing } NI/\text{pole} = \frac{0.645 \times 378 \times 800}{2 \times 6 \times 6} = 2,710$$

Since the greatest effect of the cross-magnetizing ampere-turns of armature reaction occurs in the overhanging pole shoes, it is logical to attempt
to apply corrective measures there. One method that partly counteracts
distortion and demagnetization involves a pole-shoe construction that increases the reluctance between the pole tips and the surface of the arma-

ture core; this reduces the flux produced by the armature mmf. Two designs that employ this idea are shown in Fig. 62. In one of these (Fig. 62a) the rounded surface of the pole shoe is not concentric with the circular armature core, *i.e.*, the pole shoe is chamfered. A second scheme (Fig. 62b) uses pole-core laminations with one pole tip; in assembling the laminations, the pole tips are alternated from one side to the other, so that the cross-sectional area of the iron is one-half as much under the pole tips as under the center section. A much better, though more expensive, method

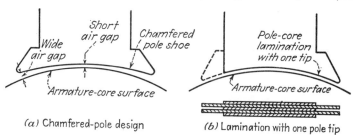

(a) Chamfered-pole design   (b) Lamination with one pole tip

Fig. 62. Special pole-core laminations to counteract the effect of cross-magnetizing armature reaction.

is to use compensating windings, but these are generally applied to large machines that must operate under wide and severe load conditions; they will be treated in a subsequent article.

Brush Shifting

When the armature of a d-c machine (without interpoles) carries current, the magnetic and mechanical neutrals do not coincide (see Figs. 58 and 59). Such displacement affects commutation, because sparking will occur at the brushes unless they occupy positions that short-circuit coil sides in the neutral zone; the brushes must, therefore, be shifted to locations that reduce sparking. Also, since the effect of armature reaction depends upon the value of the armature current, the brushes must be shifted back and forth continuously as the load changes, or they must be located in some compromise position that represents the best average load.

Assume that a dynamo is operating under load and that the brushes are shifted $\beta°$ forward for a generator or backward for a motor, so that reasonably good commutation may result. When this is done a certain number of armature ampere-turns tends to demagnetize the main field, apart from the demagnetizing action that results from field distortion. Figure 63 illustrates such a shift for a two-pole machine; under this condition the directions of the *currents* in the conductors are determined by the new brush positions, as indicated. Now then, if diametrically opposite conductors are paired in an angle $2\beta°$, it is seen that their effect, as ampere-turns, is to demagnetize the main field. In other words, a brush shift of

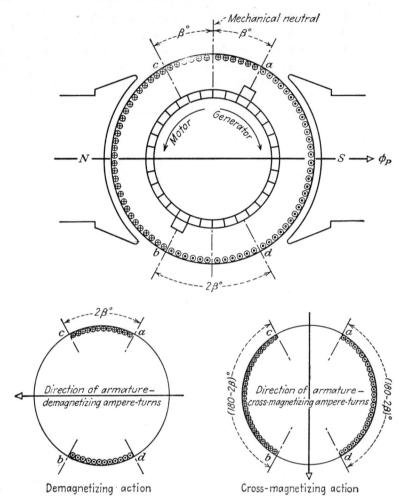

FIG. 63. Sketches illustrating the demagnetizing and cross-magnetizing armature reaction effects due to brush shift.

β degrees means that the number of conductors in 4β degrees, that is, a to c and b to d, are involved in a direct demagnetizing action of *two* main poles. Thus,

$$\text{Demagnetizing amp-conductors/pole} = \frac{1}{2} \times \frac{4\beta}{360} \times \frac{ZI_A}{a}$$

Hence

$$\text{Demagnetizing } NI/\text{pole} = \frac{1}{2} \times \frac{1}{2} \times \frac{4\beta}{360} \times \frac{ZI_A}{a} = \frac{\beta ZI_A}{360 \times a} \qquad (21)$$

The lower left sketch of Fig. 63 indicates how all the armature conductors in an angle $4\beta°$ act to demagnetize the main poles. The remaining armature conductors will obviously produce a cross-magnetizing action; this is shown in the lower right sketch of Fig. 63 where the conductors a to d and c to b are involved in creating a quadrature field. In a two-pole machine there will be $[(360 - 4\beta)/360] \times Z$ cross-magnetizing conductors, while in a P-pole machine their number will be $[(360 - 2P\beta)/360] \times Z$. It follows, therefore, that in a P-pole machine the

Total cross-magnetizing NI/pole

$$= \frac{360 - 2P\beta}{360} \times \frac{ZI_A}{2aP} = \frac{360 - 2P\beta}{720aP} \times ZI_A \quad (22)$$

EXAMPLE 2. The armature of Example 1 has a commutator whose diameter is 15 in. If the brushes are shifted 1.25 in. in the direction of rotation for the purpose of improving commutation, calculate (a) the demagnetizing ampere-turns per pole; (b) the total cross-magnetizing ampere-turns per pole.

Solution

(a)
$$\beta° = \frac{1.25}{\pi \times 15} \times 360° = 9.55°$$

$$\text{Demagnetizing } NI/\text{pole} = \frac{9.55 \times 378 \times 800}{360 \times 6} = 1{,}335$$

(b) Total cross-magnetizing NI/pole

$$= \frac{360 - (2 \times 6 \times 9.55)}{720 \times 6 \times 6} \times 378 \times 800 = 2{,}865$$

The demagnetizing action of armature reaction due to brush shift may be diminished somewhat by using armature-winding coils whose coil pitch Y_S is a little less than a pole pitch; when this is done the coils and winding are said to be *fractional pitch*. With full-pitch coils all coil sides within the angle $2\beta°$ carry currents in the same direction so that they have an additive tendency to demagnetize the pole. However, if the winding is made up of short-pitch coils, all the conductors within the angle $2\beta°$ do *not* carry currents in the same direction; under this condition the net demagnetizing action is determined by the *difference* between those conductors carrying currents in opposite directions. Thus, if the brushes are shifted β electrical degrees and the coils have a pitch of $(180 - 2\beta°)$ electrical degrees, no demagnetizing action will take place because the currents in one-half the conductors within the 2β-degree zone will be neutralized by

an equal number of conductors carrying currents in the opposite direction.
Brush shift does not alter the distortion of the flux-density distribution.
It can only improve commutation, although, as indicated above, it is
accompanied by an additional undesirable demagnetizing influence. It is
well to remember the latter point in connection with dynamo performance
under load; in the generator the terminal voltage tends to drop, while in

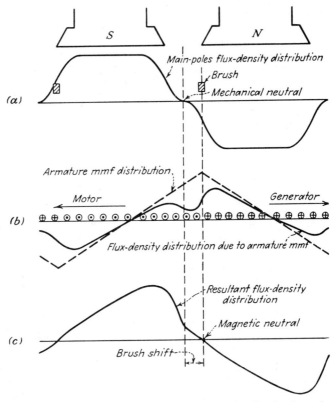

Fig. 64. Sketches illustrating armature mmf and flux-density distributions when brushes
are shifted to improve commutation.

the motor the speed tends to rise as a result of demagnetizing armature
ampere-turns.

To emphasize further the problem of brush shift, Fig. 64 is given to
show (1) how improvement is brought about by making the brush and
magnetic neutrals coincide, (2) how demagnetization is increased, (3) how
field distortion is unaffected. Note particularly that the area under the
resultant curve (Fig. 64c) is somewhat less than the similar curve of Fig.
59c, indicating that a brush shift results in demagnetization.

Voltage of Self-induction

As successive coil elements in an armature winding are commutated, the current must change from a value I_c in one direction to a value I_c in the opposite direction. Moreover, since each coil side is surrounded by a local flux that is caused by its own current flow, apart from any other magnetic fields existing in the so-called neutral zone, there must be a

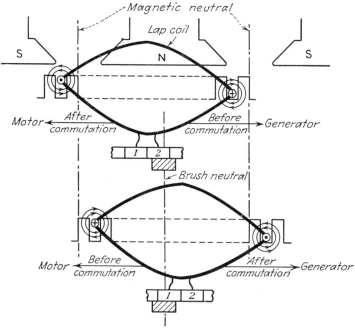

Fig. 65. Sketches illustrating how the current and flux directions change as a simple lap coil undergoes commutation.

corresponding flux change from ϕ_c in one direction to ϕ_c in the opposite direction. The total *flux change* is, therefore, $2\phi_c$, and the time during which this occurs is the short-circuit period, *i.e.*, the very small interval during which the brush short-circuits the coil element. Assuming, as a first approximation, that commutation is ideal so that the current and flux vary uniformly from $+I_c$ and $+\phi_c$ to $-I_c$ and $-\phi_c$, a constant *voltage of self-induction* will be induced in each coil, and *this voltage, by Lenz's law, will tend to oppose current reversal.*

Figure 65 illustrates a simple lap-coil element whose motion through the neutral zone is indicated for both a generator and motor. Observe that the flux passes through much air as it encircles the conductors; it is for this reason that the flux is practically proportional to the current. As a result the induced voltage of self-induction will be

$$E_i = N \times \frac{2\phi_c}{t} \times 10^{-8} \text{ volts} \qquad (23)$$

where N = number of turns in the short-circuited coil

t = time, sec, during which the coil is short-circuited

These relations are graphically represented by Fig. 66 in which the uniformly changing flux, having a slope of $-2\phi_c/t$, gives rise to a constant emf of E_i. Since this voltage acts in a circuit whose resistance is extremely low—a circuit consisting of a coil of wire, a carbon brush, and contacts between commutator and brush—a considerable current will flow in the short-circuited path and cause severe arcing at the commutator. Such a situation will obviously give rise to commutator burning and roughness, progressively poorer commutation as the brush contacts worsen, and eventual breakdown. To offset the objectionable sparking brought about by the induced emf, it is necessary to neutralize the latter by shifting the brushes *beyond* the point indicated by the magnetic neutral plane; in the generator this is *ahead*, or in the direction of rotation, while in the motor it is *behind*, or against the direction of rotation. When this is done the coil cuts flux *in advance* of the magnetic neutral so that, anticipating difficulty from the property of *self-inductance*, it develops an emf whose direction is the same as that in which the current is *about* to flow; commutation is, therefore, improved because current reversal is aided.

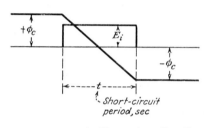

FIG. 66. Sketch illustrating the flux change and the voltage of self-induction in a coil undergoing commutation.

It should be understood that brush shifting must be employed in non-interpole machines and is, in general, an objectionable practice because the brush position must be changed for all major load changes. And, as will be shown later, modern well-designed machines usually have narrow poles in the neutral zones which automatically function to compensate for both magnetic-neutral shift and the voltage of self-induction; the use of such interpoles thereby eliminates the need for brush shifting.

EXAMPLE 3. Each of the coil elements of a 6-pole lap-wound armature winding has three turns. The armature-core and commutator diameters are 20 and 15 in., respectively, and the brush width is 1.25 in. If armature speed is 1,200 rpm and the flux surrounding each coil side is 300 maxwells per amp, calculate the voltage of self-induction for a total armature current of 800 amp.

Solution

Brush width referred to armature-core surface $= \dfrac{20}{15} \times 1.25 = 1.67$ in.

Time of commutation $= \dfrac{1.67}{\pi \times 20 \times (1{,}200/60)} = 0.00133$ sec

$\phi_c =$ flux surrounding *both* coil sides $= 300 \times \dfrac{800}{6} \times 2 = 80{,}000$ maxwells

$E_i = 3 \times \dfrac{2 \times 80{,}000}{0.00133} \times 10^{-8} = 3.6$ volts

Commutator Flashover

If a sudden heavy overload is imposed upon a d-c machine, the cross-magnetizing effect of armature reaction may distort the field so rapidly and to such an extent that an arc may be caused to form between plus and minus brushes. When this occurs the commutator is said to flashover, a condition that represents a severe short circuit.

Since a transient overload is always accompanied by a cross field that is practically proportional to the current rise, abnormal voltages of self-induction are developed in those coils which lie in the regions of high flux density. Also, the more suddenly the overload is applied, the greater will be the induced voltages because the latter depend directly upon the *rate of change of flux*. Now then, if the potential difference of the coil (or coils) that is (are) connected to adjacent commutator segments is sufficiently high, electrical breakdown will occur and an arc will form between the segments involved. Such a condition is, of course, equivalent to reducing the number of segments between plus and minus brushes; the result is that the line potential redistributes itself across the remaining active segments so that the emf between those which are adjacent is raised. This is immediately followed by the breakdown between the next pair of segments as the peak of the flux-density wave (see Fig. 64c) moves closer to the center of the pole. The sequence of flux redistributions now continues and progresses more rapidly, more segments are short-circuited, and the arc lengthens to extend eventually between brushes.

Since flashover is the result of a sudden and violent field distortion, it must be prevented by windings which carry exactly the same current— the armature current—originally responsible for the trouble and which must create an instantaneous reciprocal magnetic effect. Such windings, called *compensating windings*, are used in machines of the larger ratings, and only when the generators or motors are subjected to overloads that cause rapid inrushes of current; they are discussed in Chap. 6.

Experimental Determination of Flux-density Distribution

It should be clear that the actual flux-density distribution under the pole faces and in the interpolar zones results from the interaction of magnetic fields produced by the stationary poles and the armature mmf. Moreover, a particular distribution is determined by considerations of magnetic-circuit design and load conditions and is, in part, an indication of the manner in which the machine will perform in practice. Data for plotting such a curve may be readily obtained experimentally.

Since the average instantaneous voltage generated in a coil of wire, as it passes over a small increment of the circumference, is equal to $e =$

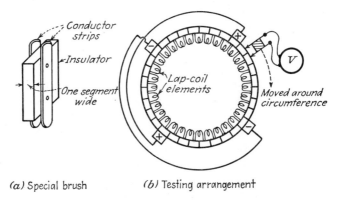

(a) Special brush   *(b)* Testing arrangement

Fig. 67. Sketches illustrating construction of test brush and procedure for determining the flux-density distribution experimentally.

$N(\Delta\phi/\Delta t) \times 10^{-8}$ volts, it is also directly proportional to the average flux density in that region. This is so because $\Delta\phi = B \times l \times \Delta\rho$, where B is the flux density, l is the axial length of the core, and $\Delta\rho$ is a small increment of armature circumference; thus, $e = NBl(\Delta\rho/\Delta t) \times 10^{-8}$. If provision is made for the measurement of a series of potential differences between a succession of equal distances $\Delta\rho$ as the armature rotates at constant speed, the terms N, l, and $\Delta\rho/\Delta t$ become constants; therefore $e = kB$ for all measurements, so that the various voltages are related to each other in exactly the same way as are the flux densities. A plot of voltages with respect to distances from a given brush can then be drawn and its shape will be a duplicate of the flux-density distribution.

Voltage measurements may conveniently be made with a special brush rigging, constructed of a piece of insulating material, such as wood or bakelite, and two brass or copper strips. The conducting strips should be fastened to opposite faces of the insulator so that the smooth, well-rounded projecting contacts are separated by a distance equal to the width of one commutator segment (see Fig. 67a). The device should then be mounted in a rocker arm with provision for radial and circumferential adjustment. Then, with the lower contacts touching adjacent commutator segments and the upper contacts connected to a low-reading voltmeter, the special brush rigging should be moved in steps, one segment at a time, from one main brush of one polarity to the adjacent brush of the opposite polarity (see Fig. 67b). A record should be made of the voltmeter deflections and the segment numbers.

Interpretation of the results is, of course, important. If the winding is simplex-lap, then the voltmeter readings represent single-coil elements; if simplex-wave, each of the deflections will be due to $P/2$ coil elements connected in series. For duplex-lap or -wave windings the insulating piece should be two segments wide or the contact strips should be bent out to touch alternate segments; corresponding adjustments must be made for other winding types.

Since the flux density at any position is a function of the *generated emf*, the measured voltages must be corrected to include the IR drop in the coil element or elements. This is easily done by calculating the proper voltage drop in the coil or coils and adding it to the recorded value; when taking data for the no-load distribution, the drop will, of course, be zero.

PROBLEMS

1. A 4-pole 100-kw 250-volt shunt generator has a wave-wound armature with 4 conductors in each of its 55 slots. If the ratio of pole arc to pole pitch is 0.72, calculate the maximum cross-magnetizing ampere-turns that magnetize or demagnetize each pole tip when the armature carries rated current. (Neglect the shunt-field current.)

2. The following information is given in connection with a 1,500-kw 600-volt 12-pole compound generator: armature diameter = 66 in., pole arc = 11.5 in., winding = frog leg, total number of armature conductors = 1,776. Neglecting the shunt-field current, calculate the full-load maximum cross-magnetizing ampere-turns at the tip of each pole.

3. The diameter of a 6-pole lap-wound armature is 22 in. and each of the 75 slots contains 4 conductors. If $\tau = 0.652$, calculate the demagnetizing ampere-turns per pole for an armature current of 1,200 amp if the brushes are shifted from the mechanical neutral to a point on the commutator directly under the tip of the pole. (The coil ends of the armature winding are connected unsymmetrically to the commutator with respect to the coil sides.)

4. Determine the total cross-magnetizing ampere-turns per pole for Example 3.

5. An 8-pole lap-wound armature, whose full-load current is 670 amp, has a core with 132 slots, each one containing 12 conductors, and a commutator having a diameter of 32 in. If the brushes are shifted on the commutator to 2.25 in. from the no-load neutral, calculate (a) the demagnetizing ampere-turns per pole; (b) the total cross-magnetizing ampere-turns per pole.

6. Calculate the voltage of self-induction in each of the 4-turn coil elements of an armature winding, given the following information: peripheral speed of the coils = 6,200 fpm (feet per minute), brush width = 1.5 in., commutator diameter is $\frac{3}{4}$ × core diameter, flux surrounding each coil side = 58,000 maxwells.

7. Each of the wave-wound armature-winding coil elements has 8 turns and carries 6.4 amp. The core and commutator diameters are 5 and 4 in., respectively, the speed is 1,750 rpm, and the brush width is 0.875 in. If the flux surrounding each coil side is 2,500 maxwells per amp, calculate the voltage of self-induction.

8. What maximum armature current can the winding of Prob. 7 carry if the voltage of self-induction must not exceed 5.5 volts?

CHAPTER 6

INTERPOLES AND COMPENSATING WINDINGS

Need for Magnetic-flux Control

When the armature winding of a dynamo—generator or motor—carries current, it produces magnetic fields of its own that disturb the desirable main-pole flux distributions and, by developing voltages of self-induction, acts against the normal function of commutation. Chapter 5 discussed armature reaction and its objectionable effects; these are field distortion and the tendency to flashover, demagnetization, continual shifting of the magnetic neutral with changing loads, and the self-induced emf that opposes current reversal during the short-circuit period. If the machine operates at a constant load, the armature current does not change and the brushes can, of course, be shifted to a position that provides sparkless commutation. In practice, however, loads are not generally steady, so that a compromise brush position must be determined, or provision must be made to move the brushes to new positions for all major changes in load. Moreover, where a motor must be used in an application requiring frequent reversal, commutation will necessarily be poor because the brushes, under this condition, are usually set on the no-load neutral.

It is obvious, therefore, that, for satisfactory performance, machines must be designed to counteract or neutralize the disturbing effects of armature reaction; moreover, this must be done so that the very current that is responsible for the original difficulties—the armature current—creates a reciprocal action of *exactly the correct magnitude and in direct proportion to the load*. Clearly, this compensation must be provided by stationary poles or windings that are electromagnetic in character and must be energized by the same current that passes through the armature winding; such poles or windings, when properly designed, will then serve to maintain sparkless commutation and good field distribution *automatically*. Commutator sparking is avoided by the use of interpoles, while field distortion is minimized when compensating windings are employed.

Interpoles for D-C Generators

The principle of interpoles has been known for many years, but it was not until the early 1900's that interpoles were designed so that they not only neutralize the effect of armature reaction in the neutral zone but compensate for the voltage of self-induction as well. Prior to their general

97

adoption, commutation difficulties were responsible for an ineffective use of the materials of construction; with them, however, armature currents are, comparatively, much higher so that outputs are correspondingly larger and commutation is greatly improved. *Interpoles* are narrow poles placed exactly halfway between the main poles, centering on the mechanical neutral planes. The exciting windings for these poles are always permanently connected in series with the armature winding because the interpoles (sometimes called *commutating poles*) must produce fluxes in their

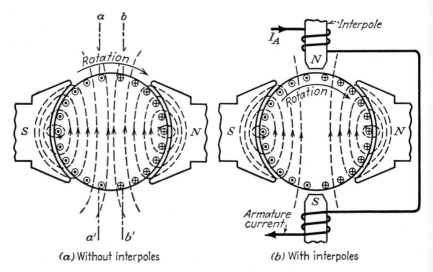

(a) Without interpoles   (b) With interpoles

Fig. 68. Sketches illustrating armature-flux distributions in a d-c generator without and with interpoles.

air gaps that are proportional to the armature current. Such a relationship can exist only when the iron portions of the magnetic circuits are unsaturated, which means that the interpoles must be operated below the knee of the magnetization curve. In practice, therefore, the interpole mmf is, at all times, capable of nullifying the armature cross-magnetizing ampere-turns per pole and injecting sufficient flux into the armature, in the commutating zone, to offset the effect of self-induction; it thus performs its useful mission of keeping the magnetic neutral fixed in space regardless of the load and counteracting the emf of self-induction.

The action of the interpole in the d-c generator may be understood by referring to Fig. 68 in connection with the following discussion. In the two-pole machine of Fig. 68a, note that the armature mmf creates a field vertically upward. Since the portion of this field that lies in the narrow interpolar zones between lines aa' and bb' is, in part, responsible for poor commutation, it should be clear that poles located in this area and creating an mmf of the proper magnitude and direction will counteract the effect of armature reaction. A pair of such poles is shown in Fig. 68b with the resultant magnetic field; observe that the commutating zones are now free of magnetism.

Now then, if the mmf is further increased so that flux is actually injected into the armature to counteract the detrimental effect of self-induction, the flux distribution will appear like that shown in Fig. 69. Observe that two separate sets of magnetic lines of force are indicated, because it helps

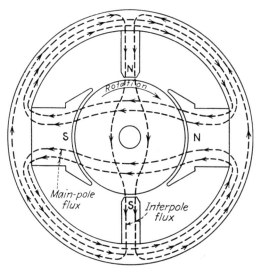

Fig. 69. Sketch showing the independent flux paths set up by the main and commutating poles in a two-pole d-c generator.

to emphasize the real functions of the main and commutating poles; it should be understood, however, that the actual flux distribution combines both into a rather complex pattern. Note particularly that *the polarities of the interpoles in a generator are the same as that of the succeeding main poles in the direction of rotation.*

Another important fact concerning *interpoles* is that they *have no effect upon the armature mmf that distorts the main field.* Field distortion is still present and, as was previously pointed out, flashover can occur if abnormally heavy loads are suddenly applied. Figure 70 illustrates the armature mmf and flux-density distributions that are set up in an interpole machine. Clearly shown in the resultant curve are (1) the excess flux that is injected into the armature to overcome the emf of self-induction and (2) the still-existing field distortion.

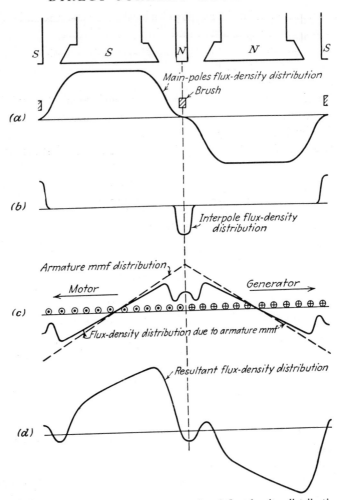

FIG. 70. Sketches illustrating the armature mmf and flux-density distributions for an interpole machine.

Interpoles for D-C Motors

The principle of interpoles discussed in connection with d-c generators applies equally well to the operation of d-c motors. There is one important difference, however, and this is that *the polarities of the interpoles in a motor must be the same as the preceding main poles in the direction of rotation.* A sketch illustrating the reason for this is given in Fig. 71 (compare with Fig. 68). Note that the cross-magnetizing field of the armature mmf is directed vertically downward; this means that the polarities of the interpoles must be such as to direct their field vertically upward if the latter is to counteract the effect of armature reaction. On the other hand, viewed from the standpoint of its *counter emf*, the interpole and main-pole polarities of the motor are exactly similar to those of the generator. It is well to understand these polarity relationships, and particularly so in connec-

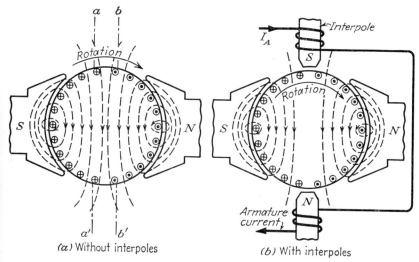

(a) Without interpoles

(b) With interpoles

Fig. 71. Sketches illustrating armature-flux distributions in a d-c motor without and with interpoles.

tion with machines that must operate interchangeably both as motors and generators.

Interpole Ampere-turns

Assuming the same number of interpoles as main poles, each one must be provided with sufficient ampere-turns to accomplish three things simultaneously. These are: (1) it must oppose the total cross-magnetizing ampere-turns of armature reaction in its own commutating zone; (2) it must inject flux into the armature to nullify the effect of self-induction and thus overcome the reluctance of its own air gap; and (3) it must overcome the reluctance of its iron magnetic-flux paths.

To oppose the total cross-magnetizing ampere-turns per pole, the interpole must develop, first of all, $ZI_A/2aP$ amp-turns. Secondly, the interpole must send ϕ_c maxwells across the air gap, whose equivalent length is $\delta_e \times 2.54$ cm, where δ_e, in inches, is slightly larger than the actual air gap because of the slotted armature. But

$$\phi_c = \frac{B_{gi}}{6.45} \times A_{gi}$$

and

$$\phi_c = \frac{\text{mmf}}{\mathcal{R}} = \frac{0.4\pi \times (NI)_{gi}}{(\delta_e \times 2.54)/A_{gi}}$$

where B_{gi} = flux density in the air gap, lines per sq in.
A_{gi} = air-gap area, sq cm
$(NI)_{gi}$ = interpole amp-turns for the air gap
Equating both values of ϕ_c

$$\frac{B_{gi} \times A_{gi}}{6.45} = \frac{0.4\pi \times (NI)_{gi} \times A_{gi}}{\delta_e \times 2.54}$$

from which

$$(NI)_{gi} = 0.313 B_{gi} \times \delta_e \qquad (24)$$

The third item, requiring that the interpole have sufficient ampere-turns to overcome the reluctance of the iron portions of the magnetic circuit, is usually estimated as being about 0.4 to 0.8 times the air-gap ampere-turns. Taking an average value of about $0.6(NI)_{gi}$ for the iron, the total interpole ampere-turns is, practically,

$$(NI)_i = \frac{ZI_A}{2aP} + (0.313 B_{gi} \times \delta_e) + (0.6 \times 0.313 B_{gi} \times \delta_e)$$

and

$$(NI)_i = \frac{ZI_A}{2aP} + 0.5 B_{gi}\delta_e = \frac{1}{2}\left(\frac{ZI_A}{aP} + B_{gi}\delta_e\right) \qquad (25$$

It is interesting to note that the interpole ampere-turns are independent of the physical dimensions of the interpoles; however, in good designs interpoles are carefully proportioned on the basis of minimum leakage flux, low flux densities, and reasonably low copper losses. Another significant point is that machines are frequently designed with half as many interpoles as main poles. When this is done, some saving is made in the cost of manufacture, although each interpole, performing the function of the usual two poles, must be about twice as large.

EXAMPLE 1. Calculate the number of ampere-turns required by an interpole to overcome the reluctance of the air gap for a flux density of 14,800 lines per sq in., if the equivalent length of the air gap is 0.28 in.

Solution

$$(NI)_{gi} = 0.313 \times 14,800 \times 0.28 = 1.300 \text{ amp-turns}$$

EXAMPLE 2. The armature of a 6-pole machine has a wave winding with a total of 328 conductors and carries a current of 280 amp at full load. If the air-gap flux density under each interpole is 12,500 lines per sq in. and the equivalent air-gap length is 0.24 in., calculate (a) the number of amp-turns required by each of the six interpoles; (b) the number of turns on each interpole.

Solution

$$(a) \quad (NI)_i = \frac{1}{2}\left[\left(\frac{328 \times 280}{2 \times 6}\right) + (12{,}500 \times 0.24)\right] = 5{,}320 \text{ amp-turns}$$

$$(b) \quad N = \frac{5{,}320}{280} = 19 \text{ turns per interpole}$$

Figure 8 illustrates a typical interpole for a d-c motor, ready for bolting to the yoke frame, and Fig. 72 shows a completely assembled field structure

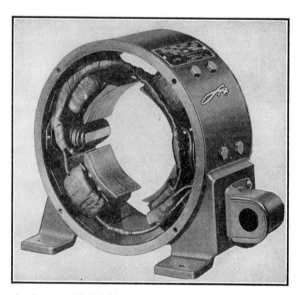

FIG. 72. Completely assembled field structure for a d-c motor. Note the four main poles and the two interpoles. (*The Louis Allis Co.*)

that has four main poles and two interpoles; one of the interpoles is clearly visible on the left.

In the design of dynamos it is usually customary to be somewhat liberal in the use of interpole-field turns and, after construction, make the necessary adjustments when the machines are actually tested under load. The reason for this practice is that Eq. (25) is, in part, empirical and, therefore, involves values that may be somewhat in question; the terms ϕ_c, δ_e, and B_{gi} are rather difficult to evaluate accurately. Two methods, both readily applied, may be employed to bring down the *effective* number of turns to the proper value for good commutation; these are (1) to shunt the interpole winding with a resistance and (2) to alter the reluctance of the interpole magnetic circuit by adjusting the air-gap length. The first of these requires that a low-resistance shunt, placed in parallel with the interpole winding, reduce the current in the latter by exactly the same percentage as the number of turns are in excess of the correct number; several trial adjustments are generally required while the machine is undergoing test. This shunt-resistance method is not particularly satisfactory when the load changes rapidly and suddenly, and this is more often the case than not. The reason for the poor operation is that the shunt resistance is noninductive while the interpole field possesses considerable self-inductance. Thus when the armature current changes suddenly because of load fluctuation, the interpole-winding current does not respond with the same rapidity as does the current through the shunt resistance; the result is that commutation may be poor since the interpole flux may be inadequate or too much during the period of load change. The second method of adjustment is more widely used since it avoids the difficulty indicated. The procedure is to employ interpoles whose radial length is somewhat shorter than required and then insert a combination of thin magnetic and nonmagnetic shims between interpole core and yoke where the two are bolted together; the shims then make up for the short core so that the correct, *actual* air-gap length is maintained. Then, when the machine is placed on test, adjustment is made by interchanging magnetic for nonmagnetic shims, or vice versa, to secure good commutation. For example, if the interpole flux is too great, more nonmagnetic shims are substituted for the magnetic type, under which condition the total reluctance of the magnetic circuit is increased and the injected flux reduced; the reverse substitution is made if the interpole flux is insufficient.

The fact that the brushes need not be shifted when interpoles are used means, of course, that the armature does not develop demagnetizing ampere-turns in accordance with Eq. (21). However, distortion resulting from the cross-magnetizing action of armature reaction is still present as indicated by Fig. 70d.

Compensating Windings

As was previously pointed out, flashover may occur between plus and minus brushes when a heavy surge is imposed upon a machine; a good example of a d-c motor operating under such conditions is a rolling-mill application in a steel mill that must be rapidly and frequently reversed. Since this kind of short circuit is brought about by the cross-magnetizing action of the armature that causes field distortion, it is logical that designers would investigate the possibility of annulling the armature mmf, the seat of the difficulty. The first practical method of compensation was proposed by Menges in Germany, and he was granted a patent for the original *compensating winding* in 1884. The winding he described consisted of groups of conductors placed in slots cut into the main-pole faces and connected together in such a manner as to create a cross field that directly opposed the one developed by the armature. Moreover, this pole-face winding was connected in series with the armature so that the same current—the armature current—was made responsible for both the armature mmf and the compensating-field mmf. This principle of compensa-

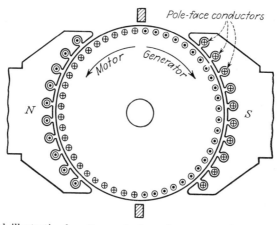

Fig. 73. Sketch illustrating how the conductors of a compensating winding are arranged in the pole faces, and the current directions with respect to those in the armature.

tion was later investigated by Ryan, Thompson, and others in the United States and, with some modifications and improvements, is the one now generally employed in modern machines.

Figure 73 illustrates how the conductors for such a winding are placed in the pole faces and indicates the current directions with respect to those in the armature winding. Heavy insulated copper bars are usually driven into the pole-face slots after which properly shaped wires connect the extended ends to form coils around the cylindrical armature. In the simple two-pole sketch (modern machines having compensating windings are multipolar) one set of connectors would join the upper five pole-face conductors on the *north* pole to the upper five conductors on the *south* pole, while similar connections would be made for the lower ten conductors of the *north* and *south* poles; the two sets would then be joined in series and connected in series with the armature winding. A diagram showing how this is done for part of a multipolar dynamo is given in Fig. 74. Note particularly that half the *even* number of conductors on the left side of one pole face are joined in series to half the conductors on the right side of the adjacent pole face and in such a manner that the current directions in these conductors are opposite to those in the wires of the armature winding directly below. In following the path of the current through the three turns (six conductors) of one of the coils, the start may be considered as being at the front of conductor a; then proceeding consecutively through conductors b, c, d, and e, the coil ends at the front of conductor f. It is, in fact, as though a coil of wire were wound in a sort of spiral with con-

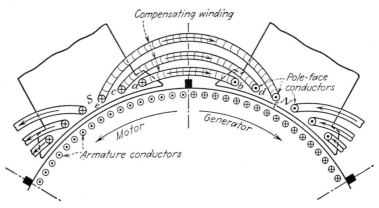

Fᴵɢ. 74. Sketch illustrating a portion of a compensating winding for a multipolar machine. Note the current directions in the pole-face conductors and the armature conductors.

ductors a and b representing part of the inside turn and conductors e and f representing part of the outside turn.

Since the compensating winding, in modern machines, must neutralize only that portion of the armature cross-magnetizing ampere-turns that lie directly under the pole faces, it must, for 100 per cent compensation, always build up an mmf that is equal to the armature mmf per *pole face;* this is, by Eq. (20), $\tau Z I_A / 2aP$ amp-turns per pole. But the compensating-winding current is the *total* armature current I_A. It follows, therefore, that

$$\frac{\tau Z I_A}{2aP} = \frac{C I_A}{2}$$

where C is the number of conductors in each pole face. Hence

$$C = \frac{\tau Z}{aP} \tag{26}$$

ExᴀᴍᴘʟE 3. A 3,000-kw 600-volt 16-pole generator has a lap-wound armature with a total of 3,250 conductors. If the pole faces cover 63 per cent of the entire circumference, calculate (a) the current in the compensating winding; (b) the number of conductors in each pole face of the compensating winding. (Neglect the shunt-field current.)

Solution

(a)
$$I_A = \frac{3,000 \text{ kw}}{0.6 \text{ kv}} = 5,000 \text{ amp}$$

(b)
$$C = \frac{0.63 \times 3,250}{16 \times 16} = 8$$

The use of compensating windings together with properly designed interpole windings in d-c machines will provide sparkless commutation and eliminate the possibility of flashover, at least insofar as armature reaction is concerned. These desirable operating characteristics come about because the resultant field is absolutely uniform and the interpolar zones are supplied with the necessary flux to combat the voltage of self-inductance; moreover, such conditions prevail at all values of armature current because the neutralizing effects are caused by the very current that is

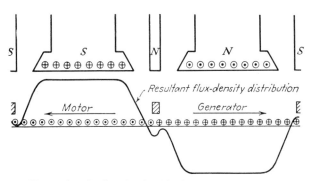

Fig. 75. Sketch illustrating the flux-density distribution that results from the combined actions of the main-pole, interpole, compensating winding, and armature mmf fields.

initially responsible for the difficulty. Figure 75 illustrates the typical flux-density distribution that results from the combined actions of the main-pole, interpole, compensating winding, and armature mmf fields.

Since the effects of armature reaction and armature reactance are virtually nullified by the use of compensating windings and interpoles, such machines usually have air gaps that are as short as mechanical clearance will permit. This is due to the fact that the reluctance of the magnetic paths, upon which the armature mmf acts, need no longer be comparatively high for the purpose of limiting the armature flux. As a result, short-air-gap machines may use fewer ampere-turns for main-field excitation with accompanying reductions in field copper and copper loss.

Summarizing the study of magnetic fields, it may be stated that a modern machine may have as many as four complete windings on the stationary frame; these are (1) the shunt-field winding, (2) the series-field winding, (3) the interpole winding, and (4) the compensating winding. Interpoles are used on most dynamos whether shunt, series, or compound. Compensating windings, on the other hand, are generally found on machines of the larger ratings and only when their special load applications justify the added expense. To emphasize further the manner in which all the field windings are interconnected and the currents that energize them, Fig. 76 is given. Note particularly that the arrow directions are drawn to indicate the relative directions of the mmfs with respect to each other.

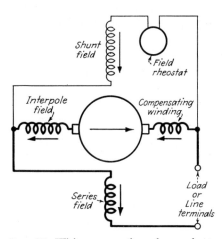

FIG. 76. Wiring connections for a short-shunt compound dynamo with four field windings. The arrow directions indicate the relative directions of the magnetic fields.

Figure 9 illustrates a completely assembled stator frame containing all four fields. Clearly seen is the pole-face compensating winding with six conductors in each pole face.

PROBLEMS

1. Each of the interpoles of a 750-kw 250-volt generator produces a flux density of 11,600 lines per sq in. in its air gap, whose equivalent length is 0.3 in. Calculate (a) the number of ampere-turns required for the air gap; (b) the current in the interpole winding at full load. (Neglect the shunt-field current.)

2. Assuming a straight-line relationship between flux density and ampere-turns, calculate the kilowatt load of the generator of Prob. 1 if the interpole air-gap flux density is 13,900 lines per sq in.

3. A 500-hp 600-volt 8-pole d-c motor has a lap-wound armature with a total of 1,584 conductors. If the flux density in the air gap of each interpole is 10,700 lines per sq in. at full load and the equivalent gap length is 0.26 in., calculate (a) the interpole field ampere-turns per pole; (b) the number of turns on each interpole. (Assume a motor efficiency of 93 per cent and neglect the shunt-field current.)

4. The leakage flux between main poles and interpoles is usually considerable so that the leakage factor [see Eq. (11), Chap. 3] for the interpoles is much more than it is for the main poles. If the interpole leakage factor of 2.5 for Prob. 3 and tapered interpoles are used, what should be the width of the laminations near the yoke if the width near the air gap is 1.5 in., assuming that the flux density at yoke section is not to exceed 16,000 lines per sq in. at full load?

5. The following information is given in connection with a 500-kw 460-volt 6-pole generator: $Z = 432$, winding-lap, interpole $\delta_e = 0.34$ in., interpole turns-per-pole = 16, number of interpoles = 3. Calculate the air-gap flux density under the interpole at full load. (Neglect the shunt-field current.)

6. A 1,500-hp 10-pole motor has a lap-wound armature with a total of 960 conductors. If the ratio of the pole arc to pole pitch is 0.625, calculate the number of pole-face conductors in each of the poles of the compensating winding.

7. An 8-pole lap-wound motor has a compensating winding with 8 conductors in each pole face. The armature diameter is 40 in. and the main-pole arc is 9.5 in. Calculate the number of armature conductors in the machine.

CHAPTER 7

GENERATOR CHARACTERISTICS

General Voltage versus Load Relations

After a d-c generator is brought up to speed and is excited so that the proper no-load voltage is established (this applies to separately and self-excited machines), it is ready for loading. This means that the armature, the source of the electric energy, can deliver current to the appliances, machines, and devices connected to its terminals. As the armature current varies with changing values of load, the voltage will, in general, tend to fall or rise at the generator or load terminals, or both, although, under ideal conditions, it is desirable that the *load* voltage remain substantially constant. Moreover, the extent to which the voltage will fluctuate *at the load* will depend upon several things, the most important of which are (1) the type of generator, *i.e.*, shunt, series, or compound; (2) the design of the generator, involving such factors as armature resistance, interpoles, magnetic-circuit proportions, and flux densities; (3) degree of compounding if the generator is a compound type; (4) distance between the generator and load; (5) whether or not the machine is equipped with a voltage regulator; and (6) the speed at which the generator is operated.

The following statements concerning the *general voltage* vs. *load characteristics* may, however, be made with regard to the three types of generators and their loads: (1) the terminal voltage of a shunt generator tends to drop as it delivers more load; (2) the degree of compounding of a compound generator will determine if the terminal voltage will rise, fall, or remain constant; (3) the voltage of a series generator tends to rise to a certain maximum value as more load is delivered and then begins to drop off as the delivered current increases further; (4) the voltage at the load diminishes as the latter is moved to greater distances from the generator; (5) the voltage of a shunt generator tends to drop less between no load and full load if the machine is operated at a lower speed; (6) the number of series-field turns with respect to the number of shunt-field turns will determine how the terminal voltage of a compound generator will vary as the load is changed.

Per Cent Voltage Regulation

To indicate the extent to which the voltage of a generator changes as the load is gradually lowered from its rated value to zero load, it is customary to use the term *voltage regulation*, or preferably *per cent voltage regulation*. As approved by the *American Standards Association*, per cent voltage regulation is defined as ". . . the final change in voltage with constant field-rheostat setting when the specified load is reduced gradually to zero, expressed as a per cent of rated voltage, the speed being kept constant." Since the speed of the prime mover and its generator usually varies somewhat between full load and no load, it is often desirable to take this into account by specifying the *over-all per cent voltage regulation*, the latter being affected by both the generator-voltage and prime-mover-speed characteristics. The foregoing may be expressed in equation form as follows:

$$\text{Per cent voltage regulation} = \frac{E - V_{FL}}{V_{FL}} \times 100 \qquad (27)$$

where V_{FL} = the full-load (rated) voltage
  E = the no-load (generated) voltage

EXAMPLE 1.   The full-load voltage of a shunt generator is 240. What is the per cent voltage regulation of the machine if the terminal emf rises to 252 when the load is reduced to zero?

Solution

$$\text{Per cent regulation} = \frac{252 - 240}{240} \times 100 = 5$$

EXAMPLE 2.   A 50-kw 460-volt shunt generator has a voltage regulation of 8.7 per cent. (*a*) Calculate the no-load terminal voltage. (*b*) Assuming that the voltage varies uniformly between no-load and full-load current, calculate the kilowatt output of the generator for a terminal voltage of 475.

Solution

(*a*) $8.7 = \dfrac{E_{NL} - 460}{460} \times 100$ $E_{NL} = \dfrac{8.7 \times 460}{100} + 460 = 500$ volts

(*b*) $I_{FL} = \dfrac{50,000}{460} = 108.7$ amp $I_{475} = 108.7 \times \dfrac{500 - 475}{500 - 460} = 68$ amp

$P_{475} = \dfrac{475 \times 68}{1,000} = 32.3$ kw

Shunt-generator Behavior under Load—No Demagnetization

Since the armature is the *source* of the electric energy, it is, therefore, the seat of all variations in the terminal voltage V_t as the load imposed upon a shunt generator rises or falls; this implies that any modification in V_t must result from a change in the generated emf E and the resistance-voltage drops in the armature circuit. Or, to put it another way, the external voltage V_t must be less than the internal voltage E by a value that is equal to the voltage drop in the armature-circuit resistance. Thus, if I_A is the armature current and R_A is the total armature-circuit resistance

$$V_t = E - I_A R_A \tag{28}$$

But $E = k\phi$ [Eq. (7), Chap. 3] for a given generator operating at constant speed. Therefore,

$$V_t = k\phi - I_A R_A \tag{28a}$$

If the generator is *separately excited,* has interpoles so that no brush shift is necessary to attain good commutation, and demagnetization due to

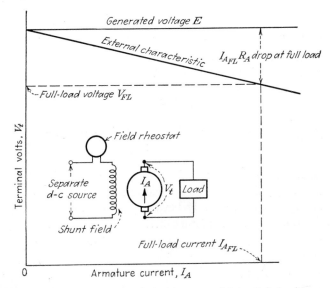

Fig. **77.** External V_t vs. I_A characteristic for a *separately excited* shunt generator with no demagnetization.

pole-tip saturation is neglected, the flux ϕ will remain constant for all values of load; under this condition Eq. (28a) becomes $V_t = k_1 - I_A R_A$, an equation of a straight line. Figure 77 shows graphically the relation between V_t and I_A, the so-called *external characteristic,* for such a machine and indicates that the full-load terminal voltage V_{FL} is less than the constant generated voltage E by the armature-resistance voltage drop $I_{A_{FL}} R_A$. For all other values of load current I_A the armature drop will obviously be less or more than the full-load value so that the terminal voltage will rise or fall correspondingly. An example will now be given to illustrate the foregoing discussion.

EXAMPLE 3. A 40-kw 250-volt separately excited interpole shunt generator has an armature-circuit resistance (includes brush contacts) of 0.12 ohm. Neglecting any demagnetizing action, (a) calculate the generated emf and the per cent regulation; (b) determine the terminal voltage and power delivered by the armature when the load current is 120 amp.

Solution

(a) $I_{A_{FL}} = \dfrac{40,000}{250} = 160$ amp $I_{A_{FL}} \times R_A = 160 \times 0.12 = 19.2$ volts

$E = 250 + 19.2 = 269.2$ Per cent regulation $= \dfrac{19.2 \times 100}{250}$

$= 7.68$

(b) $V_{120} = 269.2 - (120 \times 0.12) = 254.8$

$P_{120} = \dfrac{254.8 \times 120}{1,000} = 30.58$ kw

If a shunt generator is *self-excited*, the field winding is connected across its own armature terminals where the voltage changes under varying load conditions. This means that the flux will no longer remain constant as in the separately excited machine, and such variation will result in changing values of generated emf. It follows, therefore, that the terminal voltage V_t will not only suffer on the basis of armature-resistance drop but also because the field ampere-turns and the accompanying generated voltage E will be affected. To determine the resulting terminal voltage for a given load current delivered by the armature, it is, unfortunately, not possible to make a simple mathematical calculation as for the separately excited generator; a graphical solution is generally necessary. Referring to Eq. (28a), it should be clear that V_t depends upon two terms, one of which, $I_A R_A$, is usually known and the other of which, $k\phi$, is a function of the very result, V_t, it is desired to evaluate. A simple graphical solution for V_t is, however, possible if it is recognized that the vertical distance between a given point on the *magnetization curve* and the corresponding equal-field-current point on the *excitation line* (Fig. 47) is the $I_A R_A$ voltage drop for the particular armature current I_A. This is due to the fact that, *for a given value of field current I_f*, the generated voltage ($E = k\phi$) is located on the magnetization curve, while the voltage across the shunt-field resistance (the same value V_t as that across the armature terminals) is located on the excitation line. Thus, if a vertically scaled length equal to $I_A R_A$ ($= k\phi - V_t$) is moved between the two curves until it fits exactly *between* the magnetization curve and excitation line, the upper and lower ends will designate the values of E ($= k\phi$) and V_t, respectively.

The awkward procedure described above may be greatly simplified, and the value of V_t may be determined for any load current I_A in the following

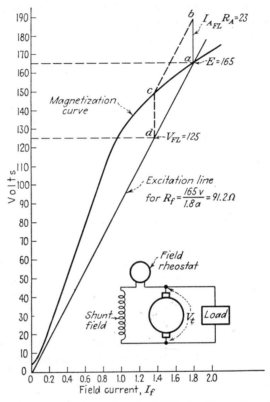

FIG. 78. Graphical method to determine the full-load voltage of a *self-excited* shunt generator with no demagnetization.

manner. Starting at the intersection of the magnetization curve and the excitation line (Fig. 78), draw a line *ab* vertically upward equal to the $I_{A_{FL}} R_A$ drop. Next, from point *b*, draw a line parallel to the excitation line, and from the point *c*, where it intersects the magnetization curve, draw another line vertically downward until, at point *d*, it intersects the excitation line; line *cd* is obviously the $I_{A_{FL}} R_A$ drop since it is equal to line *ab*. For the example selected the no-load voltage $E = 165$, the $I_{A_{FL}} R_A$ drop $= 23$, the full-load voltage $V_{FL} = 125$, and the per cent regulation $= {}^{40}/_{125} \times 100 = 32$. Also, the total shunt-field resistance, from the excitation line, is equal to $165/1.8 = 91.2$ ohms.

If it is desired to obtain the complete external characteristic for the self-excited shunt generator with no demagnetization, a number of values of V_t must be determined graphically for a series of different armature currents, after which the V_t vs. I_A curve may be drawn. This may be done as illustrated by Fig. 79 in which, for convenience, the same voltage ordinate is used for the magnetization curve—excitation line drawn to the *left* and the external characteristic plotted to the right. As before, a vertical line is erected at the intersection of the magnetization curve and the excitation line, and the length ab is made equal to the full-load armature-resistance drop $I_{A_{FL}}R_A$. Since the armature drop is directly

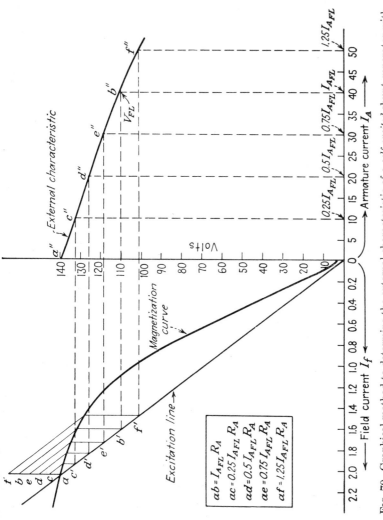

FIG. 79. Graphical method to determine the external characteristic of a *self-excited* shunt generator with no demagnetization.

proportional to I_A, points c, d, e, and f are located for selected values of armature current that are, respectively, 0.25, 0.5, 0.75, and 1.25 times I_{AFL}. To locate the points b'', c'', d'', e'', and f'' on the external characteristic, it is merely necessary to follow the procedure previously described for Fig. 78 with the exception that the terminal voltages represented by b', c', d', e', and f' are projected to the right until the extended lines intersect with vertical lines drawn vertically from corresponding armature-current values. For the example chosen, $I_{AFL} = 40$, $I_{AFL}R_A = 20$, $E = 140$, $V_{FL} = 110$, and the per cent regulation $= {}^{30}/_{110} \times 100 = 27.3$.

Shunt-generator Behavior under Load—with Demagnetization

If a shunt generator has no interpoles, its brushes must be shifted in the direction of rotation for improved commutation. Such a shift is accompanied by a demagnetizing action [Eq. (21), Chap. 5]; moreover, pole-tip saturation causes further demagnetization though to a lesser extent. As a result of such reduction in net field ampere-turns, the flux is reduced and with it the generated emf. Thus, the terminal emf suffers a greater voltage drop than do machines that are not demagnetized.

If the generator is *separately excited*, the full-load terminal voltage V_{FL} may be determined graphically in the following manner. Referring to Fig. 80, note that the *total* excitation is represented by the distance Oa', while the *net* excitation, for full-load operation, is given by the distance Ob'; the demagnetizing ampere-turns equals the horizontal distance $b'a'$. Now then, since the voltage at point b represents the value *generated* in the armature for the net magnetization, the full-load terminal emf V_{FL} will be located by point c if the $I_{AFL}R_A$ drop is subtracted from the voltage at point b.

A more desirable way to determine the terminal voltage, and one that may be extended to yield the complete external characteristic, involves the following construction and procedure. Starting at point a, draw line ad to the left equal to the demagnetizing ampere-turns previously calculated. Next draw a line de vertically upward equal to the full-load armature-resistance drop. The points a and e are then joined by what is called the *load line*. To find V_{FL}, drop a vertical line from point e to point b on the magnetization curve and then draw a parallel to the load line to intersect aa' at point c'; the full-load terminal voltage V_{FL} is thus located at c' because the *load triangle ade* is, in effect, lowered to position $c'cb$.

The next step is to determine graphically a sufficient number of points for the external characteristic; this is done in a manner similar to that described for Fig. 79. Referring to Fig. 81, note that the magnetization curve is again drawn to the left while points for the external characteristic are plotted to the right. The latter are found by duplicating the construction of Fig. 80 for armature currents that are 0.25, 0.5, 0.75, 1.0, and 1.25 times I_{FL}, the starting points for which, c, d, e, b, and f, are laid off at proportional distances from a on the load line. It should be understood that the load line may be divided in proportion to the magnitude of

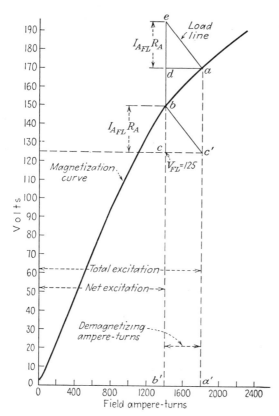

Fig. 80. Graphical method to determine the full-load voltage of a *separately excited* shunt generator with demagnetization.

the armature current because the armature-resistance drop and the demagnetizing ampere-turns are both direct functions of I_A. For the example chosen, $I_{A_{FL}} = 40$, $I_{A_{FL}}R_A = 20$, $E = 135$, $V_{FL} = 107$, and the per cent regulation $= {}^{28}\!/_{107} \times 100 = 26.2$.

To obtain the external characteristic of a *self-excited* generator, again with demagnetization, it is necessary to follow essentially the same construction procedure as previously described, with the exception that the *value of V_t*, resulting from a selected current I_A, *must terminate on the excitation line*. The latter condition must prevail because the terminal

voltage V_t is also the voltage across the shunt field, and the excitation
line merely expresses Ohm's law for the particular value of shunt-field
resistance. Figure 82 illustrates the graphical method that must be employed for this type of generator. Note particularly (1) that the load
line is drawn in the same manner as before and is divided proportionately
on the basis of I_A; (2) that a given point, such as b'' on the external characteristic, is found by drawing bb_1 parallel to the excitation line, b_1b'
parallel to the load line, and a horizontal line $b'b''$ to intersect the vertical
line at the 40-amp load; (3) that the location of a terminal voltage such
as V_{FL} involves, in effect, the fitting of the load triangle abb_2 between

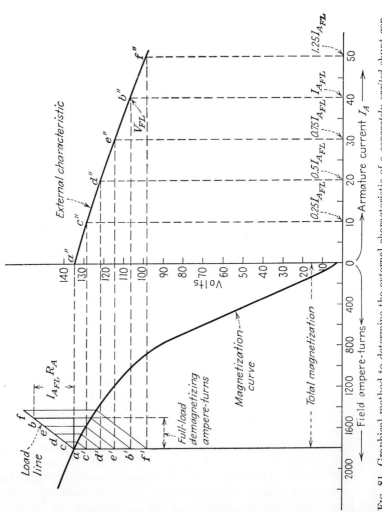

Fig. 81. Graphical method to determine the external characteristic of a separately excited shunt generator with demagnetization.

the magnetization curve and the excitation line so that it occupies the position $b'b_1b_3$; (4) that for a terminal voltage such as V_{FL} the voltage generated in the armature is located at point b_1; (5) that the armature can deliver a maximum current determined by a line drawn from a point on the load line *tangent to the magnetization curve;* (6) that after the maximum value of I_A is reached at point m'', the voltage of the generator rapidly drops to zero.

Compound-generator Behavior under Load—Cumulative

A great majority of present-day generators in service have two sources of field excitation, one of which, the shunt field, is practically independent

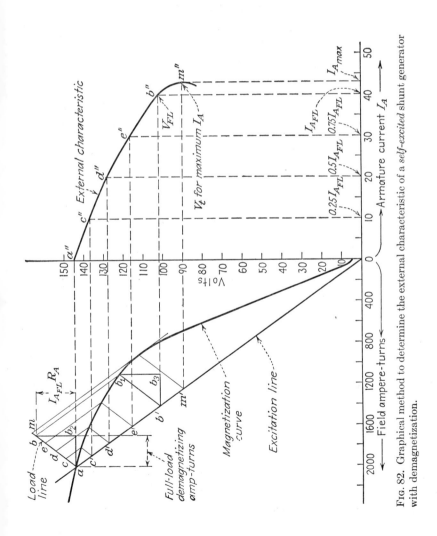

FIG. 82. Graphical method to determine the external characteristic of a *self-excited* shunt generator with demagnetization.

of the load, while the other, the series field, is energized by the load current; such machines are called *compound generators*. The addition of the series field connected to *aid* the shunt field has the important fundamental purpose of creating additional values of flux with increasing load currents so that the armature will generate greater voltages and thus compensate for the normal tendency of the shunt machine to lose terminal voltage (see Figs. 77, 79, 81, and 82). Remembering that $V_t = k\phi - I_A R_A$ [Eq. (28a)], it should be clear that V_{FL} can be made equal to V_{NL} if the term $k\phi$ is permitted to increase by an amount that is exactly equal to $I_{A_{FL}} R_A$ when the armature current changes from zero to $I_{A_{FL}}$; under this condition the machine is said to be a *flat-compound generator*. If, on the other hand, the series field has an overcompensating effect so that $k\phi$ increases to a greater extent between no load and full load than does $I_{A_{FL}} R_A$, the full-load terminal emf will exceed the no-load value; under this condition the machine is said to be *overcompounded*. Finally, if the full-load generated voltage $k\phi$ is more than the no-load value by an amount that is somewhat less than the armature-resistance drop $I_{A_{FL}} R_A$, the external characteristic may droop, though not to the same extent as for the self-excited shunt machine; under this condition the generator is said to be *undercompounded*.

Whether the generator will be flat-, over-, or undercompound will depend upon the number of series-field ampere-turns *with respect to the number of shunt-field ampere-turns*. The so-called *degree of compounding* is thus determined by the design of the main field and, once established, will yield the desired no-load and full-load terminal voltages. However, the emf between these two load conditions will not, in general, change on a proportionality basis because magnetic-saturation effects do not permit the flux to vary directly with the armature current. The result is that the external characteristics for the three general types of compound generator are not straight lines but are usually concave downwards; in the flat-compound generator, for example, the voltages *between* no load and full load will be higher than at the terminal loads.

The external characteristic of a compound generator may be determined in essentially the same way as was previously done for the shunt type of machine although, for the purposes of accuracy, the magnetization curve and the excitation line should be drawn to an enlarged scale. This was done in Fig. 83 where the useful upper portions of these graphs are shown to twice previous scales in the customary left-hand part of the drawing. Starting again as before at point a, the intersection between the magnetization curve and the excitation line, a horizontal line ab_1 is laid off to the left, its length representing the net *increase* in ampere-turns at full load over that provided at no load; the latter will be numerically equal to the series-field ampere-turns $N_{SE} I_A$ minus the total demagnetizing ampere-turns. The line $b_1 b$, equal to the full-load $I_{A_{FL}} R_A$ drop, is next scaled off vertically upward after which the load line ab and its extension to f are drawn in. Remembering that the generated emf for a given load must always lie on the magnetization curve while the terminal voltage for the same load must terminate on the excitation line, the procedure for locating a voltage such as V_{FL} involves (1) drawing bb_2 parallel to the excitation line until it intersects the magnetization curve, (2) drawing b_2b' parallel to the load line until it intersects the excitation line, and (3)

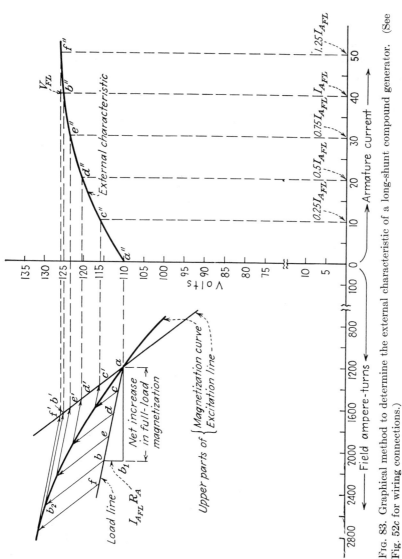

Fig. 83. Graphical method to determine the external characteristic of a long-shunt compound generator. (See Fig. 52c for wiring connections.)

drawing a horizontal line $b'b''$ until it intersects the vertical line erected at the I_{AFL} load current. This construction is actually equivalent to moving the load triangle ab_1b so that point a travels along the excitation line until it coincides with point b' under which condition point b coincides with point b_2. Other points on the external characteristic are located in the same manner for the $\frac{1}{4}$, $\frac{1}{2}$, $\frac{3}{4}$, and the 1.25 I_{AFL} loads, where the net magnetizations and the armature-resistance drops are proportional to the respective values of armature current.

In selecting the constants for Fig. 83, the net increase in the full-load magnetization was made comparatively large while the $I_{AFL}R_A$ was made rather small. This was done so that the external characteristic would be that of a typical overcompound generator; in this case $V_{NL} = 110$ and $V_{FL} = 125$.

Compound-generator Behavior under Load—Differential

Under certain special operating conditions the currents through the shunt- and series-field coils on each of the poles of a compound generator

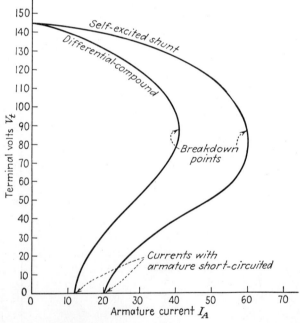

Fig. 84. Typical external-characteristic curves of a generator operated without (shunt) and with (differential-compound) the series field.

are in opposite directions; in such cases the action of the series-field mmf is to oppose the shunt-field mmf although the latter is, at all times, greater than the former. Such machines are called *differential-compound* generators since the effective flux is created by the difference between the shunt- and series-field mmfs. Their use is generally limited to such applications as booster systems and voltage-regulation equipment where they function in collaboration with other electrical units to oppose voltage fluctuations due to speed or load changes.

The analysis of this type of generator is essentially similar to that of a self-excited shunt machine with demagnetizing ampere-turns since the action of the series field to oppose the shunt field is exactly like that created by armature reaction. Considered from this point of view, therefore, it should be clear that a differential-compound generator with demagnetization will develop an external characteristic that droops, *i.e.*, loses terminal voltage, somewhat more than that illustrated by Fig. 82. In fact, a graphical plot may be carried out in an identical manner if the full-load demagnetizing ampere-turns in the load triangle, line ab_2, is made to equal the series-field ampere-turns plus the armature-reaction demagnetizing ampere-turns at rated armature current. A typical external characteristic for a differential-compound generator is shown in Fig. 84 in relation to the same machine operated without the series field, *i.e.*, as a self-excited shunt generator. Note particularly that the terminal voltage drops considerably faster when the opposing series field is used than when it is omitted.

Series-generator Behavior under Load

Because the *series generator* displays a rather unusual external characteristic, it finds very few suitable applications. In this country it is sometimes used as an auxiliary unit connected in series with a d-c system for voltage-boosting purposes or to minimize the leakage current in railway systems so that electrolytic action to underground structures may be reduced; in Europe it is sometimes employed in the *Thury* high-voltage d-c systems for the transmission of electric energy.

Since the armature, series field, and load are all connected in series, any current that is delivered to the load must, among other things, simultaneously serve to perform the following functions: (1) it must develop useful energy at the load; (2) it must provide the necessary excitation for the series field so that a voltage is generated in the armature; (3) it must create a demagnetizing armature-reaction effect. When the load is zero (on open circuit), the current is zero; under this condition the series-field ampere-turns will be zero and the generated voltage will be the residual value E_r. If the circuit is closed through a load resistance, a current I will flow, in which event the series field will create additional flux and thereby cause a higher voltage to be generated; at the same time the armature will develop a demagnetizing action, and a voltage drop will occur in the armature and series-field resistances R_A and R_{SE}. Therefore, the voltage that will appear at the series-generator terminals will be stabilized at some value that is a function of the net generated voltage (due to the net flux) and the $I(R_A + R_{SE})$ voltage drop. The terminal emf V_t will, obviously, rise with the load current so long as the over-all voltage increases more rapidly than those factors which tend to reduce it. For considerable overloads, however, the iron portions of the magnetic circuit become highly saturated, under which condition the subtractive effects exceed the slowly rising generated emf; the terminal voltage then

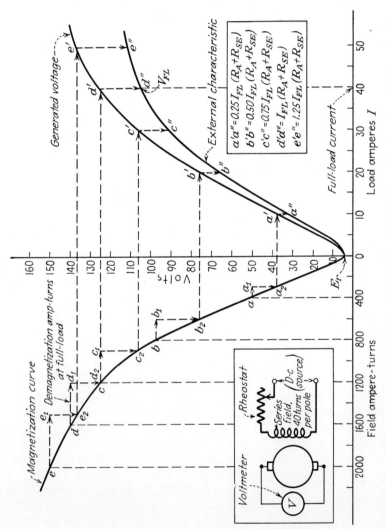

FIG. 85. Graphical method to determine the external characteristic of a series generator with demagnetization.

begins to drop. Thus, as the load current increases, the external characteristic of a series generator rises rapidly from its initial E_r value during the initial stages, then tapers off to a maximum, and finally drops to zero.

To determine graphically the external characteristic of a series generator it is necessary to follow a procedure somewhat different from the methods previously described. Remembering that data for the magnetization curve must be obtained with the exciting winding connected to a separate source while the armature carries *no* current, the series generator must be arranged for test as indicated in the lower left portion of Fig. 85. Note that the series field is disconnected from the armature and is excited by a low-voltage d-c source through a high-current rheostat; the *over-all* armature voltage, *i.e.*, with no demagnetization and no resistance drops, is then measured by a voltmeter connected to the brush terminals.

With 40 series-field turns per pole, point d on the magnetization curve locates the *over-all* generated emf when a full-load current of 40 amp passes through the exciting winding; the magnetizing force is then 1,600 amp-turns per pole. Assuming 400 demagnetizing ampere-turns per pole when the armature and series field are properly connected and the machine is actually *delivering* a full-load current of 40 amp, the *net* generated voltage is found by first subtracting dd_1 from 1,600 to yield point d_2 on the magnetization curve, and then drawing a horizontal line d_2d' until it intersects a vertical line erected at the 40-amp load in the right portion of the diagram. Finally, to find V_{FL}, the $I_{FL}(R_A + R_{SE})$ voltage drop is subtracted from the net generated voltage at d' (20 volts) to locate d''. The same procedure is used to find points a'', b'', c'', and e'', these being, respectively, the 0.25, 0.50, 0.75, and 1.25 I_{FL} current values; demagnetizing ampere-turns and armature-circuit drops are, of course, laid off on a proportionality basis. The external characteristic is then drawn through the located points as shown.

General External-characteristic Comparisons

Before proceeding with a further study of generator performance, it will be desirable to summarize the results of the foregoing articles by comparing, in a general way, the external-characteristic curves of the various types of machine. This will be done by assuming the same full-load terminal voltage and armature current in all cases; per cent values would yield similar results.

1. *Shunt Generators.* Figure 86 illustrates a set of external characteristics for the various types of shunt generator. Comparing them, it should be clear (*a*) that the voltage at full load is always less than it is at no load,

for all types; (b) the greatest per cent regulation occurs in the self-excited generator with demagnetization, while the separately excited machine without demagnetization exhibits the best performance, *i.e.*, the least per cent regulation; (c) the self-excited generator with demagnetization loses voltage rapidly beyond full-load armature current and, with the armature short-circuited, the terminal voltage is zero for an appreciable short-circuit armature current I_{Asc}.

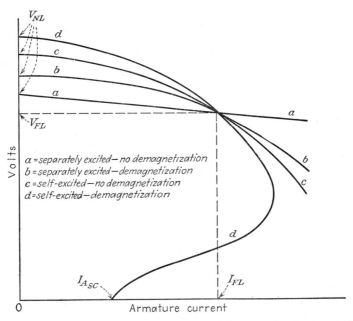

FIG. 86. Comparison of typical external-characteristic curves for shunt generators.

2. *Self-excited Shunt, Compound, and Series Generators.* Figure 87 illustrates a set of external-characteristic curves for all common types of self-excited generators. The following facts are particularly important: (a) the per cent regulation of the flat-compound machine is zero since the no-load and full-load voltages are equal; (b) the per cent regulation of the under-compound generator is greater than zero but less than that of the self-excited shunt type because of the addition of a comparatively few series-field turns; (c) when the number of turns used for the series field is comparatively greater than that of the flat-compound generator, the external characteristic has a rising tendency between no load and full load, and the machine is then said to be overcompounded; (d) the per cent regulation of the differential-compound generator is considerably greater than that of the self-excited shunt machine because of the demagnetizing action of

the series field; (e) the terminal voltage of a series generator rises rapidly from its no-load E_r value to a maximum, somewhat beyond V_{FL}, after which it tends to decrease to zero; (f) the current of a series generator

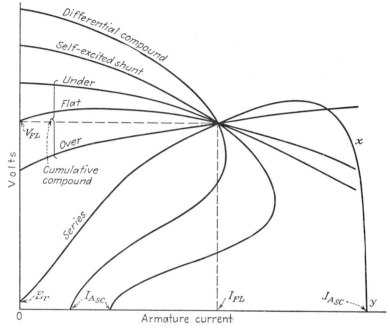

FIG. 87. Comparison of typical external-characteristic curves for self-excited shunt, compound, and series generators.

remains almost constant for considerable voltage changes in the region of x to y.

Degree of Compounding Adjustment

It is customary in manufacturing practice to equip compound generators with sufficient series-field turns so that they will operate considerably overcompounded. Then, by connecting *a very low-resistance shunt across the series field*, the no-load voltage may be brought up to almost any desired value to meet individual demands. It is thus possible, for example, to modify an overcompound generator so that it will be flat- or undercompounded. The effect of the series shunt is to by-pass or *divert* a portion of the normal load current from the flux-producing series-field winding, under which condition the *degree of compounding* is lessened.

The so-called *diverter* is generally made of *German silver* or *manganin* and is, of course, located where it will have no magnetic influence; moreover, its ohmic value, *compared with that of the series field*, will determine how much current is diverted. Thus, when the diverter resistance is extremely large, the diverted current will be small and the external characteristic will be that of an overcompound generator; on the other hand,

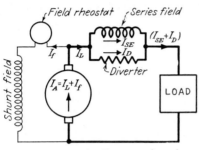

if the resistance of the diverter approaches that of a short circuit, practically all the load current will be diverted around the series field and the external characteristic will resemble that of a shunt generator. Figure 88 is a wiring diagram illustrating the connections of a short-shunt compound generator with the series field paralleled by a diverter; note that the total line current I_L divides into two parts I_{SE} and I_D, the series-field and diverter currents, respectively. Since the series-field resistance R_{SE} is in parallel with the diverter resistance R_D, the total line current I_L will divide so that I_{SE} and I_D are related to each other by an inverse ratio of the respective resistances. Thus,

FIG. 88. Schematic diagram of a short-shunt compound generator equipped with a series-field diverter.

$$\frac{I_D}{I_{SE}} = \frac{R_{SE}}{R_D} \tag{29}$$

But

$$I_L = I_D + I_{SE}$$

Therefore

$$I_{SE} = I_L \times \frac{R_D}{R_D + R_{SE}} \tag{30}$$

The correct diverter resistance is generally determined by experiment. With the machine operating at the proper speed, the no-load voltage is first set for the desired value by manipulating the field rheostat. Load is then applied so that rated current is delivered; the terminal voltage is observed under this condition. Now then, if the latter is higher than the desired value, a diverter is connected across the series field and the full-load test is repeated. If the full-load voltage is still too high, the ohmic value of the diverter resistance must be reduced; however, if the full-load voltage is less than desired, the diverter resistance must be increased. After several trials the experimenter will generally be able to make the correct diverter-resistance adjustment so that the external characteristic will fulfill the required operating conditions. In performing this test it should be remembered that the resistances of the diverter and series field are extremely low and that both elements carry comparatively high values of current. Adjustments must, therefore, be made with care, after which the junctions are permanently soldered and taped.

EXAMPLE 4. A 50-kw 250-volt short-shunt compound generator has a series field whose resistance is 0.0171 ohm. If experiment indicates that the series-field current should be 140 amp for flat compounding, calculate (a) the value of the diverter resistance; (b) the length of a rectangular manganin wire 0.20 by 0.065 in. (Resistivity = 265 ohms-cir mils/ft.)

Solution

(a) $I_L = \dfrac{50,000}{250} = 200$ amp $I_D = 200 - 140 = 60$ amp

$R_D = 0.0171 \times \dfrac{140}{60} = 0.04$ ohm

(b) $0.04 = \dfrac{265 \times l \text{ (ft)}}{(0.20 \times 0.065) \times (4/\pi \times 10^6)}$

$l = \dfrac{0.04 \times 0.013 \times 4 \times 10^6}{265 \times \pi} = 2.5$ ft, or 30 in.

EXAMPLE 5. The following information is given in connection with a short-shunt overcompound generator whose series field is equipped with a diverter: $I_L = 1,200$ amp, $R_{SE} = 0.003$ ohm, $R_D = 0.009$ ohm, series-field turns per pole = 5½. (a) Calculate the number of series-field ampere-turns per pole. What would be the number of series-field ampere-turns per pole if (b) the diverter were disconnected? (c) if the series field were short-circuited?

Solution

(a) $I_{SE} = 1,200 \times \dfrac{0.009}{(0.009 + 0.003)} = 900$ amp

$NI/\text{pole} = 900 \times 5\frac{1}{2} = 4,950$

(b) $NI/\text{pole} = 1,200 \times 5\frac{1}{2} = 6,600$

(c) $NI/\text{pole} = 0$

One of the objections to the use of a *pure resistance* as a diverter for the series-field shunt is that it possesses no inductance, whereas the series field is highly inductive. This means that the total current will *not* divide inversely as the paralleled resistances during periods of sudden load fluctuations, although the proper division will take place when the load current remains steady. In the operation of generators for railway service, for example, when the load suddenly increases (or decreases), the series field does not respond as rapidly as the diverter in taking an increase (or decrease) in current on a proportionality basis. The result is that the series field does not develop the correct excitation during the period when the total current is changing; therefore, for an increase (or decrease) in load, the rise (or fall) in series-field excitation is delayed to such an extent that the developed emf is too little (or too much). The obvious remedy for the difficulty is, of course, to convert the resistance diverter into a reactor by winding the wire around a laminated iron core of such dimensions that the unit has a time constant (L/R) equal to that of the entire series field.

Effect of Magnetic Saturation upon Generator Operation

The per cent regulation of a self-excited shunt generator will depend, among other things, upon the degree of saturation of the main field and will, in general, become smaller (better regulation) as the machine is operated higher up on the magnetization curve. This is true whether or not the dynamo is equipped with interpoles. Moreover, the maximum load current that can be delivered by the armature increases as the magnetic poles are strengthened. The first of these statements may be verified by reference to Figs. 89 and 90. Assuming first that the generator has interpoles, that the demagnetizing effect of armature reaction is negligible, and that the armature is rotated at a given constant speed, points a and b of Fig. 89 represent two conditions of operation at no load; for field current I_{f_a} the no-load voltage is E_a, while for the higher field current I_{f_b}—a higher degree of saturation—the no-load voltage is E_b. Representing the full-load armature-resistance drops by aa' and bb' (both equal), and following the procedure outlined for Fig. 79, the full-load terminal voltages will be V_c and V_d. For the lower value of field magnetization the voltage change between no load and full load is $(150 - 115) = 35$ volts, while for the higher value of field magnetization the voltage change between no load and full load is $(180 - 157) = 23$ volts. Note particularly that the lower voltage change occurs at the higher degree of saturation. Moreover, the per cent regulation for I_{f_a} equals $35/115 \times 100 = 30.4$, while the per cent regulation for I_{f_b} equals $23/157 \times 100 = 14.7$, less than half as much.

When the generator has no interpoles and the brushes are shifted so that good commutation will result, the armature will develop a demagnetizing action. Considered in this way the self-excited shunt generator will show an even better gain in performance than with interpoles if the degree of saturation is correspondingly increased. Referring to Fig. 90, two degrees of initial saturation have again been selected, and these are indicated by NI_{f_a} and NI_{f_b}; the corresponding no-load voltages are E_a and E_b. After the load triangles were drawn as shown, the full-load voltages V_c and V_d were found by following the procedure outlined for Fig. 82. For the lower value of field magnetization the voltage change is

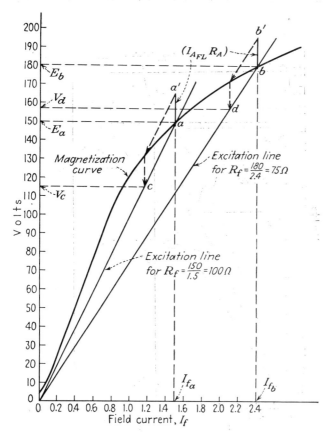

FIG. 89. Diagram illustrating that the per cent regulation of a self-excited shunt generator, without demagnetization, decreases as the magnetic saturation increases.

$(150 - 105) = 45$ volts, and the corresponding per cent regulation is $^{45}\!/_{105} \times 100 = 42.8$; for the higher value of field magnetization the voltage change is $(180 - 153) = 27$ volts, and the corresponding per cent regulation is $^{27}\!/_{153} \times 100 = 17.7$.

The second point previously made, that the maximum load current may be increased if this type of generator is operated at a higher degree of saturation, is verified by Fig. 91. Since the maximum load that may be delivered by a shunt machine is graphically determined by the largest load triangle that may be drawn between the magnetization curve and the excitation line (the lengths of the sides of the triangle are proportional to the armature current), it should be clear that the largest possible load triangle increases in size as the degree of magnetization is strengthened. Thus, for a field resistance of 100 ohms and NI_{f_a} amp-turns per pole,

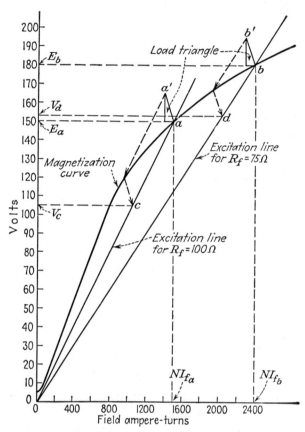

FIG. 90. Diagram illustrating that the per cent regulation of a self-excited shunt generator, with demagnetization, decreases as the magnetic saturation increases.

the largest load triangle is A and A'; for a field resistance of 75 ohms and NI_{f_b} amp-turns per pole, the largest load triangle is B and B'. Moreover, if there were no demagnetizing ampere-turns, the load triangle would shrink to vertical straight lines, but their lengths would differ correspondingly for the two degrees of magnetization.

Although the performance of a self-excited shunt generator may be improved in some respects if its magnetic circuits are highly saturated, the field must not be strengthened to such an extent that the no-load voltage greatly exceeds the demands of the load. Such a situation would generally result if the degree of saturation were increased without a change in speed (see Figs. 89 to 91). To compromise the two opposing factors it is usually necessary, therefore, to lower the generator speed somewhat if

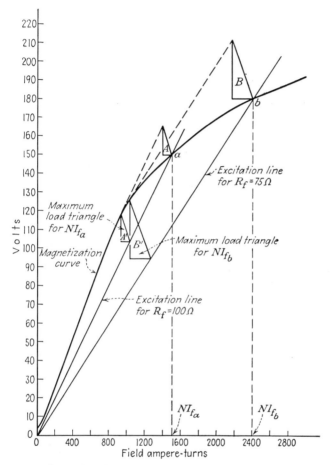

Fig. 91. Diagram illustrating that the maximum load of a self-excited shunt generator, with demagnetization, increases as the magnetic saturation increases.

it is desired to take advantage of the beneficial effects of a higher degree of saturation. This is discussed in the next article.

Effect of Speed upon Generator Operation

Since the open-circuit (no-load) voltage of a generator is directly proportional to the speed [Eq. (7), Chap. 3], the ordinates for given values of ampere-turns on one magnetization curve, obtained for one operating speed, will be related to those on a second magnetization curve, obtained for another operating speed, by the direct ratio of the speeds. Figure 92 illustrates two such curves drawn for two operating speeds, one of which is 75 per cent of the other; note, for example, that the generated voltage on the high-speed curve is 150, and for the same value of field ampere-

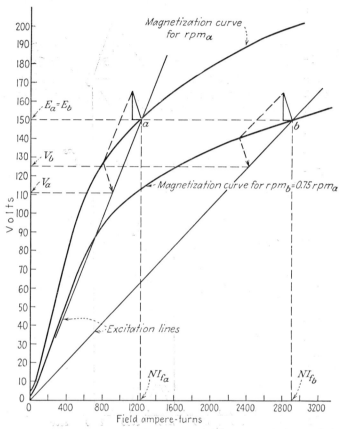

FIG. 92. Diagram illustrating that the per cent regulation of a self-excited shunt generator, with demagnetization, is improved by operating the machine at a reduced speed.

turns, the voltage on the low-speed curve is 112.5. Moreover, it is important to observe that, for a given no-load voltage, operation will always take place on the steeper portion of the high-speed curve than on the low-speed curve; this means, therefore, that the low-speed regulation will be less, $i.e.$, better, than the high-speed regulation. This important fact is clearly shown in Fig. 92 where the high-speed voltage drop between no load and full load is $(150 - 111) = 39$ volts, whereas the voltage drop for 75 per cent speed and the same load range is $(150 - 125) = 25$ volts; these operating conditions result in a high-speed regulation of $^{39}/_{111} \times$

$100 = 35.2$ per cent and a low-speed voltage regulation of $^{25}\!/_{125} \times 100 = 20$ per cent.

The operation of a generator at a speed that is lower than that for which it is designed generally involves several practical difficulties. In the first place it must be recognized that the lowest possible operating speed is limited by the desired no-load voltage and the amount of field-rheostat resistance that can be cut out. A second factor, and one that is particularly serious, involves the matter of increased field heating as the speed is lowered; this comes about because (1) the field copper loss (the I^2R loss) is increased and (2) the fanning action of the armature is lowered. In the example represented by Fig. 92, these points are especially significant because the cooling effect of the armature is considerably less at the lower speed in spite of an increase in field current of about 140 per cent.

Short-circuiting a Shunt Generator

As the load imposed upon a self-excited shunt generator is gradually increased, i.e., as the load resistance connected to the armature terminals is reduced, both the armature current and the terminal emf change. Insofar as the latter is concerned, V_t starts at its open-circuit value of E when the load resistance is infinite; then, as the load resistance is gradually diminished, the voltage continues to drop and ultimately becomes zero when the armature terminals are short-circuited. The armature current I_A, however, rises from an extremely low value—the current E/R_f required by the shunt field—to a maximum and then drops back to its so-called short-circuit current, as the load resistance is slowly changed from infinity to zero. These relations are shown graphically in Fig. 93 in which the load resistance R_L is plotted with its open-circuit value of infinity at the origin and the short-circuit condition of zero at the right.

Of particular interest and importance is the *magnitude* of the short-circuit current I_{Asc}. Assuming first that the generator has interpoles and that the demagnetizing effect of armature reaction is negligible, it should be clear that this current will be equal to the residual voltage E_r divided by the *total armature-circuit resistance*. This follows directly from Eq. (28) where $I_A = (E - V_t)/R_A$. When the armature terminals are short-circuited, V_t becomes zero and the internally generated voltage is E_r. Thus,

$$I_{Asc} = \frac{E_r}{R_A} \tag{31}$$

EXAMPLE 6. The total resistance of the armature winding and the brush contacts of a self-excited shunt generator is 0.25 ohm. Neglecting the effect of armature demagnetization, calculate the value of I_{Asc} when the armature terminals are short-circuited, if the emf due to the residual flux is 4 volts.

Solution

$$I_A = \frac{4}{0.25} = 16$$

If the armature of a self-excited shunt generator does develop a demagnetizing action, the short-circuit current results from a voltage that is slightly *less* than the open-circuit residual value; this means, therefore, that I_{Asc} will be comparatively less than that in the machine whose

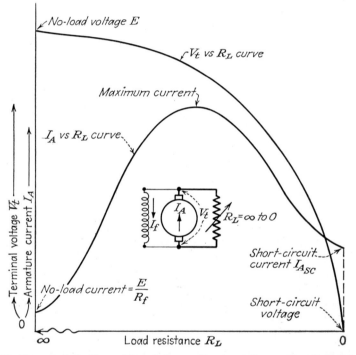

Fig. 93. Characteristic V_t vs. R_L and I_A vs. R_L curves for a self-excited shunt generator, for varying values of load resistance from infinity to zero.

armature reaction is negligible. Figure 94 illustrates why this is so. Starting at the intersection between the magnetization curve and the excitation line, observe that the load triangles move progressively toward the origin as the load resistance R_L is gradually reduced from infinity to zero; several such load triangles are indicated by *a*, *b*, *c*, *d*, and *e*. Moreover, since the size of the load triangle is an accurate measure of the armature current, it will be noted that I_A increases from zero to a maximum and then begins to decrease. When the armature terminals are finally short-circuited ($R_L = 0$), the demagnetizing ampere-turns reduces the normal residual flux so that the short-circuit residual voltage E_r' becomes less than the open-circuit residual voltage E_r; under this condition the load triangle—the so-called short-circuit load triangle—must be drawn to the left of the

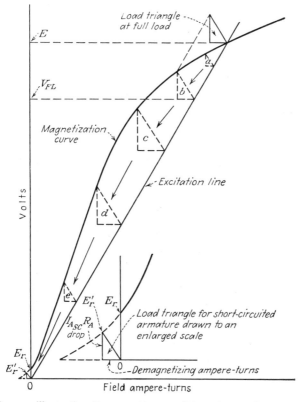

Fig. 94. Diagram illustrating the operating conditions for a self-excited shunt generator, with demagnetization, with the armature terminals short-circuited.

origin as indicated because the shunt-field ampere-turns has been reduced to zero. To determine the magnitude of I_{Asc}, it is merely necessary to divide the vertical side of the load triangle, $I_{Asc}R_A$, by the armature resistance. (The short-circuit load triangle is shown to an enlarged scale in Fig. 94.)

PROBLEMS

1. Calculate the per cent voltage regulation of a 250-volt shunt generator if the terminal voltage rises to 265 when the full load is reduced gradually to zero.

2. A 600-volt shunt generator has an 8 per cent voltage regulation. Calculate the no-load voltage.

3. The voltage of a 300-kw 250-volt shunt generator rises to 275 when the rated load is gradually reduced to zero. Assuming a straight-line relation between terminal emf and armature current, determine the output of the machine in kilowatts when the load voltage is 265.

4. Using the given data of Prob. 3, calculate the terminal voltage when the generator is delivering a load of 150 kw.

5. Calculate the total armature-circuit resistance of the machine of Prob. 3, assuming negligible armature demagnetization.

6. A separately excited interpole shunt generator has a full-load output rating of 60 kw at 460 volts. If the voltage rises to 495 when the load is removed, calculate (*a*) the per cent voltage regulation; (*b*) the terminal voltage and power delivered when the load current is 150 amp.

7. Calculate the maximum kilowatt load that can be delivered by the generator of Prob. 6 if this occurs when the load resistance is equal to the total armature-circuit resistance.

8. The following data were obtained for the magnetization curve of a 4-pole interpole shunt generator, each field coil of which has 1,000 turns.

I_f	E	I_f	E	I_f	E
0	6	0.8	160	1.56	260
0.1	20	1.0	200	1.92	280
0.4	80	1.14	220	2.40	300
0.6	120	1.32	240	3.04	320

(*a*) Draw the magnetization curve to as large a scale as possible on a good grade of graph paper.

(*b*) If the total shunt-field resistance (including the field rheostat) is 125 ohms, determine the voltage to which the machine will build up as a self-excited generator.

(*c*) Neglecting armature demagnetization, calculate the full-load voltage and the per cent regulation of the generator if the full-load armature-resistance drop is 30 volts.

(*d*) If the total armature-circuit resistance is 0.5 ohm, calculate the full-load current and power delivered by the armature.

(*e*) Determine the maximum current that can be delivered by the armature and the terminal voltage under this condition.

(*f*) What will be the armature current if the armature terminals are short-circuited?

9. Assume that the generator of Prob. 8 is operated *without interpoles* and that the brushes are shifted in the direction of rotation until reasonably good commutation occurs at full load. If the armature exerts a demagnetizing action of 300 amp-turns per pole at full load, calculate the full-load voltage and the per cent regulation of the generator.

10. For the generator of Prob. 9, calculate the maximum current that can be delivered by the armature and the terminal voltage under this condition.

11. Each of the main poles of the generator of Prob. 8 is equipped with 10 series-field turns after which the entire series field is connected in series in the armature circuit to change the machine into a cumulative compound generator. Neglect the slight additional resistance of the series field, and calculate the terminal voltage of the machine when the armature is delivering 60 amp.

12. If tests indicate that the generator of Prob. 8 must develop 900 series-field ampere-turns per pole for an armature current of 60 amp if the machine is to be flat-compound, calculate the number of series-field turns per pole.

13. The data for the saturation curve of Prob. 8 were obtained for a speed of 1,800 rpm. At what speed should the generator be operated if it is desired that it build up to 260 volts? (The shunt-field resistance is to remain 125 ohms.)

14. A short-shunt compound generator has a series field whose resistance is 0.018 ohm. For what value of diverter resistance will the series-field current always be two-thirds the total load current?

15. A 20-kw 250-volt short-shunt compound generator has a series field whose resistance is 0.022 ohm and each of whose four coils has 6½ turns. If a diverter having a resistance of 0.058 ohm is connected across the series field, calculate the series-field ampere-turns per pole at full load.

16. Calculate the total number of series-field ampere-turns for the generator of Prob. 15 if the diverter were disconnected.

17. A 10-kw 250-volt long-shunt compound generator has a no-load voltage of 230. The shunt field has 800 turns per pole and the series field 8½ turns per pole. The shunt- and series-field resistances are 80 ohms and 0.07 ohm, respectively. In order to bring the full-load voltage of 250 down to 230 so that the machine will be flat-compound, the series field must produce 225 amp-turns. Calculate (*a*) the resistance of a diverter to accomplish this change; (*b*) the number of ampere-turns produced by each pole at no load and at full load.

CHAPTER 8

GENERATOR OPERATION AND PERFORMANCE

Polarity of Self-excited Generators

Whether or not a self-excited shunt or compound generator will build up depends upon several interrelating factors and, as was pointed out in Chap. 3, these are: (1) the main poles must retain sufficient residual magnetism, (2) the total shunt-field resistance must be below a certain critical value, (3) the armature speed must be above a certain critical value, (4) the shunt-field winding must be properly connected to the armature terminals for a given direction of rotation. Moreover, the building-up process of a shunt generator is independent of the direction of the residual magnetism in the main poles.

One of the most common causes for the failure of a self-excited machine to build up (and this is particularly true of laboratory generators that are connected and operated frequently by different personnel) is that the field is improperly connected across the armature terminals; in such cases the residual voltage sends a current through the shunt field to make the machine *build down*, since the field's ampere-turns produce a bucking action upon the residual field. A simple test that may be made to determine if wrong field connections are responsible for this difficulty is to observe a voltmeter connected across the armature terminals as the field circuit is opened; if the voltmeter deflection *rises* slightly when this is done, it may be correctly assumed that the field terminals are improperly connected to the brushes. The remedy is, of course, to interchange the field ends with respect to the armature terminals.

After a self-excited generator builds up, it sometimes happens that the switchboard polarity, after the wiring is permanently installed, is incorrect. (A definite switchboard polarity is necessary when generators are connected in parallel, and for metering purposes.) Assuming that a machine builds up with the wrong polarity, either of two methods may be employed to reverse it. Figure 95 illustrates how this may be done by reversing the direction of rotation *and* interchanging the field and armature connections. In Fig. 95*a*, for clockwise rotation, the generator is shown to build up with the upper terminal plus (+) and the lower terminal minus (−); note that the field winding is connected to the armature leads so that the field ampere-turns of the upper and lower coils act to *increase the residual magnetism* of the *north* (N_R) and *south* (S_R) poles, respectively. In Fig. 95*b* the polarities of the upper and lower terminals have been reversed as indicated. Changing the direction of rotation has resulted in a reversal of the brush polarities because the armature conductors move counter-

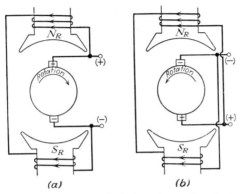

(a)   *(b)*

FIG. 95. Sketches illustrating how the polarity of a self-excited shunt generator is changed by *reversing the direction of rotation and interchanging the field and armature connections.*

clockwise to cut the same residual flux; moreover, build-up takes place because the interchanged field leads maintain the correct current directions in the upper and lower field coils to increase the residual magnetism as before. It should be pointed out that this method of reversing the

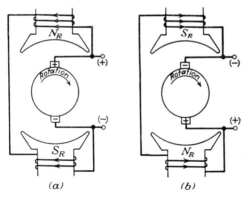

(a)   *(b)*

FIG. 96. Sketches illustrating how the polarity of a self-excited shunt generator is changed by *reversing the residual magnetism.*

polarity is not generally advisable because generators are usually designed to rotate in a given direction to accommodate the angular tilt of the brushes on the commutator as well as the correct direction of rotation of the prime mover.

Figure 96 illustrates a more satisfactory method of reversing the polarity by merely changing the direction of the residual magnetism. The latter may be accomplished in the following manner: (1) disconnect the field terminals from the armature; (2) connect a voltmeter to the armature terminals so that it deflects backwards (downscale) when the armature is rotated in the normal direction; (3) while the armature is rotating, separately excite the field from a comparatively low-voltage d-c source and observe the deflection of the voltmeter; (4) if the voltmeter deflection is now upscale, the residual magnetism is reversed; if not, reverse the separate excitation, whereupon an upscale deflection will be noted for an oppositely directed residual flux. In Fig. 96a upper and lower terminals are plus (+) and minus (−), respectively, as before. In Fig. 96b, with the residual magnetism reversed as indicated, the polarity of the upper and lower terminals become minus (−) and plus (+), respectively. Observe that the brush polarities reverse because, for the same direction of rotation, the armature conductors are cutting a field that is directed upward instead of downward; moreover, build-up takes place because, without interchanging the field connections, the correct current directions in the upper and lower field coils aid the residual field as before.

Loading a Generator

When a load is connected to a constant-potential source, *i.e.*, a source in which the voltage of the generating equipment is maintained at a constant value, the resulting line current is readily determined by dividing the *net voltage* acting in the circuit by the *equivalent resistance* of the load. If the load consists of simple resistors, the current will merely be V_t/R_e, where V_t is the line voltage and R_e is the equivalent resistance of the combination of load resistors. However, in the case of a battery load, *e.g.*, when a storage battery, having a counter voltage E_B and an internal resistance R_B, is charged by a constant-voltage generator whose terminal emf is V_t, the current is found by dividing the effective voltage $(V_t - V_B)$ by the battery resistance R_B. Such problems are entirely straightforward and involve nothing beyond the application of elementary circuit theory.

EXAMPLE 1. A d-c generator, equipped with a regulator to maintain a constant terminal voltage of 120, "feeds" two loads. Load A is a combination of three resistors connected in parallel with values of 4, 6, and 12 ohms, respectively, and load B is a storage battery, under charge, having 48 cells in series, each with an open-circuit emf of 2.15 volts and an internal resistance of 0.0104 ohm. Calculate (a) the current delivered to load A; (b) the battery-charging current in load B; (c) the total power delivered by the generator.

Solution

(a) $I_A = \dfrac{120}{1/(0.25 + 0.167 + 0.083)} = \dfrac{120}{2} = 60$ amp

(b) $V_B = 48 \times 2.15 = 103.2$ volts $R_B = 48 \times 0.0104 = 0.5$ ohm

$I_B = \dfrac{120 - 103.2}{0.5} = 33.6$ amp

(c) $P_{total} = 120(60 + 33.6) = 11{,}232$ watts

Figure 97 is a sketch showing the wiring connections and all identifying values for the problem.

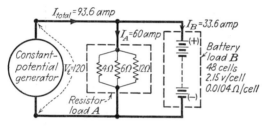

Fig. 97. Sketch illustrating Example 1.

When the terminal voltage of a generator is *not* constant but varies with the delivered load current, it is necessary to follow a somewhat more involved procedure than the one illustrated by Example 1. In such cases the problem generally resolves itself into one of matching a point on the external characteristics of the generator with a corresponding point on the so-called *load characteristic*, *i.e.*, the *voltage* vs. *current* relationship of the load. A mathematical solution for the various quantities is possible, of course, if the equations of the characteristic curves are known; however, since the latter are often difficult to obtain, it is desirable to apply the simpler graphical method to problems of this kind.

If the load is a combination of resistors whose equivalent value is R_e, the current it will "take" will be directly proportional to the voltage impressed across its terminals, *i.e.*, $I = V/R_e = kV$, because the resistance is constant. This means that the load characteristic for a constant resistance is an oblique line with a slope of $V/I = R_e$. Now then, if the external characteristic of the generator and the load characteristic of the resistor are plotted to the same scale, the point of intersection is the *matching point* that indicates the voltage and current values for the particular combination of generator and load. Figure 98 illustrates the foregoing discussion as applied to a self-excited shunt generator that delivers a load current I_R to a resistor of value R_e. Note that the matching point is the only point on *both* characteristics for which the same voltage corresponds to the *same* current; this is an essential requirement because the terminal voltage of the generator is simultaneously the load voltage, and the generator-output current is the very same current that is delivered to the load.

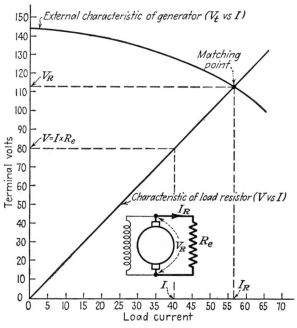

FIG. 98. Sketch illustrating how the current delivered to a resistor by a self-excited shunt generator is determined. (See Example 2.)

EXAMPLE 2. Referring to Fig. 98, determine (a) the load voltage and current for a load resistance of 2 ohms; (b) the load resistance and current for a generator terminal voltage of 120.

Solution

(a) Since the load characteristic is a straight line passing through the origin, it is merely necessary to locate one other point; this is arbitrarily selected for a current of 40 amp which yields 80 volts ($V = I \times R_e = 40 \times 2 = 80$). Extending the load characteristic until it intersects the external characteristic, the matching point corresponds to an emf of 113 volts and a current of 56.5 amp.

(b) For a terminal voltage of 120 the current is 50 amp. Thus, the load resistance, to match these values, must be $^{120}\!/_{50} = 2.4$ ohms.

Essentially the same procedure as the foregoing is followed when it is necessary to find the charging current delivered by a generator to a battery. However, since a major portion of the generator emf must overcome the open-circuit voltage E_B of the battery, the load characteristic of the latter

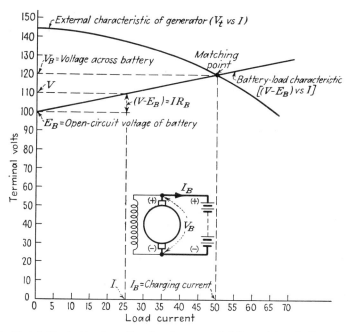

FIG. 99. Sketch illustrating how the charging current delivered to a battery by a self-excited generator is determined.

does not pass through the origin but has an intercept on the ordinate at a point that is equal to E_B. Moreover, the slope of the battery-load characteristics is $IR_B/I = R_B$; note that in this case, as in that of the resistor load, the slope is in terms of *ohms*. Figure 99 illustrates how the graphical method is applied to this type of problem. After the external characteristic of the generator is plotted, the battery-load characteristic is drawn in. The latter is a straight line with an intercept of E_B on the ordinate and a slope equal to $(V - E_B)/I$; the value of $(V - E_B)$ is, of course, equal to the voltage drop in the battery for any arbitrarily assumed current I. Finally, the matching point is found by extending the battery-load characteristic until it intersects the generator characteristic.

EXAMPLE 3.   Referring to Fig. 99, determine the charging current delivered by a self-excited shunt generator to a battery having an internal resistance R_B of 0.4 ohm and an open-circuit emf of 100 volts.

Solution

It is first necessary to draw in the battery-load characteristic. This is a straight line with a 100-volt intercept on the ordinate and a slope of 0.4; for an arbitrary value of 25 amp, the IR_B drop is $25 \times 0.4 = 10$ volts. The matching point is then found to yield a charging current of 50 amp, for which current the generator terminal emf is 120 volts.

When a generator delivers current to two types of load consisting of batteries on charge and resistors, the individual load characteristics must first be combined to form a single composite load characteristic before

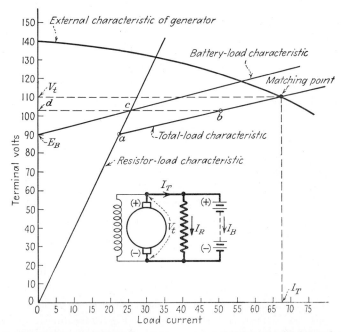

FIG. 100. Sketch illustrating how the total current delivered to a resistor and a battery by a self-excited generator is determined.

the matching point is determined. The resulting total current delivered by the generator can then be properly proportioned into the individual parts taken by the separate loads. Referring to Fig. 100, assume that a generator, whose external characteristic is shown, delivers current to two loads, one a resistor and the other a battery on charge. Since the same

erminal voltage is impressed across *both* loads simultaneously, it should
)e clear that this emf is common to the resistor and the battery; moreover,
he total current delivered by the generator at the corresponding terminal
voltage V_t must divide properly into the two components demanded by
he resistor and battery loads. The graphical solution previously applied
o similar types of loads is equally effective for dissimilar units if the
separate load characteristics are added as shown to give the *total-load*
characteristic; the intersection of the latter with the generator character-
stic then yields the matching point. The total-load characteristic is obviously a straight line (it is graphically the sum of two straight lines) and
s readily plotted after determining two points. One point a is on the
resistor-load characteristic at voltage E_B when the battery current is zero;
another point b is conveniently located by drawing a horizontal line
hrough the intersection c between the resistor-load and battery-load characteristics and making db equal to $2 \times dc$.

EXAMPLE 4. Referring to Fig. 100, a self-excited shunt generator delivers
current to two loads, one of them a resistor of 4 ohms and the other a
)attery having an internal resistance R_B of 0.5 ohm and an open-circuit
emf of 90 volts. Calculate (a) the terminal voltage of the generator V_t
and the total current delivered to both loads; (b) the current and power
lelivered to the resistor; (c) the battery-charging current.

Solution

The resistor-load and the battery-load characteristics are first drawn,
as in Examples 2 and 3. The total-load characteristic is then found by
ocating points a and b as previously explained. Finally, the matching
)oint is determined by extending the total-load characteristic until it intersects the generator characteristic.

a) $V_t = 110$ volts and $I_T = 67.5$ amp

b) $I_R = \dfrac{110}{4} = 27.5$ amp $\quad P_R = 110 \times 27.5 = 3{,}025$ watts

c) $I_B = 67.5 - 27.5 = 40$ amp or $\quad I_B = \dfrac{110 - 90}{0.5} = 40$ amp

Three-wire (115/230-volt) Systems

The types of generator most commonly found in practice develop a
single terminal voltage that is permitted to vary between rather narrow
imits or, when equipped with a voltage regulator, is maintained at a
airly constant value. Furthermore, the so-called voltage rating of the
machine is also the potential at which the electric energy is transmitted and

utilized; the generated voltage cannot be readily raised to permit long-distance transmission or changed to accommodate both appliance and power loads. (Alternating-current systems using transformers make voltage changes simple and efficient.)

The difficulty indicated may, however, be compromised to a limited extent by providing the transmission system with a third wire—a *neutral wire*—that has a potential with respect to the positive *or* negative brush that is one-half the normal generator voltage; under such conditions the transmission system becomes a three-wire system. In practice it is customary to design the generator for 230-volt service so that, with the addition of the neutral wire, it is possible to serve 115-volt lighting and appliance loads as well as 230-volt heavy power loads. To obtain the neutral for the half voltage, two methods are generally employed. In one of them a supplementary coupled motor-generator set—a balancer set—is connected across the 230-volt main generator, with the junction between the added units supplying the neutral; in the arrangement that is more frequently employed the machine is originally designed as a three-wire generator.

Balancer Sets

The wiring diagram of Fig. 101 shows how a *balancer set*—two compound machines coupled together—is connected to a so-called main generator to

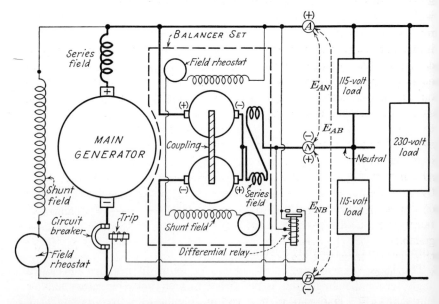

FIG. 101. Wiring diagram showing a compound-type 230-volt main generator equipped with a balancer set for three-wire 115/230-volt service. Note that the series fields of the balancer set function only when the 115-volt loads are unbalanced.

supply the neutral for a 115/230-volt service. In operation the main generator serves the 230-volt load directly through lines A and B, acting independently of the balancer set in this respect. Moreover, if the two 115-volt loads are exactly equal, no current will flow in the neutral wire, in which event the balancer set is again without function; the equal individual 115-volt load resistances may then be considered as connected in series across the 230-volt source. However, if the two 115-volt loads are unequal, a current represented by the unbalance will flow in the neutral wire. If the load connected to E_{AN} is greater than that connected to E_{NB}, the current will be directed *toward* N, whereas the current will be *away from* N when load AN is less than load NB; under either of these conditions the unbalanced current must divide between, and pass through, the two units of the balancer set, causing one of them to act as a motor to drive the other as a generator. Furthermore, the unit that functions as the generator is always the one that happens to be connected to the more heavily loaded side, while the motor unit is joined to the less heavily loaded side. Thus, either unit of the balancer set may perform as a motor or generator when the 115-volt loads are unequal, while both units become motors—connected in series to the 230-volt source and running idly— when the 115-volt loads are equal.

In practice it is customary to provide a balancer set capable of handling an unbalance of about 10 to 25 per cent; this means that the neutral wire will carry a current that is 10 to 25 per cent of the full-load current of the main generator under maximum permissible conditions of unbalance. An important reason for such limitation is the objectionable tendency that causes the two voltages between each line and neutral to depart from equality; in fact, the greater the unbalance, the more does the voltage on the lightly loaded side rise above the voltage on the heavily loaded side. To forestall possible injury to appliances that may be subjected to excessive line-to-neutral voltages, since a drop in the voltage on one side of the line is always accompanied by a rise in voltage on the other, it is customary to equip the three-wire system with a differential relay as shown in Fig. 101. Thus, when E_{AN} and E_{NB} depart from each other by more than a permissible value, the differing currents in the two halves of the relay cause the latter to operate; this action closes the relay contacts which in turn permits the *circuit-breaker trip* to disconnect the main generator from the line. Two examples will now be given to illustrate this type of three-wire transmission system, often called the *Edison* three-wire system.

EXAMPLE 5. Referring to Fig. 102, the following information is given in connection with a three-wire system formed by a main generator and a balancer set: $E_{AB} = 230$, $E_{AN} = 115$, $E_{NB} = 115$, load $AB = 46$ kw, load $AN = 8.05$ kw, load $NB = 4.6$ kw. Neglecting the losses in the balancer set (*i.e.*, assuming a balancer-set efficiency of 100 per cent), calculate (*a*) the currents I_{AN}, I_{NB}, I_{AB}, I_N, I_A, I_B, I_G, I_M, I_T; (*b*) the power P_T delivered by the main generator; (*c*) the power P_G delivered

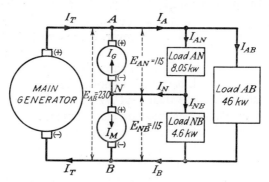

Fig. 102. Wiring diagram illustrating Examples 5 and 6.

by unit G of the balancer set; (*d*) the power P_M taken by unit M of the balancer set.

Solution

(*a*) $I_{AN} = \dfrac{8{,}050}{115} = 70$ amp $I_{NB} = \dfrac{4{,}600}{115} = 40$ amp

$I_{AB} = \dfrac{46{,}000}{230} = 200$ amp

$I_N = 70 - 40 = 30$ amp $I_A = 70 + 200 = 270$ amp

$I_B = 40 + 200 = 240$ amp

$I_G = I_M = \dfrac{30}{2} = 15$ amp

$I_T = I_A - I_G = I_B + I_M = 270 - 15 = 240 + 15 = 255$ amp

(*b*) $P_T = \dfrac{230 \times 255}{1{,}000} = 58.65$ kw   or

$P_T = 46 + 8.05 + 4.6 = 58.65$ kw

(*c*) $P_G = \dfrac{115 \times 15}{1{,}000} = 1.725$ kw

(*d*) $P_M = \dfrac{115 \times 15}{1{,}000} = 1.725$ kw

EXAMPLE 6. Using the same given data of Example 5, but assuming that each unit of the balancer set has an efficiency of 90 per cent, calculate (a) I_G, I_M, I_T; (b) the power P_G delivered by unit G of the balancer set; (c) the power P_M taken by unit M of the balancer set; (d) the power P_T delivered by the main generator.

Solution

The currents I_{AN}, I_{NB}, I_{AB}, I_N, I_A, and I_B are exactly the same as those calculated in Example 5 (refer to Fig. 102).

(a) Balancer-set efficiency = (gen. unit eff.) × (motor unit eff.)

$$= 0.90 \times 0.90 = 0.81$$

Also

$$\text{Balancer-set efficiency} = \frac{\text{gen. unit output}}{\text{motor unit input}} = \frac{115 \times I_G}{115 \times I_M} = \frac{I_G}{I_M}$$

But

$$I_M = I_N - I_G = 30 - I_G$$

Therefore

$$\frac{I_G}{30 - I_G} = 0.81$$

Hence

$$I_G = \frac{0.81 \times 30}{1.81} = \frac{24.3}{1.81} = 13.4 \text{ amp}$$

and

$$I_M = 30 - 13.4 = 16.6 \text{ amp}$$

$$I_T = I_A - I_G = I_B + I_M = 270 - 13.4 = 240 + 16.6 = 256.6 \text{ amp}$$

(b)
$$P_G = \frac{115 \times 13.4}{1,000} = 1.54 \text{ kw (output of gen. unit)}$$

(c)
$$P_M = \frac{115 \times 16.6}{1,000} = 1.91 \text{ kw (input to motor unit)}$$

(d)
$$P_T = \frac{230 \times 256.6}{1,000} = 59.0 \text{ kw}$$

Also

$$P_T = \text{(total-load power)} + \text{(balancer-set power loss)}$$

$$= (58.65) + (1.91 - 1.54) = 59.0 \text{ kw}$$

Three-wire Generators

The use of a balancer set in a three-wire distribution system to obtain the neutral involves a comparatively costly piece of rotating equipment—two commutator-type machines—with its added problems of service and maintenance. A more satisfactory arrangement, originally proposed by Dobrowolsky, makes use of a specially designed d-c generator which, with the addition of an externally connected reactance coil—a static device—

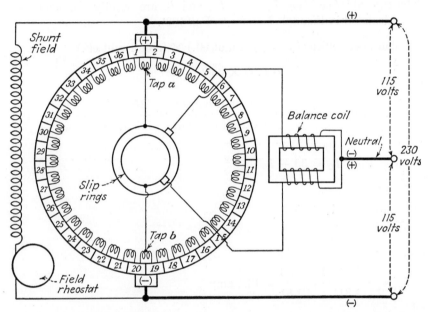

Fig. 103. Sketch illustrating the wiring connections of a two-pole three-wire shunt generator for 115/230-volt service.

furnishes the neutral without the need for an auxiliary M-G (motor-generator) unit. Such a machine, called a *three-wire generator*, is usually a standard 230-volt shunt or compound generator whose armature is provided with two, three, or four slip rings on either end of the armature; taps taken from properly selected points on the armature winding are then connected to the slip rings. Brushes riding on the latter are joined to a suitable reactance which furnishes the neutral for the desired 115/230-volt distribution system.

To understand how such a machine functions, it is first necessary to remember that any d-c generator develops an a-c voltage in its armature winding; in fact, if slip rings are provided instead of a commutator, the current will be alternating. In a two-ring three-wire generator, therefore, if a high-inductance coil is connected through slip rings and brushes to points on the armature that are exactly 180 electrical degrees apart, the *mid-point* on the reactance coil will always have a potential exactly halfway between the d-c voltage existing between positive and negative brushes. Figure 103 illustrates the general arrangement and wiring connections for a simple two-pole three-wire generator designed for 115/230-volt operation. Since the potential difference between the tapped points *a* and *b* is alternating, a low value of alternating current will flow through the highly inductive reactance coil whose exact mid-point serves as the neutral. And, as in the balancer-set three-wire system, the current in the neutral will always be the difference between the two unbalanced 115-volt load currents; moreover, since the two halves of the reactance coil are identical, the d-c neutral current will divide equally between them. Note also that equal mmfs developed in the two parts of the reactance coil are oppositely directed so that the iron core around which the winding is placed will not become saturated. The latter requirement is extremely important because a saturated core would tend to reduce the self-inductance of the unit and thereby cause a large value of alternating current to pass through the reactor winding; this would then result in a demagnetizing action that would alternately affect each half and thus give rise to a rather high a-c potential on the neutral.

A reactance coil, generally called a balance coil, has one objectionable feature in a three-wire system because of its tendency to cause unbalanced voltages between the two outside wires and the neutral when the 115-volt loads are unbalanced. This action results because the two halves of the balance coil possess resistance, thereby incurring a voltage drop on the more heavily loaded side and a voltage rise on the less heavily loaded side. Since good operating conditions make it necessary to limit the degree of voltage unbalance to about 3 per cent, standard construction generally provides for unbalanced 115-volt loads of 10 per cent. Generators can, however, be built for 25 or 50 per cent degrees of unbalance.

The performance of a three-wire generator may be improved somewhat if, instead of having two rings and a single balance coil, it is equipped with four rings and two balance coils, or three rings and a three-unit balance coil. Figure 104 illustrates how the winding is tapped and connected to the four rings of a four-pole three-wire shunt generator, and the manner in which the external connections are made to the two balance coils to obtain the neutral. Note particularly that the ends of each reactor are joined to points on the armature winding that are 180 electrical degrees apart, and that the two reactors are connected to rings so that they are displaced 90 electrical degrees with respect to each other. Figure 105 is a sketch showing how a four-pole three-wire compound generator is arranged for three-ring three-reactor operation. In such a machine the armature winding is tapped at points that are 120 electrical degrees apart and

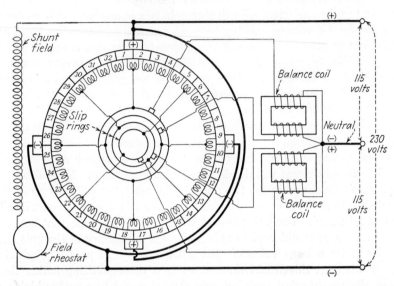

Fig. 104. Sketch illustrating the wiring connections of a four-pole three-wire shunt generator for 115/230-volt service.

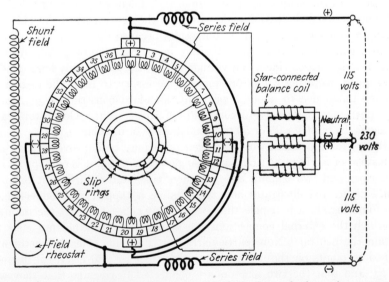

Fig. 105. Sketch illustrating the wiring connections of a four-pole three-wire compound generator for 115/230-volt service.

the brushes are joined to a composite three-unit balancer connected in star. Observe also that the series field is divided into two equal sections, with one part, *consisting of the north poles,* connected in series with the outer positive line and the other part, *consisting of the south poles,* in series with the outer negative line; this procedure permits the generator to operate compound with respect to the independent 115-volt loads on each side of the neutral as well as the 230-volt load.

Three-wire generators are, for the most part, comparatively high-capacity machines and, therefore, have many more commutator segments and a

Fig. 106. Completely wound d-c armature with two rings for a 125/250-volt three-wire generator. (*General Electric Co.*)

greater number of poles than those illustrated by Figs. 103 to 105. The wiring arrangements are, however, similar to those shown.

With the usual conditions of unbalance in practice, it is customary to employ two-ring three-wire generators because the three- and four-ring armatures, and their accompanying balance coils, do not improve operation sufficiently to justify the greater complexity of the wiring connections and the added cost of manufacture. However, when the degree of unbalance is expected to be considerable, three-ring generator installations may be desirable, while four-ring machines may be warranted in special cases. An important point in this connection is that the *maximum out-of-balance current in the armature winding* is given by the expression

$$I'_A = \frac{I_N}{a}\left(0.5 + \frac{0.5}{r}\right) \tag{32}$$

where I'_A = maximum out-of-balance armature current
  I_N = neutral current due to the unbalanced line-to-neutral loads
  a = number of armature winding paths
  r = number of rings

Equation (32) therefore indicates that the maximum out-of-balance current in the armature winding decreases as the number of rings is increased, being $0.75I_N/a$ for two rings, $0.667I_N/a$ for three rings, and $0.625I_N/a$ for four rings.

Figure 106 is a photograph of a completely wound armature with two rings for a 125/250-volt three-wire d-c generator; note the two rings adjacent to the commutator. A balance coil for this type of machine is illustrated by Fig. 107.

Fi3. 107. Balance coil for a 100-kw 2-ring 3-wire 125/250-volt d-c generator. (*Allis-Chalmers Mfg. Co.*)

Need for Parallel Operation of Generators

The steady growth of electrical distribution systems has been accompanied by corresponding increases in the number and size (generating capacity) of power plants. The latter will usually be found to have several generator units each of which may be operated singly or in combination with others to serve the common load. Multiple-unit stations, both d-c and a-c, are considered extremely desirable because of the great importance of service continuity; moreover, such power plants may be operated more efficiently than those in which single generators must supply widely varying loads.

The standard load chart in a power plant indicates that the load demands fluctuate considerably, usually being a maximum sometime during the day and a minimum during the night hours. Since a generator is most efficient when it is delivering power at or near its rated capacity, the best practice is to have a small machine in operation when the load is light and to substitute a larger unit, or connect two or more generators in parallel, when the load increases sufficiently. This must obviously be done without disturbing the continuity of service and implies, therefore, that the switching be carried out smoothly and without the slightest interruption.

Although the breakdown of a generator, its prime mover, or the auxiliary equipment is no longer as common as in earlier days, provision must be made for such a possibility. It is also considered good practice to inspect and service each machine carefully and periodically to forestall possible failure, and this can be done most efficiently when the unit is at rest. These requirements can be met only if other generating equipment is available to maintain service. Furthermore, when failure of a unit does occur, repairs can be made with care and without rush if other equipment is available to provide the necessary service.

Finally, as distribution systems are extended and the load demands increase, power plants must be enlarged by the addition of new equipment. Such extensions are made, of course, only when existing facilities begin to prove inadequate or become unreliable, inefficient, or obsolete, and when the installation of new machines is considered economically advisable.

Operation of Shunt Generators in Parallel

When generators are operated in parallel, they function together to supply power to a common load; moreover, under ideal conditions, (1) the combined rating of the several machines is approximately equal to the total load, and (2) each generator assumes its proportionate share of the total load on the basis of its rating in comparison with those of the others. Thus, if three generators having ratings of 250, 400, and 600 kw are connected in parallel, they should, for example, share an 1,100-kw load by respectively assuming individual portions of about 220, 350, and 530 kw. To achieve such a load division, the generators must have identical external *voltage* vs. *load characteristics*, *i.e.*, the voltage changes of all machines must be exactly the same for equal changes in *per cent change of load*.

Shunt generators are completely stable when operating in parallel, whether or not their external *voltage* vs. *load* characteristics are identical; this is true because of the drooping nature of these curves (see Figs. 82, 84, and 86) which, in general, has the effect of opposing any tendency on the part of any one of the parallel machines from momentarily assuming a greater portion of the existing common load once a certain load division has been established. Since the terminal voltage—the bus-bar voltage— must be the same for all shunt generators when they are operating in parallel, it should be clear that any attempt by one of them to take on more load at the expense of the others implies a reduction of its terminal emf and a corresponding rise in the potential of the others, a condition that is immediately accompanied by actions that oppose the attempted change. However, should the common load, *i.e.*, the system load, change, the bus-bar voltage must do likewise (the voltage drops when the load increases, and vice versa) as each of the parallel generators delivers more or less current; in any event shunt generators in parallel may be said to be in stable equilibrium under all load conditions.

A circuit diagram illustrating how the wiring connections should be made for the operation of two shunt generators in parallel is shown in

Fig. 108. Assume that generator A is in operation, with switch M_A closed, and that the load it is delivering is about to be increased sufficiently to require (1) the use of a machine of larger rating than A or (2) the connection of a second generator to operate in parallel with A. The procedure for doing this is accomplished in the following manner. (1) Generator B is brought up to rated speed by its prime mover. (2) The field switch F_B is closed whereupon the voltage will build up, assuming of course that all conditions for build-up are satisfied (see Chap. 3, page 55). (3) The

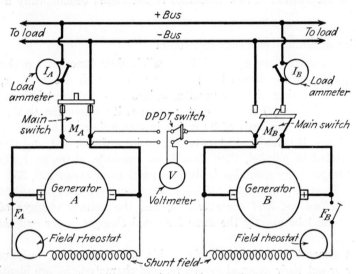

FIG. 108. Circuit diagram showing the wiring connections for the operation of two shunt generators in parallel.

voltage of generator B is adjusted until it is equal to, or slightly higher than, that of generator A, the field rheostat of the incoming machine being manipulated for this purpose; special care should be taken that the polarity of B is exactly the same as that of A w th respect to the load, i.e., the plus and minus terminals of the incoming machine must be traced to corresponding bus polarities across open switch M_B. (4) With adjustments made and precautions taken as indicated, main switch M_B is closed; this places generator B in parallel with A but with the latter still supplying the entire load and machine B running idle, i.e., "floating." (5) To shift the load from A to B it is merely necessary to adjust the field rheostats of the two generators simultaneously, cutting in resistance in the field circuit of A and at the same time cutting out resistance in the field circuit of B. Any desired load shifting may be readily accomplished in this way; in fact, the entire load may be transferred to B, after which the main switch M_A can be opened to disconnect generator A from the line. During the load-shifting period load ammeters I_A and I_B should be carefully watched to make sure that the incoming machine is not overloaded. Finally, it is particularly important that field-rheostat adjustments are not carried beyond the point where A is receiving power from B (ammeter I_A will reverse) because, under this condition, machine A will attempt to act as a motor and thus drive its prime mover.

EXAMPLE 7. Two shunt generators A and B, with ratings of 250 and 400 kw, respectively, and having identical *straight-line voltage* vs. *per cent kilowatt-output* external characteristic, are connected in parallel. If the no-load voltage is 260 and the full-load voltage is 240, calculate (a) the kilowatt output of each machine and the total kilowatt load when the terminal voltage is 245; (b) the kilowatt output of each machine and the terminal voltage when the total output is 575 kw.

Solution

$$(a) \quad kw_A = \frac{260 - 245}{260 - 240} \times 250 = 187.5$$

$$kw_B = \frac{260 - 245}{260 - 240} \times 400 = 300$$

Total kw $= 187.5 + 300 = 487.5$

$$(b) \quad kw_A = \frac{250}{250 + 400} \times 575 = 221$$

$$kw_B = \frac{400}{250 + 400} \times 575 = 354$$

Per cent kw_A = per cent $kw_B = \frac{221}{250} \times 100 = \frac{354}{400} \times 100 = 88.5$

$$\frac{88.5}{100} = \frac{260 - V_t}{260 - 240} \qquad V_t = 260 - \left(\frac{88.5}{100} \times 20\right) = 242.3 \text{ volts}$$

EXAMPLE 8. Two shunt generators A and B, with ratings of 500 and 750 kw, respectively, and having the *voltage* vs. *per cent current* external characteristics shown in Fig. 109, are connected in parallel. Calculate (a) the kilowatt output of each generator and the total kilowatt load when the terminal emf is 630 volts; (b) the kilowatt load delivered by generator A when generator B is "floating."

Solution

(*a*) At 630 volts, generators A and B deliver 57.5 and 41 per cent of their respective current ratings. Therefore

$$kw_A = 0.575 \times \frac{500,000}{600} \times 0.630 = 302$$

$$kw_B = 0.41 \times \frac{750,000}{600} \times 0.630 = 323$$

and

$$\text{Total load kw} = 302 + 323 = 625$$

(*b*) When generator B is delivering no load ("floating"), the terminal emf is 635 volts. Under this condition generator A delivers 47.5 per cent of its rated current. Therefore

$$kw_A = 0.475 \times \frac{500,000}{600} \times 0.635 = 251$$

An interesting problem is one involving the determination of the power delivered by each of two shunt generators that are operating in parallel when a resistance load of known value is connected to the bus bars. Here

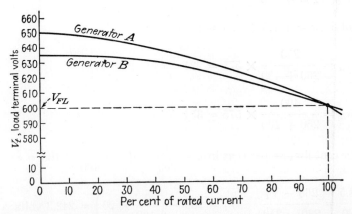

Fig. 109. Characteristic *voltage* vs. *per cent rated current* curves for two shunt generators operated in parallel. (See Example 8.)

again a graphical solution is generally preferable, particularly if the external characteristics of the two machines are dissimilar. The procedure requires (1) the drawing of a so-called *total characteristic* for the two generators, which, in effect, is a curve representing the relation between the voltage and current of a fictitious generator having a capacity of the two machines, (2) the drawing of the load characteristic, (3) determining the total current and the terminal emf from the intersection between the total and load characteristics, and (4) the calculation of the power delivered by the individual generators. The following example illustrates the foregoing method.

EXAMPLE 9. Two shunt generators A and B, whose external characteristics are given in Fig. 110, are operating in parallel and deliver power to a resistance load of 2.5 ohms. Calculate (a) the total current, the terminal

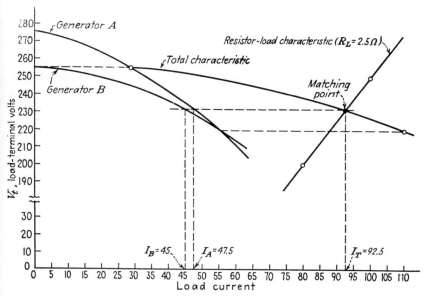

FIG. 110. Sketch illustrating the graphical method for determining the load division between two shunt generators when operating in parallel and connected to a resistor load. (See Example 9.)

voltage, and the power delivered by both machines; (b) the current and power delivered by each generator.

Solution

(1) Since the terminal voltage for any given load must be exactly the same for generators A and B and for the fictitious combination generator, it is a simple matter to locate several points for the total characteristic. The first point is on the A characteristic for the voltage at which $I_B = 0$. A second convenient point is at the voltage when $I_A = I_B$; thus $V_t = 220$ at $I_t = 110$. Any other point may be found by selecting an arbitrary voltage V_x, adding the values of I_A and I_B at that voltage, and then

plotting this current sum I_x at V_x. (2) The load characteristic is, of course, a straight line. Two points are located, one at 80 amp when the terminal volts must be $80 \times 2.5 = 200$, and the other at 100 amp when the terminal volts must be $100 \times 2.5 = 250$. (3) The matching point is then the intersection between the total and load characteristics.

(a) $I_T = 92.5$ amp $V_t = 232$ volts $P_T = \dfrac{232 \times 92.5}{1,000} = 21.5$ kw

(b) $I_A = 47.5$ amp $I_B = 45$ amp

$$P_A = \frac{232 \times 47.5}{1,000} = 11.0 \text{ kw} \qquad P_B = \frac{232 \times 45}{1,000} = 10.5 \text{ kw}$$

Operation of Compound Generators in Parallel

Shunt generators are not considered satisfactory for power-plant service because the terminal voltage of such machines drops as they deliver increasing values of load current (see Fig. 86). Moreover, the voltage changes at the load end of a transmission system are affected to an even greater extent because of the IR *drop* due to line resistance. Compound generators do, however, have desirable characteristics for central-station work because they can be designed with the proper degree of compounding; for loads that are near the machines, the latter are generally flat compound or very slightly overcompound, whereas a high degree of overcompounding is employed when transmission distances are considerable, as, for example, in street-railway service (see Fig. 87).

When operated in parallel to supply power to a common load, compound generators that are overcompounded must be provided with an *equalizer connection* if they are to be in stable equilibrium. An *equalizer* is merely an extremely low-resistance copper wire that joins together identical ends of the series fields not otherwise electrically connected. Figure 111 is a simple schematic wiring diagram showing how this is done for two compound generators. Note particularly that the two series fields are permanently connected in parallel, a condition that results in a division of the total current I_T so that the ratio of the two series-field currents I_{SE_A} and I_{SE_B} are inversely proportional to their respective resistances, that is, $I_{SE_A}/I_{SE_B} = R_{SE_B}/R_{SE_A}$.

Referring to Fig. 112, consider two identical overcompound generators operating in parallel *without an equalizer* and delivering a total current I_T. Under ideal conditions I_A will equal I_B and, neglecting the small values of shunt-field currents, their sum will equal I_T; the machines may thus be said to be in *unstable equilibrium* because, as explained below, any slight mechanical or electrical disturbance will immediately initiate a series of reactions that will cause complete instability and the resulting opening of protective circuit breakers. If, for illustrative purposes, it is assumed that the speed of generator B increases momentarily, its *generated emf* will increase; this is the initial cause of the instability since B immediately delivers a slightly greater share of the total load while A supplies a corre-

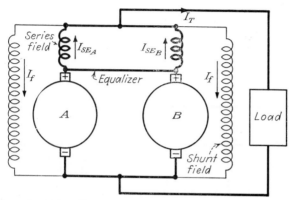

Fig. 111. Schematic wiring diagram showing two compound generators connected in parallel, *with an equalizer*, delivering current to a common load.

spondingly lower value of current than before, the terminal voltage and the total current remaining substantially constant. Remembering that both machines have rising *voltage* vs. *load* characteristics, the increased current through the series field of B will cause its flux to increase and

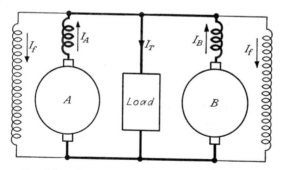

Fig. 112. Schematic wiring diagram showing two compound generators connected in parallel, *without an equalizer*, delivering current to a common load.

raise the generated voltage further; conversely, the small decrease of the current through the series field of A will reduce its flux and lower the generated voltage. The result of these incremental changes is to make B take a still larger part of the total load, while A is losing more of its portion. This process of load transfer having once been started continues until generator B delivers the entire load while that of A falls to zero. At this point further action, if permitted to continue, will reverse the current in machine A and cause it to operate as a differential-compound motor to drive its prime mover; under this condition, A, taking its power from B, imposes a still greater load on the latter. The final stage—a most serious one—occurs when the series-field flux completely nullifies the shunt-field flux so that the counter emf of A falls to zero; machine A then becomes a virtual short circuit on machine B.

As previously pointed out, the simple addition of an equalizer prevents the instability described because the series fields, being in parallel, are no

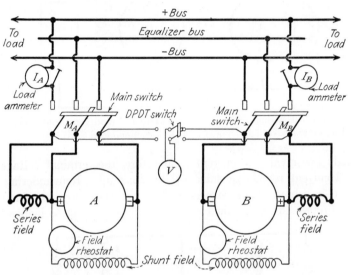

Fig. 113. Circuit diagram showing the wiring connections for the operation of two compound generators in parallel.

longer permitted to act independently of each other, the primary cause of the difficulty. Thus, any tendency on the part of one generator to assume a greater share of the total load than it should is immediately accompanied by the strengthening of *both* series fields, one portion of the increased current passing directly into one series field and the other flowing to the second series field through the equalizer. It should be clear, therefore, that both generators are affected similarly when any disturbance occurs, which implies complete stability of operation.

When compound generators are not identical, they will function most satisfactorily in parallel when (1) their external characteristics, *i.e.*, *terminal volts* vs. *per cent load*, are similar and (2) the resistances of the series fields are inversely proportional to the ratings of the machines. The first condition is attained by carefully adjusting the diverter resistance across the series field of either machine (see Fig. 88), while a very low resistance *in series* with one of the series fields will fulfill the second condition. It is also well to remember that the equalizer resistance should be extremely low, *i.e.*, below a certain critical value. Moreover, the series fields of the parallel generators must be on the *same side*—the positive *or* negative side—of the line; if not, the series field of one machine will become a short circuit across the armature of the other when the paralleling switch is closed.

Figure 113 shows a complete wiring diagram for the parallel operation of two compound generators. Note particularly that each of the main switches M_A and M_B has three blades, with the middle one acting to join the machines through the equalizer. The method for connecting one compound generator in parallel with another already supplying load current follows essentially the same procedure outlined in the previous article concerning the parallel operation of shunt generators. Load transfer, or disconnecting one machine from the line, may be accomplished in a similar manner.

Compound Generators in Parallel for Three-wire Service

When three-wire generators are designed for compound operation, it is necessary to divide the series field into two equal parts, half of the turns of that winding being placed on the positive side of the line and the other

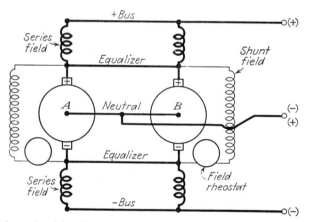

Fig. 114. Schematic wiring diagram showing two three-wire compound generators connected in parallel. Note that the series field of each machine is divided into two halves and that two equalizers are used.

half on the negative side of the line (see Fig. 105). The purpose of such an arrangement is to provide each of the half-voltage loads (the 115-volt loads) with independent compound-generator service; if the entire series field were connected on one side of the line, the generator would be compounded only with respect to *that* half-voltage side and the full-voltage service. This means that *two equalizers* must be used when three-wire compound generators are to be operated in parallel; each of the equalizers must join together corresponding ends of the series fields that are not otherwise connected. Figure 114 illustrates schematically how this must be accomplished for two three-wire compound generators. The sketch has

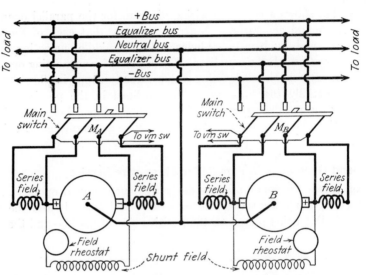

Fig. 115. Circuit diagram showing the wiring connections for the operation of two three-wire compound generators in parallel.

been greatly simplified by omitting the ring and balancer-coil connections, for which the student is referred to Figs. 103 to 105. A more detailed wiring diagram for the operation of two such machines is given in Fig. 115. This clearly shows why each of the main switches must be provided with four blades, two for the plus and minus lines and two for the equalizers.

Tirrill Regulator for Voltage Control

One of the important operating requirements of modern distribution systems is the necessity of maintaining constant voltage at the load; when the latter is near a flat-compound generator, or in the case of a distant load that is served by a properly adjusted overcompound machine, the load voltage may be kept reasonably steady. A shunt generator, on the other hand, has an inherent tendency to lose voltage with increasing values of load. Moreover, speed changes of the prime mover resulting, for example, from changes in the steam pressure will affect the compounding action of compound generators. For these and other reasons, it is usually necessary to have some method of *voltage control* for the purpose of keeping the normal voltage fluctuations between rather narrow limits. A simple *manual* scheme is to adjust the shunt-field rheostat, as the voltage changes, in accordance with load or other requirements; this is satisfactory if the voltage changes are not too frequent or violent. For example, if the voltage falls with increase in load, the field-rheostat resistance must be decreased; this raises the flux and with it the generated emf.

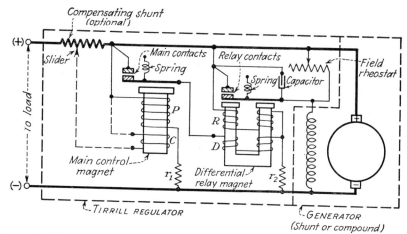

FIG. 116. Wiring diagram showing a Tirrill regulator connected to a generator for automatic voltage control.

Automatic control is, of course, much more desirable and satisfactory, not only because it eliminates the need for watching the generator as it operates but also because it performs its regulating function quickly and accurately without attention. One form of such equipment is the *Tirrill regulator* which operates on a simple principle that requires the use of electromagnets and moving contacts. A pair of short-circuiting contacts are connected across a portion of a preset field rheostat and are actuated by the electromagnetic action of a so-called relay. When the terminal voltage drops, the relay causes the short-circuiting contacts to close; this is accompanied by a decrease in the field resistance, an increase in the field current, and an increase in the field flux. The generated and terminal voltages then rise. On the other hand, if the terminal voltage rises, the relay causes the contacts to open; this decreases the field flux and with it the generated and terminal voltages.

Figure 116 shows a wiring diagram of a Tirrill regulator connected to a shunt generator whose voltage it is intended to control automatically. Note that there are two electromagnets, namely, the *main control magnet* and the *differential relay magnet;* the first one operates the spring-loaded *main contacts* and the second operates the spring-loaded *relay contacts.* The field rheostat is usually adjusted so that the generator terminal voltage is about 30 to 40 per cent *below* rated value when the machine is delivering full-load current with the relay contacts held open. To describe the operation, assume initially that the main and relay contacts are open; under this condition (1) the field-rheostat resistance is *in*, (2) the potential coil P of the main control magnet is normally excited through its limiting resistor r_1, (3) the relay coil R is normally excited through its limiting resistor r_2. Now then, if the line voltage falls, the following sequence of actions takes place: (1) the main contacts close because the excitation of P falls; (2) coil D of the differential relay is excited through the main contacts and the limiting resistor r_2; (3) the net excitation on the differenti l relay is reduced because the excitations of coils R and D oppose one another; (4) relay contacts close to short-circuit the field rheostat; (5) the generator voltage rises. When the terminal emf has risen sufficiently, coil P is again normally excited to open the main contacts; the latter operation causes coil D to become deenergized, thus permitting the relay contacts to open and remove the field-rheostat short circuit. The small capacitor shown reduces the sparking at the relay contacts. If it is desired to impose a delaying action on the opening of the main contacts, the *compensating shunt* and *differential coil* C on the main control magnet may be used; when the slider is properly adjusted for the desired degree of compounding, the differential action of coil C makes it necessary for the terminal voltage to rise to a higher value than previously before the main contacts are permitted to open.

In practice the relay contacts continually open and close many times a second so that the field-rheostat resistance is inserted and short-circuited with great rapidity; as a result the terminal votage is unable to follow the field-current resistance changes. What happens then is that the contacts remain closed a relatively longer period when the terminal emf is low and remain open a relatively longer period when the terminal emf is high.

Diactor * (Direct-acting) Regulator

The direct-acting type of automatic regulator eliminates the need for vibrating contacts and is comparatively simple in construction, operation, and adjustment. It consists essentially of an electromagnetic, voltage-sensitive *torque element* that functions to operate directly a wide-range, quick-acting rheostat of new and novel design. The rheostat element is connected in the shunt-field circuit of the generator, and any change in terminal voltage is corrected by the direct action of the torque element

---

* See reference 25 in Bibliography.

on the rheostatic element. The latter consists of stacks of special non-metallic resistance material whose resistance may be varied from practically zero to any desired maximum value. The stacks are assembled in such a manner that contact between the plates is made at the center only by interleaved contact plates; the latter also act as fulcrums on which the resistance plates are tilted. When the stacks are *tilted* back by the torque element so that the front ends of the plates are separated, the rheostat

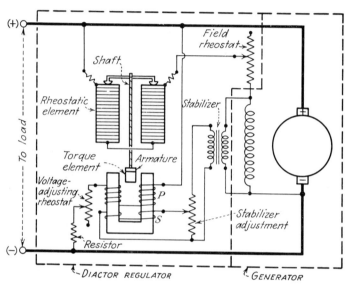

Fig. 117. Wiring diagram showing a Diactor regulator connected to a generator for automatic voltage control.

is in the maximum-resistance position; however, if the stacks are *gradually* tilted forward, the resistance is *gradually* reduced. Note particularly that vibrating contacts do not repeatedly short-circuit and open-circuit a *block of resistance* as is done in the Tirrill regulator; the Diactor regulator is, therefore, smoother in operation and subject to fewer service interruptions.

A wiring diagram showing a Diactor (*type GGD, General Electric Company*) regulator connected to a shunt generator is given in Fig. 117. The unit is normally at rest, functioning only when a change in excitation is required. Operation consists of a slight motion of the armature, suspended between the poles of the U-shaped core of the torque element, which tends to align itself with the pole pieces when the potential coils P are energized. The armature is fastened to a lever and linkage which acts with or against a main spring (not shown) to operate the rheostatic element. This tilts the rheostatic stacks slightly, one way or the other, changing the resistance to provide the correct value of excitation. All the resistance may be inserted or removed within a small fraction of a second, or the resistance may be varied slowly in an infinite number of steps, depending upon the required excitation change. A voltage-adjusting rheostat, mounted on the regulator panel, is connected in series with coil P of the torque element and, when properly adjusted, permits the regulated d-c voltage to be changed

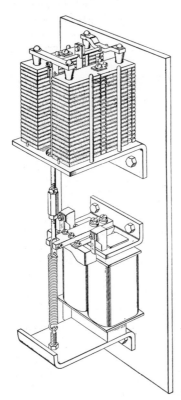

Fig. 118. Perspective drawing of a Diactor voltage regulator. (*General Electric Co.*)

Fig. 119. Photograph of a Diactor voltage regulator with the cover removed. (*General Electric Co.*)

a total of approximately 5 per cent above or below normal. To prevent any overshooting tendency of the moving parts, an antihunting stabilizer is generally provided with the equipment. This is merely a small transformer with its primary winding across the generator field and the secondary connected to coils S on the torque element through a *stabilizer adjustment* unit. While the generator-field voltage is *increasing*, a voltage appears temporarily across the secondary winding because of transformer action. This secondary voltage is in the proper direction to add to the voltage obtained from the generator terminals, so that the voltage applied to the torque-element winding P is temporarily increased. The resulting action, therefore, tends to halt the original movement of the rheostatic element and thus prevents overshooting.

Figure 118 shows a perspective drawing of the Diactor voltage regulator in which the various parts may be readily identified by comparing it with Fig. 117. Particular attention is called to the following: the rheostatic element; the horizontal bar resting on top of rheostatic element and fastened to the vertical lever; the strong coil spring, attached to vertical lever, that opposes the armature torque; the stator core, armature, and coils of the torque element.

Since this type of regulator is an individual-generator voltage regulator, it must be used with *one* generator or exciter. This means that each generator or exciter must be equipped with its individual regulator if two or more machines are to be operated in parallel.

Figure 119 is a photograph of the voltage regulator, shown with the cover removed.

PROBLEMS

1. A 115-volt constant-potential d-c generator delivers power to three loads connected in parallel. Load A is a resistor of 5.75 ohms, load B consists of 21 60-watt lamps, and load C is a storage battery on charge whose open-circuit emf and internal resistance are 104.5 volts and 0.35 ohm, respectively. Calculate the output current and power of the generator.

2. A shunt generator has an external characteristic whose terminal voltage is given by the equation $V_t = (250 - 0.4I)$, where I is the load current. What current and power will be supplied by the machine to a load resistor of 5.85 ohms?

3. Using the given data of Prob. 2, calculate the current delivered by the generator and its terminal voltage when the load power is 13.56 kw.

4. Referring to Fig. 98, determine the load voltage, current, and power for a load resistance of 2.5 ohms.

5. Using the external characteristic of Fig. 99, calculate the charging current delivered to a storage battery whose open-circuit emf and internal resistance are, respectively, 105 volts and 0.3 ohm.

6. The generator represented by the external characteristic of Fig. 100 delivers two loads, one of which is a parallel combination of resistors of 6 ohms and 12 ohms, and the other being a storage battery on charge whose open-circuit emf and internal resistance are 100 volts and 0.5 ohm, respectively. Calculate (*a*) the generator terminal voltage; (*b*) the currents delivered to the resistor and battery loads; (*c*) the power output of the generator.

7. A 115/230-volt three-wire system is formed by a main generator and a balancer set as shown in Fig. 101 and supplies the following loads:

$AN = 5.75$ kw, $NB = 10.35$ kw, $AB = 36.8$ kw. Neglecting the losses in the balancer set, calculate (a) the line currents I_A, I_N, and I_B; (b) total power P_T delivered by the main generator; (c) the power P_G delivered by unit G (which one?) of the balancer set; (d) the power P_M taken by unit M (which one?) of the balancer set.

8. Using the given data of Prob. 7, assume that each unit of the balancer set has an efficiency of 86.6 per cent, and calculate (a) the current and power delivered by unit G (which one?) of the balancer set; (b) the current and power taken by unit M (which one?) of the balancer set; (c) the total current and power delivered by the main generator.

9. Two shunt generators A and B, with ratings of 100 and 150 kw, respectively, and having identical straight-line external *voltage* vs. *per cent-kw output* characteristics, are connected in parallel. If the no-load and full-load voltages are, respectively, 255 and 230, calculate (a) kw output of each machine and the total load when the terminal emf is 235; (b) the terminal voltage and the kw output of each machine when the total load is 280 kw.

10. Two shunt generators, A and B, are connected in parallel to deliver a common load. Generator A has a no-load voltage of 240 and a voltage of 220 when it delivers 120 amp. Generator B has a no-load voltage of 235 and a voltage of 220 when it delivers the same current as A. Assuming straight-line external characteristics for both machines, calculate (a) the line voltage and total kw load when generator B is "floating"; (b) the load delivered by each machine and the total load when the terminal emf is 225.

11. Two shunt generators A and B, with ratings of 150 and 250 kw, respectively, have external characteristics shown in Fig. 109 and are connected for parallel operation. (a) What load in kilowatts will be delivered by generator A when B is "floating"? (b) Calculate the kw output of each machine and the total load when the terminal emf is 615.

12. Using the external characteristic curves shown in Fig. 110, calculate the total power and the power delivered by each machine if generators A and B, operating in parallel, deliver current to a resistor of 3 ohms.

13. (a) What must be the load resistance for the generators of Fig. 110, operating in parallel, if both machines are to divide the total load equally? (b) What will be the kw output of each machine when they are operating as in (a)?

14. An automatic regulator is adjusted so that the terminal emf of a 250-volt generator, to which it is connected, is permitted to vary ±4 per cent during normal operation. What maximum and minimum line voltages may be expected?

CHAPTER 9

MOTOR CHARACTERISTICS

Manual Starters for Shunt and Compound Motors

Direct-current motor starting, the principles of which were discussed in Chap. 4, requires the insertion of a variable resistor in the armature circuit during the accelerating period; the resistor is gradually *cut out* as the motor, gaining speed, develops increasing values of counter emf. In practice it is customary to tap the properly designed resistor at several points, connect the latter to studs or contactors, and arrange (1) manually to cut out successive portions of the resistor by the movement of a lever arm or (2) automatically to short-circuit portions of the resistor, in steps, by the operation of electromagnetic relays.

There are two standard types of starter for shunt and compound motors, namely, *three-point* and *four-point*. Either type may be used when speed control does not require an increase in the speed of the motor by the insertion of considerable resistance in the shunt-field circuit. When the application necessitates a substantial speed increase, accomplished by weakening the shunt-field flux of the motor, three-point starters are not completely satisfactory. (This point will be clarified in a subsequent article dealing with speed control of motors.)

The wiring connections of a motor and its starter always involve a major circuit—the high-current circuit—in parallel with one or more auxiliary, low-current circuits; to distinguish the two kinds of circuit they will, therefore, be shown with heavy and light lines in the diagrams to follow. The major circuit always consists of the motor armature and its starting resistor and, when used, the interpole winding, the series field, and the compensating winding; the auxiliary circuit or circuits contain such low-current units as the shunt-field winding and its field rheostat and the holding coil in the starter. Of particular importance is the fact that the starting resistor, designed for short-duty service, must be cut out in a comparatively short time if overheating is to be avoided; this generally implies that the duration of the motor starting period is but a few seconds.

Figure 120 is a diagram of connections of a *three-point starter* and a shunt motor. Note that the starter has three terminals labeled L, F, and A that are connected respectively to one line terminal, one shunt-field terminal, and one armature terminal; the remaining armature, shunt-field, and line terminals are joined together, with the field rheostat placed in series with the shunt field. When the motor is at rest, the starter arm is held in the *off* position by a strong spiral spring.

To start the motor, one hand grasps the handle of the open main switch while the starter arm is rotated to the first stud with the other hand; the main switch is then closed. Assuming that all wiring connections are in order and the armature is free to turn, the motor will start. After the armature accelerates sufficiently on the first stud, the starter arm is moved slowly to studs 2, 3, 4, 5, etc., until the iron keeper rests firmly against the iron poles of the *holding-coil* electromagnet. The entire starting process should be completed in about 5 to 10 sec. In the final position, the holding-coil electromagnet exerts a greater force than the spiral spring. In the event of a power failure, or should the field circuit be opened accidentally,

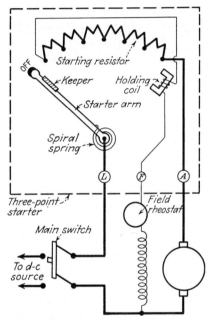

Fig. 120. Wiring diagram of a three-point starter connected to a shunt motor.

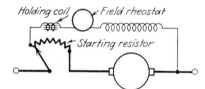

Fig. 121. Schematic wiring diagram of a three-point starter connected to a shunt motor. Note two parallel circuits. (See Fig. 120.)

the starter arm will fall back to its *off* position. This function of the starter is particularly important because (1) if the starter arm is not returned to the *off* position when the power fails, the motor might be damaged should the fuses or circuit breaker fail to function promptly when the power comes on again; (2) if the shunt-field circuit were opened accidentally and the starter arm did not return to the *off* position quickly, the motor would tend to operate at a dangerously high speed.

To stop the motor, it is necessary to open the main switch. Under this condition the emfs across the opened switch blades will be a minimum because the armature counter emf effectively opposes the line voltage; little or no arcing will, therefore, occur. Moreover, with the line potential removed at the switch, the electromagnetic energy stored in the shunt field is gradually discharged through the armature resistance as the arm returns to the *off* position. However, if an attempt is made to stop the motor by throwing back the starter arm *without opening the main switch*, the highly inductive field will be opened on the last returning stud, with consequent arcing and burning at this point.

To show clearly that the three-point starter and its connected shunt motor form two electrical circuits in parallel, the schematic sketch of Fig. 121 is given. Note that the

FIG. 122. Enclosed standard-duty three-point starter, shown with cover removed. (*Cutler-Hammer, Inc.*)

major circuit, in heavy lines, consists of the starter resistor and the motor armature. The auxiliary circuit includes the shunt field with its rheostat and the holding coil. Concerning the latter circuit, note that the *same* current passes through the shunt field and the holding coil; thus, if sufficient field-rheostat resistance is *cut in* so that the holding-coil current is no longer able to create an electromagnetic pull strong enough to overcome the spring tension, the starter arm will fall back to the *off* position. In fact, it is this undesirable feature of the three-point starter that makes it unsuitable for use with speed-controlled motors and that has resulted in the general application of four-point starters. Figure 122 is a photograph of a three-point enclosed type of starter with the cover removed; with the cover in place no live parts are exposed.

Figure 123 shows a wiring diagram of a four-point starter connected to a short-shunt compound

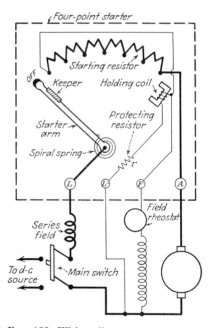

FIG. 123. Wiring diagram of a four-point starter connected to a short-shunt compound motor.

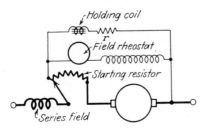

FIG. 124. Schematic wiring diagram of a four-point starter connected to a short-shunt compound motor. Note three parallel circuits. (See Fig. 123.)

motor. Of particular importance, compared with the internal connections of a three-point starter (Fig. 120), it should be noted that one change has been made. The holding coil has been removed from the shunt-field circuit and, in series with a current-limiting resistor r, has been placed in a separate circuit in parallel with the armature and shunt field. With this arrangement the holding-coil current is independent of any field-rheostat changes and thus overcomes the objection to the three-point starter. Figure 124 is a simple schematic sketch of the four-point starter and compound-motor connections and clearly shows the major armature circuit and the two parallel auxiliary circuits.

Series-motor Controllers

Whenever a starter, whose duty it is to accelerate a motor from rest to normal speed, is equipped with a means of governing, in some predetermined manner, the electric power delivered to the apparatus to which it is connected, it is called an *electric controller*. The basic functions of a controller are acceleration, retardation, line closing, reversing, braking, protection, and others. In this respect, a device used in connection with the operation of a series motor is a controller because, in addition to its accelerating feature, it generally serves for speed-control and reversing purposes. As manufactured, it is usually designated as a *drum* controller because it utilizes a drum switch as the main switching element. Figure 125 is a photograph of one such type of controller with the cover removed; clearly seen are the contact fingers arranged vertically on the left

FIG. 125. Drum controller used principally with speed-controlled motors employing resistance in the armature circuit. (*Cutler-Hammer, Inc.*)

and the insulating baffle plates swung out to the right. The variable series resistor in the armature circuit, mounted externally to the controller, has a continuous-duty rating, unlike those used in three-point and four-point starters, which are designed for short-duty service only. A series-motor controller, therefore, has no spring that tends to restore the starter arm to the *off* position. Moreover, the drum may be revolved clockwise or counterclockwise from a marked *off* position so that the direction of rotation of the motor may be changed. In construction, the drum controller consists of a central shaft to which are attached a group of copper cams that make contact with spring-loaded copper fingers or contactors as the drum is revolved. Since the currents are comparatively high, the breaking of contacts is usually accompanied by much arcing; it is for this reason that fireproof baffles, previously mentioned, are placed between successive sets of contacts to prevent dangerous short circuits that result from arcing. To improve further the operation and service requirements of such controllers, it is customary to employ magnetic blowout coils for the purpose of blowing out the arcs quickly when the contacts open.

Shunt- and Compound-motor Controllers

In the practical installation of a shunt or compound motor it is customary to include a shunt-field rheostat for the purposes of speed control. Referring again to Figs. 120 and 123, it will be noted that field rheostats are shown in the shunt-field circuits. A subsequent article will fully consider the problems of speed control, but for the present discussion it is sufficient to state that the motor speed rises with increasing values of field-rheostat resistance; also, at comparatively high speeds the field flux must be weakened considerably. Now then, should a motor, connected to a three- or four-point starter, be stopped when it is operating with a large part of the field-rheostat resistance *cut in* and then started again *before the rheostat is reset in the all-out position*, the motor will attempt to start too rapidly; under this condition the armature current would rise to an excessively high value to compensate for the low field current, because the developed motor torque depends upon the product of both the flux and the armature current [see Eq. (18a), Chap. 4]. Moreover, should the starting current be sufficiently high, the line fuses would blow or the circuit breaker would open.

To avoid the foregoing difficulty, controllers are available that incorporate both starting resistors and field rheostats in compact, panel-mounted units and are designed so that a motor will always be started with the field rheostat set in the *all-out* position; field resistance can be cut in only after the machine has been brought up to normal speed. Since such units have a double function, to start a motor and control its speed, they are properly called controllers. A complete wiring diagram of this type of controller, connected to a long-shunt compound motor, is given in Fig. 126.

Before describing the operation of the controller, the following points should be noted: (1) there are two arms, the longer of which moves over the upper arc of field-rheostat contact points, the shorter one moving over the lower arc of armature-resistance contact points; (2) the handle for moving *both arms forward* is fastened to the longer one and, when moved clockwise, pushes the short arm; (3) the spiral spring is fastened to the short armature-resistor arm only, while the long, field-resistance arm is free of any spring loading; (4) a wiper is fastened to the armature-resistor arm and wipes over a copper segment as it moves forward; (5) in the final position of the armature-resistor arm, the wiper makes contact with one end of the holding coil at point d; (6) also in the final position, the armature-resistor arm is held by the holding-coil electromagnet, while the field-resistance arm is free to be moved *counterclockwise* to any of the upper arc of contacts.

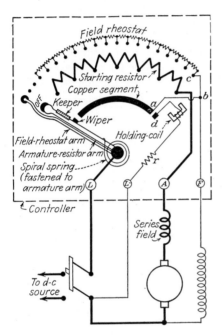

To start the motor the two arms move forward simultaneously, the long one pushing the spring-loaded short one. Resistance is inserted and gradually cut out of the armature circuit as the armature accelerates. The shunt field receives maximum excitation since current passes directly to it from L to a to b to F. In the final position of the armature-resistance arm, the latter is held by the holding-coil electromagnet; simultaneously, the connection between a and b is broken, so that the field current must now pass to point c before proceeding to point F. With the motor up to normal speed, the long arm may be rotated counterclockwise to insert resistance in the shunt-field circuit further to increase the speed. It should, therefore, be clear that the motor must always be started with full field (no field-rheostat resistance).

FIG. 126. Wiring diagram of a controller (four-point) connected to a long-shunt compound motor.

Automatic Starters

The use of starters that will perform the function of accelerating motors automatically, although somewhat more expensive, is preferable to the manual types previously discussed. There are several reasons for such preference: (1) *automatic starters* are reliable and, when properly adjusted, will bring motors up to speed without the blowing of fuses or the opening of circuit breakers under all conditions of loading; (2) push-button stations for starting and stopping may be conveniently located for remote-control operation; (3) the starting resistors may be cut out at a desired time rate so that acceleration may be uniform and in accordance with the demands of the load; (4) to conserve power, a motor is more likely to be stopped when it is idle by simply pressing a button; (5) electric braking facilities may be readily provided so that a motor may be brought to rest quickly and smoothly; (6) overload and temperature protection of equipment is usually incorporated.

There are three general operating principles of automatic starters, one or more of which may be employed in their design. These are (1) counter emf (speed-limit) acceleration, (2) current-limit (series relay) acceleration, and (3) time-limit acceleration. In the counter-emf control scheme advantage is taken of the fact that the counter emf increases as the motor accelerates; relay coils may, therefore, be adjusted and connected so that their operation, depending upon definite values of developed counter emfs, will short-circuit portions of the armature resistor in time succession. The current-limit method of control involves a group of relays that carry and respond to changes in the armature current; the relays are made to operate in sequence, one following the other in time, to cut out the armature resistor in steps. Special devices are employed in time-limit acceleration to cut out successive sections of the armature resistor in a preset and adjustable time sequence; some of the time-delay methods are (*a*) an escapement device controlled by a pendulum or balance wheel, like a clock or watch, (*b*) a timer operated by a small motor, (*c*) an air or oil dashpot, (*d*) a ratcheting device with a reciprocal drive, (*e*) a mechanical or magnetic drag element, (*f*) an inductively coupled electromagnetic unit whose delaying action is created by a collapsing magnetic field.

Counter EMF (Speed-limit) Controller. The wiring diagram of Fig. 127 shows a counter-emf type of automatic controller connected to a long-shunt compound motor; provision is made for starting and stopping the machine from a push-button station. Before describing its operation the following preliminary points should be noted: (1) the starter relays must be adjusted to operate at predetermined values of voltage to close their respective contactors; (2) the field rheostat may be preset to yield a desired, final speed, although it is short-circuited during the initial accelerating period; (3) should the load be too high, the excessive line current would cause the overload relay to open its contacts and disconnect the motor from the line.

To start the motor it is merely necessary to close the main switch and press the spring-loaded "start" button. This immediately energizes the electromagnet M causing its core and the lever L to be pulled to the left;

contacts s, m, and r close. The closing of the s contacts permits the electromagnet current to by-pass the "start" button; the "start" button can now be released because M will be energized through the "stop" button. With m closed, current passes into three circuits; these are (1) the armature circuit, (2) the field circuit, and (3) the relay circuit. The armature circuit may be traced through the *h avy lines*—the major circuit—and consists of the armature, series field, and the three starting resistors R_C, R_B, and R_A. The second circuit is through the shunt field, while the third circuit

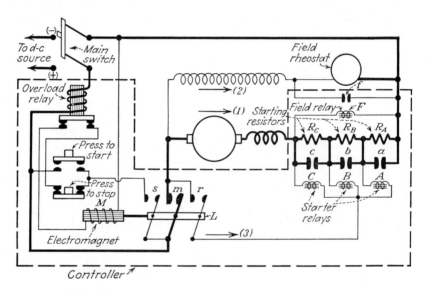

Fig. 127. Wiring diagram showing a *counter-emf* type of automatic starter connected to a long-shunt compound motor.

is through the three relays C, B, and A. At the starting instant the counter emf in the armature is zero. This means that the voltage drop across the armature and series field is low, because their combined resistance is considerably less than $R_C + R_B + R_A$; as a result, the voltage drops across C, B, and A are not sufficient to actuate the plungers, because each voltage drop includes the potential across the armature and series field. However, the voltage drop across $R_C + R_B + R_A$ is sufficiently high to actuate relay F which closes contacts f; this short-circuits the field rheostat until the motor reaches normal speed. As the motor accelerates, the counter emf increases and thereby raises the voltage drop across the armature and series field with a consequent lowering of the three resistance-voltage drops. When the potential across relay A reaches a predetermined value, contacts a close; this short-circuits resistor R_A. The motor accelerates further until relay B operates to close contacts b

and short-circuit the second resistor R_B. Finally, when the motor speed is high enough, relay C operates to close contact c and short-circuit the third resistor R_C; the motor is now operating normally without the starting resistors. The last action is the opening of contacts f across the field rheostat, because the voltage across field relay F is zero; this increases the motor speed to a value that is determined by the preset field rheostat. To stop the motor it is necessary only to press the stop button; doing so deenergizes electromagnet M and causes contacts s, m, and r to open.

Series Relay (Current-limit) Controller. Figure 128 shows a wiring diagram of a series-relay type of automatic controller connected to a shunt

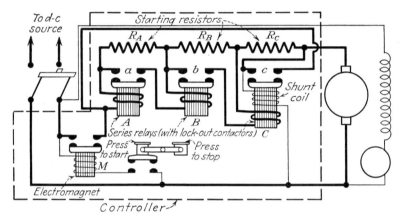

Fig. 128. Wiring diagram showing a *series-relay* type of automatic starter connected to a shunt motor.

motor. Its operation depends upon a group of relays that are specially designed to respond to *current changes* and whose windings carry the comparatively high values of armature current. In operation the contacts are held in the *open* position when the current exceeds a predetermined value; when the current drops to the adjusted setting of the relay, the contacts close to short-circuit a portion of the armature resistor and, if necessary, complete an electrical circuit for the next relay and its step of resistance.

When the main switch is closed, the shunt field is immediately excited. To start the motor the "start" button must be pressed; this energizes the electromagnet M, causes its contacts to close, and permits current to pass through relay A, the entire starting resistor $R_A + R_B + R_C$, and the armature. Since the initial rush of armature current is high, relay A is *locked out* and contacts a are held *open* by the delaying action of the relay. As the motor accelerates, the armature current falls, and at a predetermined value the relay operates to close contacts a; this action short-

circuits resistor R_A and provides a path for the coil of relay B. With the
closing of contacts a the armature current rises again so that the operation
of relay B is delayed until the motor accelerates further. At the proper
value of current contacts b close, short-circuiting resistor R_B and providing
a path for the coil of relay C; the armature current, therefore, increases
for the third time and permits the motor to speed up still further. After
the armature current drops sufficiently, relay C operates to close contacts
c; when this happens current is "fed" directly to the armature from one
side of the line through contacts c. Simultaneously, the shunt coil of relay

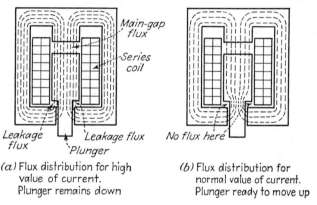

(a) Flux distribution for high
value of current.
Plunger remains down

(b) Flux distribution for
normal value of current.
Plunger ready to move up

Fig. 129. Section of a lockout type of series relay showing the flux distributions for
high and normal values of current.

C is energized—it is connected across the armature terminals—to keep
contacts c closed until the "stop" button is pressed; also relay coils A and
B are released because they are connected across resistors that carry no
current.

One method of delaying the action of a series relay is shown in a design
illustrated by Fig. 129; it is generally referred to as a *lockout contactor* of
the coil and plunger type. Under conditions of rather large values of
exciting current (Fig. 129*a*), the high flux density tends to saturate the
lower end of the plunger where the cross-sectional area is reduced; this
causes some of the flux to "spill over" into the bottom air gap, where it is
indicated as *leakage flux*. Since the upward magnetic force in the upper
main air gap is opposed by the downward magnetic force in the lower
leakage-flux air gap, the resultant force is not sufficient to raise the plunger.
However, when the exciting current decreases to a predetermined value,
the flux distribution becomes normal as in Fig. 129*b*, so that no leakage
flux passes through the lower air gap; thus, the upward magnetic force is
increased sufficiently to lift the plunger, which in turn closes the lockout
contacts (not shown).

Time-limit Acceleration. As previously mentioned, the time-limit acceleration method of control depends upon the use of mechanical or electromagnetic devices that provide definite time-delaying actions to a group of successive relays that short-circuit the several starting resistors, *i.e.*, contacts are closed in a regular sequence, and at a *preset rate*, to cut out the starting resistors as the motor accelerates to normal speed. Such controllers are widely used, particularly because of their comparative rugged simplicity and low cost. They do have the disadvantage, however, that the rate of acceleration of the motor is independent of the load; therefore, under conditions of heavy load the current peaks may become extremely high.

A popular style of time-limit automatic starter for small motors employs a ratcheting and escapement construction similar to that found in motor-driven clocks. When an electromagnet is energized, it operates a plunger, which in turn causes a reciprocating ratcheting drive to actuate a pawl and ratchet wheel. The period of the oscillating pendulum may be readily adjusted by moving a threaded weight up or down so that a desired timing may be obtained. A set of contact fingers, mounted on a rotating bar, then short-circuits successive portions of a starting resistor as the motor accelerates to normal speed.

Oil and air dashpot devices are sometimes used to provide the necessary delaying action of an electromagnetic plunger as it is pulled into its solenoid. Although simple in design and construction, they are subject to timing changes caused by dirt and gummy substances and, if oil is used, variation in viscosity with temperature; frequent cleaning and adjustment are, therefore, necessary. These automatic controllers are generally employed in applications requiring short periods of acceleration or where accurate timing is not particularly important.

Time-current Acceleration. To combine the advantages of both time-limit and current-limit acceleration, the *time-current* relay was developed by The Electric Controller and Manufacturing Company. In this unique relay design, motor acceleration proceeds at a definite time rate but does so more slowly as the mechanical load increases. Thus, more time is allowed between steps for the heavier loads, with the result that the motor has an opportunity to develop higher values of counter emf before the starting resistors are cut out; current peaks are thereby reduced.

A sketch illustrating the general construction of the time-current acceleration relay is given in Fig. 130. When armature current passes through the series coil (in series with the two sets of contacts shown in the upper part of the drawing), magnetic flux is created that passes through the adjustable solid-steel core and the outer cylindrical core. As the flux rapidly builds up, a current is induced in the aluminum sleeve surrounding the upper portion of the steel plug. Since, by Lenz's law, the induced current creates a flux that opposes the very action that produces it, a momentary force of repulsion exists between the plug and the aluminum sleeve. The sleeve, carrying the upper movable contacts, therefore jumps up to break the two sets of contacts, with the result that a starting resistor, connected between the lower stationary contacts, is inserted in the armature circuit. As motor acceleration proceeds, the series-coil current and its accompanying flux ceases to build up, the aluminum sleeve starts to drop but is retarded somewhat in its fall by eddy currents that are induced in the opposite direction; moreover, with increasing values of armature current the rate of fall of the sleeve diminishes. When the aluminum piece finally reaches its lowest point of travel, both sets of contacts close to short-

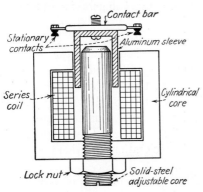

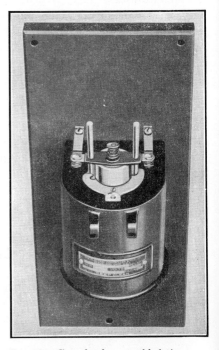

Fig. 130. Sketch showing construction of time-current acceleration relay.

Fig. 131. Completely assembled time-current acceleration relay. (*The Electric Controller & Mfg. Co.*)

circuit the resistor; this brings in the next accelerating contactor, if one is provided. Time adjustment is effected by screwing the steel plug up or down, after the lock nut is loosened; screwing the core down reduces the time interval for a given coil current, and vice versa. A photograph of a completely assembled unit is shown in Fig. 131; clearly seen are the upper part of the aluminum sleeve and the two sets of contacts.

The Magnetic Blowout

When any pair of contacts in a controller is opened while carrying current, an arc will occur. Since electric arcing is always accompanied by an extremely high temperature, burning of the copper contactors will take place unless the arc is quickly extinguished. The most satisfactory method of accomplishing the latter is to provide each set of arc-forming contacts with a magnetic *blowout* and a pair of insulating barriers that confine the arc to a restricted space, out of the reach of adjacent parts. The principle of the magnetic blowout is, in fact, that of motor action (see Chap. 4 and Fig. 49), wherein a current-carrying conductor, placed perpendicularly to a magnetic field, is subjected to a force that is normal to both the field and the conductor. Now then, if the ex-

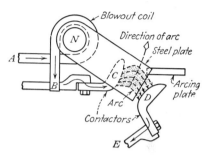

FIG. 132. Sketch illustrating the action of the magnetic blowout.

tremely hot arc is considered as a flexible conductor, capable of elongating at will as it tends to rise naturally, it may be given a *violent* upward thrust if the very current that forms the arc and is being interrupted is

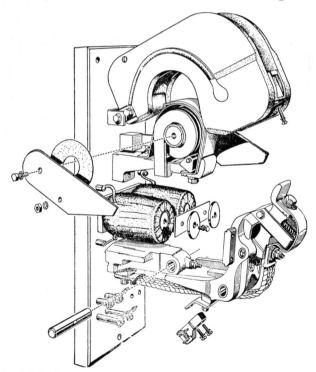

FIG. 133. Exploded view of a line-arc contactor and its blowout coil. (*The Electric Controller & Mfg. Co.*)

made to create a strong magnetic field at right angles to the arc path. Under this condition the arc is quickly moved away from the contactors and, after being "stretched" sufficiently, ruptures of its own accord. Figure 132 is a simplified sketch illustrating the principle of the magnetic blowout. Assuming the current to enter at A, it passes through several turns of very heavy copper (usually rectangular in cross section and wound on edge) wrapped around an iron core flanged by two steel plates that

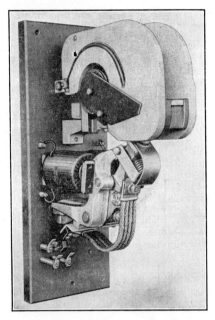

extend to the arc space; the current path proceeds to B, C, across the opened contactors, and thence to D and E. For the current path indicated, the direction of the magnetic field between the ends of the steel plates in the arc space will, therefore, be away from the observer, *i.e.*, with the front plate a *north* pole and the rear plate a *south* pole. Thus, the arc will be forced up and away from the contactors where the sides of the arc shield and the air cools and ruptures the elongated arc.

An exploded view of a *line-arc* type of contactor and its blowout coil is shown in Fig. 133. In operation the arc is automatically transferred from the contacts (where the arc starts) to the arcing plate and the circular guard over the blowout coil at the instant the contactors start to separate. Clearly visible are the insulating barriers (arc shields)

Fig. 134. Completely assembled line-arc contactor and its blowout coil. (*The Electric Controller & Mfg. Co.*)

raised to expose the blowout coil and core; also seen are the two steel blowout plates, between which a strong magnetic field is set up in the arc space. A completely assembled unit is illustrated by Fig. 134.

Direction of Rotation

Many motors are designed to have a given direction of rotation to conform with a certain position and tilt of the brushes on the commutator; under such conditions the manufacturer often places a stenciled arrow on the machine to indicate the proper direction in which armature should revolve. In other cases, as in cranes, streetcars, and in some rolling-mill applications, the motors must be reversible. Since the direction of the developed torque in a motor depends upon the simultaneous directions of the magnetic field and the current in the armature winding, it should be clear that the rotation of a motor may be reversed (1) by changing the current flow through the armature, *i.e.*, reversing the brush polarity, or (2) by changing the current flow through the field circuit or circuits, *i.e.*, reversing the magnetic polarity. The direction of rotation of a d-c motor *cannot* be reversed by changing *both* the brush and magnetic polarities. (Refer to Chap. 4 and Fig. 49 for the principle of motor action and the direction of the force exerted upon a current-carrying conductor placed in a magnetic field.) Figure 135 illustrates how a shunt motor, connected to a three-point starter, may have its direction of rotation changed by reversing either the current through the armature winding (Fig. 135*b*) or by reversing the current through the field winding (Fig. 135*c*); in both of the

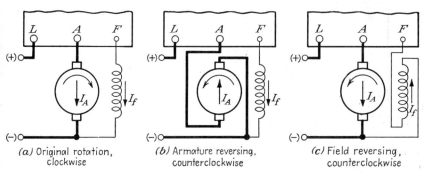

(a) Original rotation, clockwise   *(b)* Armature reversing, counterclockwise   *(c)* Field reversing, counterclockwise

FIG. 135. Sketches illustrating how the direction of rotation of a shunt motor, connected to a three-point starter, is reversed.

latter cases the motor will rotate counterclockwise if the original rotation (Fig. 135*a*) is clockwise. It is particularly important to understand that *the armature- and field-current arrows* I_A and I_f are simplified notations that *indicate the directions of the currents in the armature conductors with reference to the respective magnetic polarities of the poles.*

Compound motors are reversed in essentially the same way as are shunt machines, *i.e.*, by reversing either the current through the armature winding or the *currents* through *both* the shunt *and* series fields. If the latter method is applied, it is imperative to recognize the fact that failure to reverse both fields simultaneously will result in a differential action between them, with a consequent tendency on the part of the machine to become unstable. Remembering that the speed of a motor varies *inversely* with the flux [see Eq. (19), page 71], it should be apparent that the imposition of load on the machine will cause the series-field flux to buck the shunt-field flux and thus cause the motor to run faster. Moreover, since the increased speed requires an additional increment in load current, the series field creates a greater bucking action, and this results in a further increase in speed; the conditions described being cumulative, the motor will, therefore, tend to "run away." In fact, if the relative series-field strength is high enough, the circuit breaker will open when the motor is started, the reason being that the required starting torque must be made up by a much larger value of armature current to compensate for the reduction in total flux [see Eq. (18a), page 67]. Figure 136 illustrates how a compound motor, connected to a four-point starter, may be reversed by either of the methods indicated above. Note particularly that fewer connections must be changed in Fig. 136b—armature reversing—than in

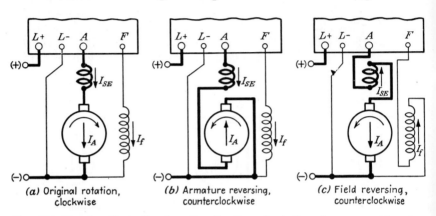

(a) Original rotation, clockwise   *(b)* Armature reversing, counterclockwise   *(c)* Field reversing, counterclockwise

Fig. 136. Sketches illustrating how the direction of rotation of a compound motor, connected to a four-point starter, is reversed.

Fig. 136c—field reversing; in practice it is generally more desirable to reverse the direction of rotation of a compound motor by changing the armature connections.

Reversing Interpole Motors

Most modern d-c motors are equipped with interpoles whose windings are *permanently* connected in series with the armature winding through the plus and minus brushes. This implies, therefore, that the interpole field is automatically reversed when the direction of rotation of a motor is changed by reversing the armature circuit. Moreover, if the polarities of the main poles are reversed to effect a similar change in rotation, the relative polarities of the interpoles will be modified with respect to the main poles. Both of the changes indicated are precisely those required, as the following analysis will show.

Referring to the upper sketch of Fig. 137a, it will be observed that the armature, interpole, and shunt-field currents are given for an assumed clockwise rotation; also note in the corresponding lower sketch that the polarities of the main poles and the interpoles are correctly shown, since these are in accordance with the rule that the interpoles must be the same as the preceding main poles, considered from the standpoint of the direction of rotation (see Chap. 6, page 100, and Fig. 71). Now then, if the motor is to be reversed by a field change (Fig. 137*b*), the upper sketch indicates how this is done, while the lower one shows that the relative main pole and interpole polarities remain correct. Finally, if the motor is to be reversed by an armature-circuit change (Fig. 137*c*), the upper

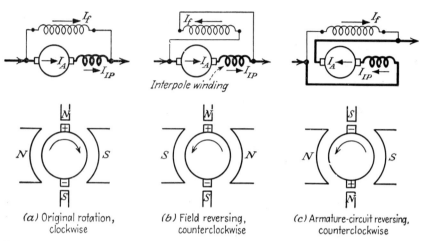

(a) Original rotation, clockwise

(b) Field reversing, counterclockwise

(c) Armature-circuit reversing, counterclockwise

Fig. 137. Sketches illustrating how the *relative* main-pole and interpole *polarities* are maintained when an interpole shunt motor is reversed.

sketch shows how the new connections are made, while the lower one indicates that the proper magnetic polarities are maintained.

Speed Regulation of Motors

The name-plate listings of voltage, current, horsepower, speed, temperature rise, etc., on a d-c motor refer to the *full-load* operating conditions. These data imply that a machine will run at a given speed and draw the specified line current when it is connected to the indicated voltage source and delivers the rated mechanical-horsepower output; moreover, if rated load is carried continuously, the average temperature of the motor will level off to a value that will not exceed the ambient (surrounding cooling medium) temperature by the name-plate temperature rise. Assuming that a shunt or compound motor (not a series motor) is operating in accordance with the name-plate data, its speed will rise to the so-called no-load value when the load is gradually reduced to zero with constant applied voltage and field-rheostat setting. The *speed regulation is then specified as the change in speed between rated load and no load, expressed as a per cent of the speed at rated load.* Thus,

$$\text{Per cent regulation} = \frac{\text{rpm}_{nl} - \text{rpm}_{rated}}{\text{rpm}_{rated}} \times 100 \qquad (33)$$

The speed regulation of shunt motors is generally of the order of 2 to 8 per cent, while that of compound machines varies between about 10 to 25 per cent.

EXAMPLE 1.   The name-plate speed of a 25-hp shunt motor is 1,150 rpm. (a) If the motor speed rises to 1,210 rpm when the load is removed, calculate the per cent regulation. (b) Assuming a straight-line speed-load variation (approximately correct), determine the motor speed when the output is 15 hp.

Solution

(a)   Per cent regulation $= \dfrac{1,210 - 1,150}{1,150} \times 100 = 5.22$

(b) $\text{rpm}_{15} = 1,150 + \left(\dfrac{10}{25} \times 60\right) = 1,174$ (by similar triangles)

EXAMPLE 2.   The no-load speed of a compound motor is 1,650 rpm. How fast will it operate when it delivers rated horsepower output, if the speed regulation is 12.5 per cent?

Solution

$$0.125 = \frac{1,650 - \text{rpm}_{\text{rated}}}{\text{rpm}_{\text{rated}}} \qquad \text{rpm}_{\text{rated}} = \frac{1,650}{1.125} = 1,467$$

The fact that a compound motor has two fields—a constant-flux shunt field and a varying-flux series field—means that the total flux per pole will be greater at rated load than at no load. Therefore, neglecting the effect of armature reaction, it should be clear that the basic difference between a compound motor and a shunt motor is that the former creates more flux at rated load than at no load—about 8 to 25 per cent more—while the latter is essentially a constant-flux machine. Moreover, since *the speed of a motor is inversely proportional to the flux* [see Eq. (19), page 71], it may be inferred that it is this very difference in the flux-producing abilities of the two types of machine that is mainly responsible for their dissimilar speed-regulation characteristics. Two examples will now be given to illustrate the foregoing discussion.

EXAMPLE 3.   The following information is given in connection with a 230-volt *shunt motor:* line current at a rated speed of 1,200 rpm = 20 amp, line current at no load = 5 amp, armature resistance = 0.3 ohm, shunt-field resistance = 115 ohms, brush drops at rated load and no load equal 2 volts and 1 volt, respectively. Calculate the per cent speed regulation of the motor. (Assume no flux change between rated load and no load.)

Solution

$$\text{rpm}_{nl} = \frac{(230 - 1) - (5 - 2)0.3}{k\phi} \qquad 1{,}200 = \frac{(230 - 2) - (20 - 2)0.3}{k\phi}$$

$$\text{rpm}_{nl} = 1{,}200 \times \frac{228.1}{222.6} = 1{,}230$$

$$\text{Per cent regulation} = \frac{1{,}230 - 1{,}200}{1{,}200} \times 100 = 2.5$$

EXAMPLE 4. The motor of Example 3 is equipped with a series field having a resistance of 0.05 ohm and is connected for *long-shunt compound* operation. The torque applied to the motor is then adjusted to the same value as that in Example 3; under this condition the speed drops to 1,075 rpm, the line current is 18.4 amp, and the shunt-field current 2 amp as before. If calculations show that the flux per pole is increased by 10 per cent over the shunt-motor operation, determine the per cent speed regulation. (Assume the same brush drops and no-load current as in Example 3.)

Solution

$$\text{rpm}_{nl} = \frac{(230 - 1) - (5 - 2)0.3}{k\phi}$$

$$1{,}075 = \frac{[230 - 2 - (0.05 \times 16.4)] - (18.4 - 2)0.3}{1.1 \times k\phi}$$

$$\text{rpm}_{nl} = 1{,}075 \times \frac{228.1}{222.3} \times 1.1 = 1{,}210$$

$$\text{Per cent regulation} = \frac{1{,}210 - 1{,}075}{1{,}075} \times 100 = 12.6$$

Comparing the results of Examples 3 and 4, it should be noted particularly that the greater speed change (per cent speed regulation) of the compound motor resulted primarily because the series-field ampere-turns were added to the shunt-field ampere-turns at full load to increase the flux.

In noninterpole machines, where it is customary to shift the brushes backwards to improve commutation, the effect of armature reaction is to demagnetize the main field somewhat between no load and full load. This generally results in a slightly lower value of speed regulation in both types of motor. Moreover, if the demagnetizing effect of armature reaction is especially severe, a shunt machine will tend to have a rising speed-torque characteristic and may thus become unstable.

The designations *constant speed* and *variable speed* are arbitrarily applied to shunt and compound motors, respectively, because (1) the speed regulation of a shunt machine is usually low enough to indicate that, for practical purposes, the speed variation between no load and full load is negligible, and (2) the speed regulation of a compound machine is considerable when compared with the shunt type. In some applications, such as wood planers, circular saws, grinders, polishers, and line shafts, it has been found that constant-speed shunt motors give satisfactory service. Variable-speed compound motors should, however, be applied to loads requiring considerable torque upon starting or to loads that are subject to rapid change. Good examples of such applications are compressors, pumps, and pressure blowers.

Differential-compound Motors

If the series field of a compound motor is connected so that its *varying mmf* opposes the constant mmf of the shunt field, the resulting differential magnetomotive-force action of the two fields will tend to reduce the total flux with increasing values of load current. At light loads the demagnetizing action of the series-field mmf is low so that it has little effect upon the shunt-field mmf. However, at heavy loads, the series-field current is comparatively high, which means that the total flux may be considerably less than at no load. In any event, it should be clear that this differential action of the two fields attempts to speed up the motor with increasing values of load. Thus, if the motor is designed with the series-field ampere-turns properly proportioned with respect to shunt-field ampere-turns, it is possible to have a speed characteristic that is almost flat over a good portion of the operating range, *i.e.*, negligible speed variation (practically zero speed regulation) will result because the armature IR drop, which tends to slow down the motor, is mostly offset by a reduction in flux, which has an equivalent tendency to raise the speed. *Differential-compound motors*, as they are called, are, however, very unstable when the load increases sufficiently to initiate a perceptible increase in speed; under this condition the motor attempts to "run away" because every slight increase in speed is accompanied by corresponding rise in load current, which, passing through the series field, reduces the total flux and causes the speed to increase further. Moreover, such a machine must be started with caution, preferably with the series field short-circuited, for the reason that a large series-field current may cause the motor to start up in the wrong direction; such instability may result because the high starting current in the low-inductance series field builds up much more rapidly than does the current in the highly inductive shunt field, in which case the series-field mmf exceeds the shunt-field mmf, reverses the normal polarity of the magnetic field, and causes the motor to rotate in the wrong direction. As the motor

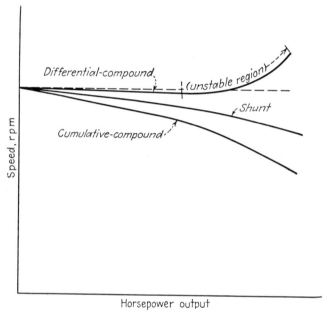

Fig. 138. Typical characteristic *speed* vs. *horsepower output* curves for shunt, cumulative-compound, and differential-compound motors.

accelerates, the shunt-field current and mmf build up sufficiently to nullify the series-field mmf; this in turn reduces the torque to a value that is incapable of maintaining rotation, so the motor stops. At this point the counter emf becomes zero, which means that there is another heavy rush of current through the armature winding and the series field; the motor now starts up in the proper direction because the shunt field is established, but if the series-field mmf is sufficiently high to overpower the shunt-field mmf, the machine again comes to a stop and starts up with another reversal of rotation. Such instability will continue indefinitely unless the circuit breaker is opened or the natural period of oscillation of the rotating structure is such as to exert a damping action upon successive impulses.

It should be obvious from the foregoing discussion that specially designed differential-compound motors can be employed only where the operation and loading is carefully controlled; their practical application is, therefore, extremely limited. Figure 138 shows typical characteristic curves for shunt, cumulative-compound, and differential-compound motors.

Effect of Field-rheostat Resistance upon Speed and Torque

Shunt- and compound-motor installations are generally provided with rheostats, placed in the shunt-field circuit, for purposes of speed control; Figs. 120 and 123 are typical wiring diagrams indicating how field rheostats are connected, and Chap. 10 discusses the principles of motor control in some detail. To understand how a motor reacts to a change in field-rheostat resistance, it is helpful to apply the fundamental relationships for torque and speed [Eqs. (18a) and (19)], respectively.

Assuming, for example, that a shunt motor is developing a given torque and driving a mechanical load, an increase in field-rheostat resistance results in a reduction in flux and a corresponding rise in speed; this is in accordance with the equation rpm $= (V - I_A R_A)/k\phi$ which indicates that the speed is *inversely proportional* to the flux. However, if the speed is to increase, the motor must develop a value of torque that is sufficiently greater than that demanded by the load so that acceleration can proceed to the higher speed, and this must be accomplished by a comparatively large rush of armature current. Now then, since the torque is *directly proportional* to both the armature current *and* the flux, $T = k\phi I_A$, it should be obvious that I_A alone must account for the required increase in torque because the flux is diminished to raise the speed. It should be clear, therefore, that an increase in field-rheostat resistance is accompanied by three successive changes, namely, (1) a permanent reduction in flux, (2) a short-duration rise in armature current and torque for the purposes of acceleration, and (3) a final drop in armature current and torque to values necessary to power the load at the higher speed. The foregoing analysis is illustrated by the following practical example.

EXAMPLE 5. A 5-hp 230-volt shunt motor has an armature resistance of 0.3 ohm and takes an armature current of 18 amp when delivering rated horsepower output at a speed of 1,750 rpm. (a) Calculate the full-load torque. (b) Assume a brush drop of 2 volts and determine the initial rush of armature current and the corresponding momentary maximum torque at the instant the field-rheostat resistance is increased to reduce the field flux to 0.96 of the original value. (c) Calculate the final armature current, speed, and horsepower output, assuming that the motor develops the same torque as that found in (a).

Solution

(a) $\quad T = \dfrac{5 \times 5{,}250}{1{,}750} = 15$ lb-ft

(b) $\quad 1{,}750 = \dfrac{(230 - 2) - (18 \times 0.3)}{k\phi} \qquad k\phi = \dfrac{228 - 5.4}{1{,}750} = 0.1273$

$$0.96 \times 0.1273 = \dfrac{(230 - 2) - (I_A \times 0.3)}{1{,}750}$$

$$I_A = \dfrac{228 - 214}{0.3} = 46.7$$

$$T = 15 \times \dfrac{0.96\,\phi}{\phi} \times \dfrac{46.7}{18} = 37.4 \text{ lb-ft}$$

Note that, *at the instant the flux is decreased*, and while the speed is still 1,750 rpm, the armature current and torque increase 160 and 150 per cent, respectively.

(c) $\qquad I_A = 18 \times \dfrac{\phi}{0.96\,\phi} = 18.75$ amp

$$\text{rpm} = \dfrac{(230 - 2) - (18.75 \times 0.3)}{0.96 \times 0.1273} = \dfrac{222.4}{0.1222} = 1{,}820$$

$$\text{hp} = \dfrac{15 \times 1{,}820}{5{,}250} = 5.2$$

When the field-rheostat resistance is increased (or decreased) in order to raise (or lower) the motor speed, the shunt-field current falls (or rises) proportionately, since $I_f = V/(R_f + R_{rh})$; however, owing to the magnetic saturation of the iron, the flux changes to a *lesser* extent than does the field current. To determine the relation between the *final* and *initial* fluxes, *i.e.*, ϕ_f/ϕ_i, it is merely necessary to refer to a magnetization curve similar to Fig. 38, from which the ratio of E_f/E_i may be taken as equal to the flux ratio; the two ratios are equal to each other because data for the magnetization curve of the motor, tested as a separately excited shunt generator, are obtained for a constant speed, which means that $E_f/E_i = k\phi_f/k\phi_i = \phi_f/\phi_i$. In Example 5, therefore, the ratio of $\phi_f/\phi_i = 0.96$ was found in precisely this way. Armature reaction may be neglected in interpole machines.

Compound motors behave essentially like shunt motors when the field-rheostat resistance is altered, *i.e.*, an increase in shunt-field circuit resistance is immediately accompanied by a large momentary surge of armature current, which, in turn, causes the motor to develop sufficient additional torque and accelerate to a higher speed. Moreover, calculations for the final armature current, speed, and horsepower can generally be made by following the method given in Example 5, neglecting the minor changes in mmf and voltage drop that occur in the series field.

Torque and Speed Relations in Series Motors

When a series motor is in operation, driving a mechanical load, the so-called load current passes through the field winding and the armature winding to energize *both* the stationary and rotating elements of the machine; this basic fact is fundamental to an understanding of the torque and speed relations in series motors. Now then, since the torque is a function of both the field flux *and* the armature current, $(T = k\phi I_A)$, every increase or decrease in the load is met by a corresponding change in two factors, *i.e.*, I_A and ϕ, although the latter may or may not be pro-

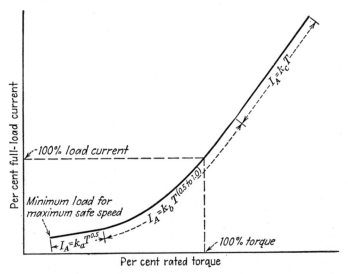

Fig. 139. Typical *per cent current* vs. *per cent torque* characteristic for a series motor.

portional to the former. At light loads, when the magnetic-circuit iron is unsaturated, the flux varies almost directly with the load current, under which condition $T = k\phi I_A = k(k'I_A)I_A = k_1 I_A^2$; therefore $I_A = k_a T^{0.5}$. However, as the load approaches rated value and the iron tends to saturate, the flux rises at a progressively diminishing rate, while the armature current increases more rapidly than before, so that $I_A = k_b T^{(0.5 \text{ to } 1.0)}$. Finally, at considerable overloads, when the iron is highly saturated and few or no flux changes occur with increasing values of I_A, the armature current alone must meet the demands of the load; under this condition $I_A = k_c T$. The typical *per cent current* vs. *per cent torque* characteristic curve of Fig. 139 graphically illustrates how the current varies with changing values of torque and clearly indicates the nonlinear relation between I_A and T in the usual operating range of a series motor. The following numerical example further emphasizes the foregoing discussion.

EXAMPLE 6. A 20-hp 230-volt series motor takes 80 amp when operating at full load at a speed of 1,450 rpm. What load torque will be developed by the machine when the line current rises to 100 amp, assuming that a 25 per cent increase in field current results in a 12 per cent increase in flux?

Solution

$$T_{FL} = \frac{20 \times 5,250}{1,450} = 72.5 \text{ lb-ft}$$

$$T_{100} = T_{FL} \times \frac{\phi_{100}}{\phi_{80}} \times \frac{100}{80} = 72.5 \times 1.12 \times 1.25 = 101.5 \text{ lb-ft}$$

The fact that the field magnetization of a series motor changes considerably under normal operating conditions also means that the speed will fluctuate greatly as the load varies; this is true because the fundamental speed equation of a motor, rpm $= [V - I_A(R_A + R_{SE})]/k\phi$, indicates that two factors are responsible for the rpm vs. load variations. Note particularly that the speed, being inversely proportional to the flux, is mainly affected by the latter, whereas the $I_A(R_A + R_{SE})$ drop, only a minor part of the numerator, influences the speed very slightly. A typical rpm vs. output characteristic curve for a series motor is given in Fig. 54 and clearly indicates the wide speed variation for this type of machine; the figure further illustrates that such a motor tends to "run away" at light loads. The latter condition is brought about by a greatly weakened magnetic field which requires that the armature winding move very rapidly if it is to generate a sufficiently high counter emf. This statement should be clear if the general speed equation is written in the form rpm $= E_c/k\phi$, from which $E_c = k\phi \times$ rpm; thus, if the counter emf E_c is to have a value that is only several per cent less than the impressed voltage, it should be obvious that every reduction in the magnitude of the flux must be accompanied by a corresponding rise in the speed. It is for this reason that a series motor must be installed so that it cannot "lose" its load, which generally implies a direct coupling or gearing between the two. Referring again to Fig. 139, it will be noted that the lower limit of the characteristic curve is indicated as the minimum load for the *maximum safe speed*.

Assuming that a series motor is taking a known current when driving a given load at a known speed, it is possible to determine the speed and horsepower output of the machine at *another* value of line current only if the magnetization curve is available. Such a curve may be plotted from experimental data obtained by driving the armature with another motor at any reasonable constant speed while the series field is *separately excited* through a high-current rheostat from a d-c source. Figure 85 illustrates the wiring connections required. Since the motor operates as an unloaded generator at a constant speed in such a test, *the generated emfs on the magnetization curves are directly proportional to the respective values of flux;* thus $E_{g2}/E_{g1} = \phi_2/\phi_1$. This means that the *ratio* of any two voltages on the curve, picked off for two desired values of load current I_{A2} and I_{A1}, is equal to the *ratio* of the two flux magnitudes. Now then, since the torque is proportional to both the flux and the armature current, it follows that a torque at current I_{A2} may be found by multiplying the known torque at I_{A1} by the two ratios, namely, I_{A2}/I_{A1} and E_{g2}/E_{g1}. The speed and horsepower output of the motor can then be obtained by applying methods previously discussed. An example will now be given to illustrate the procedure suggested.

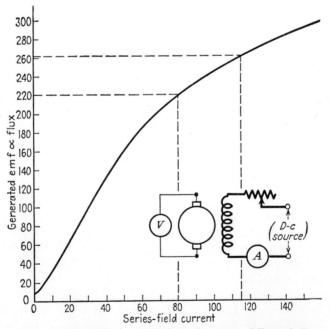

Fig. 140. Magnetization curve for series motor of Example 7.

EXAMPLE 7. The motor of Example 6 was operated at a constant speed of 1,500 rpm and data for the magnetization curve of Fig. 140 were obtained. Calculate the torque, speed, and horsepower output of the motor when the line current is 115 amp. The total armature and series-field resistance is 0.14 ohm, and a brush drop of 3 volts is assumed for both loads. Neglect the effect of armature reaction.

Solution

Referring to Fig. 140, $E_{80} = 220$, $E_{115} = 262$.

$$\frac{E_{115}}{E_{80}} = \frac{\phi_{115}}{\phi_{80}} = \frac{262}{220} = 1.19$$

$$\frac{I_{115}}{I_{80}} = \frac{115}{80} = 1.44$$

$$T_{115} = 72.5 \times 1.19 \times 1.44 = 124 \text{ lb-ft}$$

$$\text{rpm}_{115} = \frac{[(230 - 3) - (115 \times 0.14)]/1.19\phi}{[(230 - 3) - (80 \times 0.14)]/\phi} \times 1,450$$

$$= \frac{210.9}{215.8 \times 1.19} \times 1,450 = 1,195$$

$$\text{hp}_{115} = \frac{124 \times 1,195}{5,250} = 28.3$$

Starting Torque and Overload Capacity of Motors

The ability of a motor to start a load, overcoming the static friction and the inertia of heavy moving parts of its own rotor and the application to which it is connected, is frequently an important requirement in certain installations; this is usually referred to as the *per cent starting torque* or *per cent "breakaway" torque*, based upon the rated full-load torque. Since torque is, in general, proportional to both the armature current and the field flux, it should be clear that, for a given large initial starting current in the armature circuit, the shunt motor will develop less starting torque than the series motor; this is true because the shunt motor creates the same magnetic-field strength regardless of the permissible initial armature current, whereas the flux established by the series field in a series motor is considerably more during the starting period than the full-load value. The cumulative compound motor will, on the other hand, develop starting torque that is somewhat more than a shunt machine of equal full-load rating although less than an equivalent series motor.

The maximum starting torque that can be developed by a motor is determined primarily by the permissible armature current that can be commutated without destructive sparking; also, unduly high values of armature current cause excessive heating, especially if motors are started frequently. Moreover, the bearing load must be kept within reasonable levels if mechanical failure is to be avoided. Thus, with the indicated limitations that must be placed upon the rotating part of the machine, it is seen that a motor must be designed with a strong series field, whether in a compound or series machine, if it is to perform exceptionally well from the standpoint of good starting torque. Actual starting-torque maximums now attainable are approximately 300 per cent for shunt motors, up to 450 per cent for compound motors depending upon the degree of compounding, and 500 per cent for series motors.

After a motor has been placed in operation, it will often be called upon to deliver loads, for short periods of time, that are considerably in excess of its name-plate rating. Whether or not it will be capable of doing so, however, will, in general, be determined by (1) its ability to create higher flux densities with increasing increments of load and (2) its inherent tendency to slow down under similar conditions. Remembering that a shunt motor is essentially a constant-flux machine whose speed tends to drop only by virtue of the armature $I_A R_A$ drop [rpm $= (V - I_A R_A)/k\phi = k_1 - k_2 I_A R_A$], it should be clear that its overload capacity is extremely limited; such motors will, in fact, break down or stall when the torque is somewhat less than 300 per cent of rated value. A series motor, on the other hand, is especially suited to severe overload service because it can provide increasing values of magnetization, up to saturation, as the field current rises with the load, and because it does slow down considerably with rising torque demands; such motors may usually be expected to have *pull-out torques* that are well over 400 per cent of rated value. Since a compound motor is a sort of combination shunt-series machine, whose flux and speed will, respectively, rise and drop with increases in load, its overload capacity will be found to fall between the two types indicated above; such motors will ordinarily pull out, *i.e.*, stall, at about 350 per cent of full-load torque.

The following points should be noted in summarizing the foregoing. (1) Shunt motors develop moderate starting and maximum torques, about 300 and 275 per cent, respectively, operate within a speed variation of about 10 per cent, and should be applied to such loads as line shafts, fans, blowers, centrifugal pumps, metal and woodworking machines, elevators, conveyors, laundry washing machines, and vacuum cleaners. (2) Series motors develop extremely high values of starting and maximum torque, about 500 and 425 per cent, respectively, operate over a considerable range of speed, tend to race at very light loads, and should be applied to such loads as cranes, traction machines, coal and ore bridges, bucket and mine hoists, gates, car dumpers, turntables, and car retarders. (3) Compound motors have medium starting and maximum torques, about 450 and 350 per cent, respectively, operate within a speed range that varies up to 30 per cent, and should be used in such applications as plunger pumps, shears, crushers, rotary and flat-bed presses, rolling mills, punch presses, geared elevators, hoists, pressure blowers, compressors, circular saws, bending rolls, and hydroextractors.

PROBLEMS

1. A 5-hp 230-volt shunt motor has a full-load efficiency of 87 per cent, an armature resistance of 0.22 ohm, and a field resistance of 115 ohms. Calculate (a) the total resistance in a starting box to limit the armature current to 140 per cent of its full-load value; (b) the resistance which is cut out in moving the starter arm to the second contact point if the range of armature current between contacts is 140 to 100 per cent. Assume a 3-volt brush drop.

2. A 20-hp 220-volt 540-rpm shunt motor has an armature resistance of 0.12 ohm and a field resistance of 52.4 ohms. If the resistance of a starter is 1.93 ohms, what line current does the motor take at the instant of starting? Assume a motor efficiency of 88 per cent and a brush drop of 3 volts.

3. Using the data of Prob. 2, calculate the speed to which the motor will accelerate on the first stud if it develops 50 per cent of rated torque.

4. The armature resistance of a 60-hp 240-volt shunt motor is 0.067 ohm and the field resistance is 40 ohms. It is desired that the motor develop 150 per cent of its rated torque on starting. Calculate the total starter resistance, assuming a full-load motor efficiency of 83.8 per cent and a brush drop of 3 volts.

5. A 75-hp shunt motor has a full-load speed of 1,200 rpm. (a) If the motor operates at 1,275 rpm when the load is removed, calculate the per cent regulation. (b) Assuming a straight-line speed-torque curve, determine the horsepower output of the motor when it is operating at 1,230 rpm.

6. The following information is given in connection with a 25-hp 550-volt 900-rpm long-shunt compound motor: $R_A = 0.42$ ohm, $R_{SH} = 183$ ohms, $R_{SE} = 0.06$ ohm, full-load efficiency = 87 per cent.

If the no-load line current is 5 amp and the full-load flux is 10 per cent greater than the no-load value, calculate the per cent speed regulation. Assume brush drops of 4 and 2 volts at full and no load, respectively.

7. A 240-volt series motor has an armature resistance of 0.23 ohm and a series-field resistance of 0.12 ohm. If the speed is 800 rpm when the load current is 45 amp, what will be the motor speed when the load increases the current to 60 amp while the voltage drops to 236 volts. Assume a 3-volt brush drop and that the flux increase is 50 per cent as great as the current increase.

8. On a level track a streetcar, with two series motors connected in parallel, runs at 35 mph, and each motor takes 40 amp from the 600-volt trolley. On a hill, where the required torque is five times as much as on the level, the motors are connected in series. If the trolley voltage is now 500 volts and the flux is assumed to be proportional to the field current (not strictly true), (a) what current will be required? (b) At what speed will the car operate? The total armature, field, and brush-contact resistance per motor is 0.6 ohm.

9. A 550-volt long-shunt compound motor has an armature resistance of 0.82 ohm and a series-field resistance of 0.18 ohm. The full-load speed is 1,600 rpm when the armature current is 26 amp. (a) At what speed will the motor operate at no load if the armature current drops to 3 amp with a corresponding drop in flux to 84 per cent of the full-load value? (Assume a brush drop of 5 volts at full load and 3 volts at no load.) (b) Calculate the per cent regulation of the motor.

10. A 50-hp 550-volt shunt motor has an armature resistance of 0.088 ohm and takes an armature current of 74 amp when delivering rated horsepower output at a speed of 1,350 rpm. (a) Calculate the full-load torque. (b) Assume a brush drop of 5 volts and determine the initial rush of armature current and the corresponding momentary maximum torque at the instant the field-rheostat resistance is increased in order to reduce the field flux to 97 per cent of its original value. (c) Calculate the final armature current, speed, and horsepower output, assuming the same torque as that found in (a).

11. A series motor has a rating of 500 hp at 600 volts under which condition it takes 660 amp and operates at 750 rpm. Calculate the torque developed by the motor when the load increases to cause the line current to rise to 725 amp, assuming that the flux rises 40 per cent as much as the current.

12. Calculate the torque developed by the motor of Prob. 11 for a current of 600 amp, assuming a flux change that is 60 per cent of the current change.

13. Referring to the given data of Example 6, p. 197, and the magnetization curve of Fig. 140, calculate the torque, speed, and horsepower output of the series motor when the line current is (a) 60 amp, (b) 100 amp.

14. A 60-hp 1,200-rpm shunt motor has a maximum starting torque of 280 per cent and a pull-out torque of 260 per cent. Calculate the values of starting torque and maximum torque in pound-feet.

15. A compound motor was tested and found to have a maximum starting torque of 135 lb-ft. If this is assumed to be three times the normal developed torque at a speed of 1,750 rpm, calculate the horsepower rating of the motor.

CHAPTER 10

CONTROL OF MOTORS

Speed Control and Speed Regulation

Direct-current motors are especially suited to applications that require considerable speed adjustment, both above and below rated values. Such *speed control* is, of course, accomplished at the discretion of the operator who makes the necessary resistance or voltage adjustment at his disposal; whether or not the motor speed will vary *inherently with changes in load*, at a given resistance or voltage setting, will depend upon the *speed regulation* of the particular type of motor employed. It is extremely important that this distinction between speed control and speed regulation be recognized because, as noted, speed variations may occur in either or both of two ways, *i.e.*, by a physical adjustment on the part of an operator or by the self-regulation characteristic of the motor.

There are two *general* methods of controlling the speed of a d-c motor; these are (1) by changing the voltage across the armature (brush) terminals and (2) by varying the magnetic flux. When either or both schemes of adjustment are applied, the machine is said to be an *adjustable-speed* motor. However, if, in addition to the feature of adjustability, the speed changes with varying loads, the machine is said to be an *adjustable-varying-speed* motor. A shunt motor employing the field-rheostat method of control is an example of an adjustable-speed application; an adjustable-varying-speed motor is represented by a series machine with a line rheostat.

General Principle and Speed-control Methods

The most common methods of controlling the speed of shunt, series, or compound motors employ rheostats connected (1) in series with the armature circuit, (2) in series with the shunt-field circuit, (3) in parallel with the series field, or (4) in parallel with the armature circuit; combinations of the foregoing are sometimes used. A more desirable, though more expensive, arrangement is to connect a variable-voltage source, such as multivoltage or adjustable-voltage generator, across the controlled motor. All control schemes are, however, based upon the basic principle that *the speed of a motor is directly proportional to the counter emf and inversely proportional to the flux*, *i.e.*, rpm $= E_c/\phi$.

Armature Series-resistance Control

Figure 141 illustrates how a series rheostat is connected in the armature circuit for the purpose of adjusting the speed of a series, shunt, or compound motor. In all cases the physical size of the control unit must be large

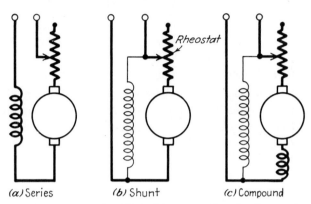

(a) Series   (b) Shunt   (c) Compound

FIG. 141. Sketches showing the simplified wiring connections for the armature-resistance method of speed control.

enough to handle the high values of armature current. Moreover, an increase in rheostat resistance R_{RH} will decrease the speed of the motor in accordance with the equation

$$\text{rpm} = \frac{V - I_A(R_A + R_{RH})}{k\phi} \tag{34}$$

Characteristic speed-torque curves for the three types of motor, with and without series armature resistance, are given in Fig. 142. Note particularly that with this method of control the speed of the motor depends upon the load as well as the amount of resistance inserted; furthermore, in all cases the speed regulations are greatly increased, for which reason they are properly designated adjustable-varying-speed motors.

The fact that resistance is inserted in the armature circuit, through which all or a major portion of the line current passes, means, of course, that there will be a considerable power loss, that is, $I_A{}^2 R_{RH}$ loss; this, then, represents one of the chief objections to the arrangement. In practice, therefore, the scheme is employed when the application requires a speed reduction to about 50 per cent of rated value and where a low operating efficiency can be tolerated. An example will now be given to illustrate quantitatively this control procedure as applied to a shunt motor.

EXAMPLE 1.   A 10-hp 230-volt 1,750-rpm shunt motor has an armature resistance of 0.35 ohm and a shunt-field resistance of 62.2 ohms. (a) If the motor takes 7.7 amp at no load and the full-load efficiency is 86 per cent, calculate the per cent regulation, assuming brush drops of 3 volts and 1 volt at full load and no load, respectively. (*b*) If a rheostat having 2.65 ohms is placed in the armature circuit to lower the speed, calculate the

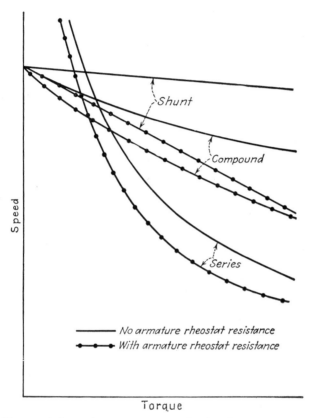

Fig. 142. Characteristic *speed* vs. *torque* curves, showing the effect of adding armature resistance to control the motor speed. (See Fig. 141 for the wiring connections.)

speed, the per cent regulation, and the power loss in the rheostat as a per cent of the total power input to the armature, when the motor is developing full-load torque.

Solution

(*a*) $I_{FL} = \dfrac{10 \times 746}{230 \times 0.86} = 37.7$ amp $I_{SH} = \dfrac{230}{62.2} = 3.7$ amp

$I_{A_{FL}} = 37.7 - 3.7 = 34$ amp $I_{A_{NL}} = 7.7 - 3.7 = 4$ amp

$\text{rpm}_{NL} = 1{,}750 \times \dfrac{(230 - 1) - (4 \times 0.35)}{(230 - 3) - (34 \times 0.35)} = 1{,}750 \times \dfrac{227.6}{215.1} = 1{,}850$

$$\text{Per cent regulation} = \frac{1,850 - 1,750}{1,750} \times 100 = 5.7$$

$$(b)\ \text{rpm}_{FL} = 1,750 \times \frac{(230 - 3) - (34 \times 3)}{(230 - 3) - (34 \times 0.35)} = 1,750 \times \frac{125}{215.1} = 1,020$$

$$\text{Per cent regulation} = \frac{1,850 - 1,020}{1,020} \times 100 = 81.5$$

$$I_{RH}{}^2 R_{RH} = (34)^2 \times 2.65 = 3,060 \text{ watts}$$

$$\text{Total armature power} = 230 \times 34 = 7,820 \text{ watts}$$

$$\text{Per cent power loss in rheostat} = \frac{3,060}{7,820} \times 100 = 39.2$$

Shunt-field-resistance Control

The most satisfactory and economical way to control the speed of a shunt motor is to insert a rheostat in the field circuit. This method provides for speed adjustments that are *above* rated values only and, for general-purpose machines, is limited to about 25 per cent. However, when the speed increase is to be much greater than this, it is necessary to use a specially designed adjustable-speed shunt motor that permits speed ranges of as much as 6 to 1; thus, if the rated speed is 450 rpm, the field can be weakened to increase the speed to 2,700 rpm. Figures 123 and 128 illustrate the wiring connections for this method of control.

Unlike the armature-circuit rheostat which is bulky and involves a considerable power loss (see Example 1), the shunt-field rheostat is a comparatively small unit and handles only about 4 to 10 per cent of the total current supplied to the motor; the rheostat $I_f{}^2 R_{RH}$ is, therefore, small. In many applications it is a necessary part of the installation or, as in Fig. 126, is incorporated in the starter, in which case the latter is known as a controller.

EXAMPLE 2. Using the given data of Example 1, calculate the speed to which the shunt motor will rise if a field-rheostat resistance is added to reduce the field current to 2.7 amp, assuming that the flux is reduced to 80 per cent of its original value and that the motor torque remains unchanged. Also determine the power loss in the rheostat.

Solution

Since $T = k\phi I_A$, I_A must increase by as much as ϕ decreases if the developed torque is to remain unchanged.

Therefore

$$I_A = \frac{34}{0.8} = 42.5 \text{ amp}$$

$$\text{rpm} = 1,750 \times \frac{[(230 - 3) - (42.5 \times 0.35)]/0.8k\phi}{[(230 - 3) - (34 \times 0.35)]/k\phi}$$

$$= 1,750 \times \frac{212.1}{215.1 \times 0.8} = 2,160$$

$$R_{RH} = \frac{230}{2.7} - 62.2 = 23.0 \text{ ohms}$$

$$I_f^2 R_{RH} = (2.7)^2 \times 23.0 = 167.5 \text{ watts loss in rheostat}$$

The speed of compound motors may also be adjusted by the insertion of resistance in the shunt-field circuit, although the method is not quite so satisfactorily applied as in the shunt machine. The reason for this is that any weakening of the shunt field for the purpose of increasing the speed is partly compensated by an increase in the series-field strength, since the current in the latter must rise if the motor torque is to be maintained. Moreover, as the magnetizing action of the shunt field is reduced, the series-field winding becomes more effective. For the best results, therefore, it is customary to apply this method of control to compound motors having comparatively small degrees of compounding and to restrict the speed adjustment to rather narrow ranges. On some applications, where a wide speed range is required, the series-field winding performs for starting duty only, being cut out (short-circuited) when the motor comes up to speed; the speed can then be adjusted by shunt-field rheostat control as in the ordinary shunt type of machine.

Armature-voltage Control

If an independent d-c source, in the form of a *variable-voltage generator*, is available for the controlled shunt motor, the latter may have its speed varied over an extremely wide range; such a system is a comparatively expensive installation and has a low over-all efficiency. It does, however, offer excellent possibilities for speed adjustment above and below rated value, provides a stepless control, and gives good (low) speed regulation. Generally referred to as the *Ward Leonard* system, the speed is controlled in accordance with the basic equation

$$\text{rpm} = \frac{V_{var} - I_A R_A}{k\phi} \tag{35}$$

Moreover, if the motor field is connected to a separate, constant-voltage source so that the flux is constant, the speed will be almost directly proportional to the variable armature (brush) potential V_{var} for a given developed torque. Thus

$$\text{rpm} = \frac{V_{var} - I_A R_A}{k\phi} = k_1 V_{var} - k_2 \qquad (35a)$$

the equation of a straight line. Figure 143 illustrates the elementary wiring connections for this unique scheme, in which a separate three-unit motor-

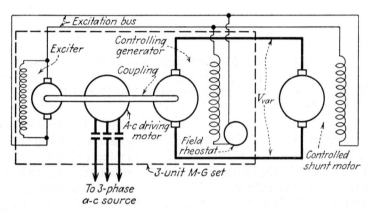

FIG. 143. Wiring connections for a *Ward Leonard* variable-voltage system of control for a shunt motor.

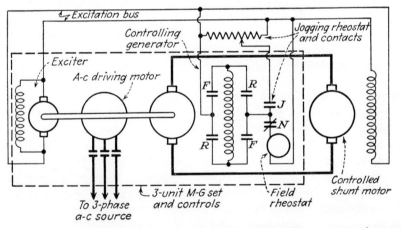

FIG. 144. Wiring connections for a *Ward Leonard* variable-voltage system of control with provisions for reversing and jogging.

generator (M-G) set is required to control the shunt motor. Note particularly that a three-phase a-c motor drives the separately excited controlling generator and the small d-c exciter; the latter, through the excitation bus, separately excites the shunt fields of the controlling generator and the controlled motor. *All control is centered in a small, low-power-consuming field rheostat* which is used to adjust the voltage V_{var} impressed across the armature terminals of the motor that drives the load.

This variable-voltage drive may be equipped with a "jogging" or "inching" control for fine speed adjustments and a method of reversing. Provision for such added features are shown in Fig. 144 in which push-button relays (not shown) are employed to operate the contactors for the

Fig. 145. Three-unit motor-generator set used in the armature-voltage method of control. (*Reliance Electric and Engineering Co.*)

"jogger" and the "reverser" devices. With the N contacts made (normally closed), the field rheostat controls the speed of the shunt motor in the normal way, either in a forward direction (with the F contacts closed) or in the reversed direction (with the R contacts closed); however, when the jogging contacts J are made to close (normally open), the N contacts open automatically so that the jogging rheostat may be used instead without affecting the other.

A photograph illustrating a three-unit set, mounted on a common base, is shown in Fig. 145. Note that the center a-c three-phase motor is coupled to the small exciter on the left and the controlling generator on the right.

Series-field Shunt-resistor Control

When a series motor must drive a given load—rated load for example—at a speed that is above its normal operating value, a rheostat must be connected *in parallel* with the series field. The effect of this arrangement is to cause a portion of the load current to by-pass the series field with the

result that less flux will be created.   The motor, therefore, speeds up to
satisfy the general equation rpm $= (V - I_A R_A)/k\phi$, although in doing so
the armature current (as well as the
line current) must increase somewhat to fulfill the torque demand.
Note that the effect of $k\phi$ to increase the speed is greater than
that of the $I_A R_A$ drop to decrease
the speed.   Figure 146 shows a
wiring diagram for controlling the
speed above as well as below

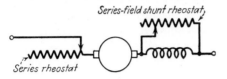

Series-field shunt rheostat

Series rheostat

FIG. 146. Wiring connections for controlling
a series motor above and below normal
speed.

normal.   The shunt-resistor method is seldom used in practice because, having an extremely low ohmic value, it is difficult to adjust; it is
also bulky and wasteful of energy.

Armature Shunt-resistance Control

It was pointed out that the use of a series resistor in the armature
circuit, to reduce the speed of a shunt motor, results in considerable
power loss.   Also, as Example 1 clearly illustrates, the per cent regulation
is greatly increased so that the speed varies over an extremely wide range
between full-load torque and no-load operation.   Moreover, the greater
the speed reduction by the insertion of increasing values of series resistance, the greater will be the wasted power and the more the speed will
vary with the load.   It is for these reasons, therefore, that this method of
control is limited to speeds that are rarely below 50 per cent of normal.
To show further how the addition of more armature series resistance
affects the power loss and the regulation, and how the latter characteristic
may be improved by the use of an *armature shunt resistance*, several problems will be solved; for this purpose the given data of Example 1 will be
used.

EXAMPLE 3.   Referring to the information given for the shunt motor of
Example 1, calculate the per cent regulation and the power loss in the
rheostat, if a resistance of 3.15 ohms is inserted in series in the armature
circuit for the purpose of lowering the speed to about one-half of rated
value.   The motor is to develop rated torque.

Solution

$$\mathrm{rpm}_{FL} = 1{,}750 \times \frac{(230 - 3) - (34 \times 3.5)}{(230 - 3) - (34 \times 0.35)} = 880 \text{ (approx.)}$$

$$\text{Per cent regulation} = \frac{1{,}850 - 880}{880} \times 100 = 110 \text{ (approx.)}$$

$$I_{RH}{}^2 R_H = (34)^2 \times 3.15 = 3{,}640 \text{ watts}$$

EXAMPLE 4. In order to reduce the speed still further, to about 375 rpm, a series resistance of 4.95 ohms is added in the armature circuit. Determine the per cent regulation and the power wasted in the rheostat for this lowered speed condition, assuming the same motor torque.

Solution

$$\text{rpm}_{FL} = 1,750 \times \frac{(230 - 3) - (34 \times 5.3)}{(230 - 3) - (34 \times 0.35)} = 380 \text{ (approx.)}$$

$$\text{Per cent regulation} = \frac{1,850 - 380}{380} \times 100 = 387 \text{ (approx.)}$$

$$I_{RH}{}^2 R_{RH} = (34)^2 \times 4.95 = 5,720 \text{ watts}$$

Note particularly in Examples 3 and 4 that a change in armature series resistance from 3.15 to 4.95 ohms results in a considerable rise in the speed regulation, from 110 to 387 per cent, as well as a rather large increase in rheostat power loss, from 3,640 to 5,720 watts. A better regulated method of speed control below the 50 per cent speed value of 875 rpm may, however, be obtained by means of an armature shunting resistance. This is illustrated by Fig. 147, in which an *armature shunt-resistance* method of control is added to the 3.15-ohm armature series-resistance control. Thus, when a shunting resistor of 3.15 ohms is added to the armature, in addition to the 3.15-ohm series resistor, the shunt-motor speed will drop to approximately 375 rpm, but at a greatly improved value of regulation. The following example shows this.

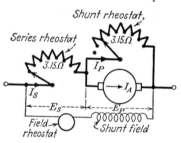

FIG. 147. Wiring connections showing the armature shunt-resistance, the armature series-resistance, and the shunt field-resistance methods of control. (Refer to Example 5.)

EXAMPLE 5. Referring to Fig. 147, calculate the speed regulation of the motor of Example 1 if an armature series resistor of 3.15 ohms and an armature shunt resistor of 3.15 ohms are connected as shown. Also determine the total power loss in the two rheostats. The motor is assumed to develop rated full-load torque at the low speed.

Solution

Calculations indicate that the current values through, and the voltage drops across, the various parts of the motor circuit, at full load and at no load, are as follows:

$I_{A_{FL}} = 34$ $I_{S_{FL}} = 53.5$ $I_{P_{FL}} = 19.5$ $E_{S_{FL}} = 168.5$ $E_{P_{FL}} = 61.5$

$I_{A_{NL}} = 4$ $I_{S_{NL}} = 38.5$ $I_{P_{NL}} = 34.5$ $E_{S_{NL}} = 121.5$ $E_{P_{NL}} = 108.5$

Therefore

$$\text{rpm}_{FL} = 1{,}750 \times \frac{(61.5 - 3) - (34 \times 0.35)}{(230 - 3) - (34 \times 0.35)} = 380 \text{ (approx.)}$$

and

$$\text{rpm}_{NL} = 1{,}750 \times \frac{(108.5 - 1) - (4 \times 0.35)}{(230 - 3) - (34 \times 0.35)} = 865 \text{ (approx.)}$$

$$\text{Per cent regulation} = \frac{865 - 380}{380} \times 100 = 128 \text{ (approx.)}$$

$$\text{Rheostat losses at full load} = (53.5)^2 \times 3.15 + (19.5)^2 \times 3.15$$

$$= 10{,}200 \text{ watts}$$

$$\text{Rheostat losses at no load} = (38.5)^2 \times 3.15 + (34.5)^2 \times 3.15$$

$$= 8{,}420 \text{ watts}$$

Multivoltage Control

A speed-control method that, in principle, is similar to the Ward Leonard system, page 207, makes use of two or more series-connected generators to supply two or more definite voltages to a controlled motor. The ad-

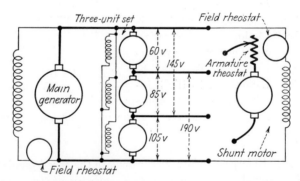

Fig. 148. Wiring diagram showing a multivoltage speed-control system.

vantage of this method is, of course, that less power is wasted at low speed, although, as in the *armature-voltage* control scheme, the additional rotating equipment increases the initial cost of the installation and involves added servicing. In the two-generator arrangement each of the machines is generally designed for a different voltage in which case three definite voltages become available to the operated motor or motors. Thus, for example, with an 80-volt 160-volt combination, the load may receive power at 80 volts, 160 volts, and 240 volts; moreover, if the controlled shunt motor is equipped with armature and field rheostats, intermediate speed adjustments can be made with limited controls. In some cases it has been found satisfactory to employ an equal-voltage balancer set (see Fig. 101), or balance coils (see Figs. 103 to 105), under which conditions only two definite voltages are provided. Three-unit sets are sometimes employed, particularly in elevator service where several elevators must be started frequently, and often simultaneously. In such installations the individual generators are designed for different armature voltages in which case six values of voltage become available. Figure 148 illustrates a three-unit combination of generators connected to a 250-volt main generator; with single-voltage supplies of 60, 85, and 105, the available six voltages are 60, 85, 105, 145, 190, and 250.

Series-parallel Control

When two motors are mechanically connected to drive a load, their speed may be controlled by the *series-parallel* method. The scheme is

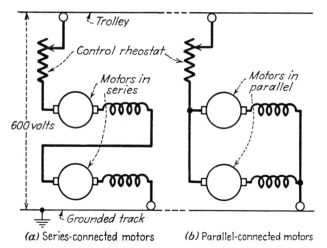

(a) Series-connected motors   *(b)* Parallel-connected motors

FIG. 149. Two-motor series-parallel control system for traction service.

particularly suited to the use of series-type motors whose characteristics are well adapted to such applications as street-railway and interurban service, electric locomotives, ore bridges, and cars used in the yards of steel mills and coke plants. In a small moving car, for example, each of the two motors is mounted on a truck that is geared to the driving wheels. In the starting position a drum controller (see Fig. 125) connects the two machines in *series* and in series with a control rheostat (Fig. 149a). As the car gains speed, the rheostat is cut out gradually until the two motors are in series across the full voltage supply, usually 600 volts; under this condition each motor receives one-half of the line potential. With further increase in speed the two motors are connected in *parallel* and in series with the same control rheostat (Fig. 149b). As acceleration progresses, the rheostat is again gradually cut out until each machine is connected directly across the full line potential. An important point to be noted is that half speed is obtained with the motors in series, with no external resistance in the circuit and, consequently, with no rheostatic power loss;

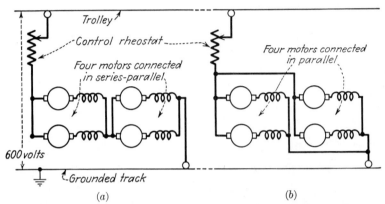

FIG. 150. Four-motor series-parallel control system for traction service.

the scheme has the advantage where half speed is frequently required. Moreover, when the accelerating period is comparatively long, a further saving in power is obtained because, with the motors in series, the line current is about half as much as would be required if they were in parallel.

When four motors are used in the larger traction installations, the control method is similar to that described above for the two-motor application, with the exception that there are always *two-pairs* of parallel-connected motors that may be joined in series or parallel. During the initial accelerating period the two pairs of motors are in series, and in series with a control rheostat (Fig. 150a). As the machines gain speed, the resistance is cut out until, at about half speed, each motor receives one-half of line potential. With further acceleration, the drum-controller handle is moved to the position that joins the four motors in parallel and in series with the same control rheostat (Fig. 150b). The latter is again gradually cut out until, at full speed, all four motors are connected directly across the full line voltage.

Flux Adjustment by Mechanical Control

All the methods thus far considered for the speed control of d-c motors involve electrical-circuit adjustments in which rheostats are changed or machines rearranged to raise or lower the flux or voltage. Still another scheme makes use of *mechanical* devices that alter the position of the poles with respect to the armature core; these change the magnetic reluctance within the machine. The result is that the flux will vary inversely with the reluctance of the magnetic circuit, for a given shunt-field mmf. Since an important part of the magnetic circuit is made up of a comparatively short air gap whose reluctance is given by the equation $\mathfrak{R} = \delta/A$ ($\mu = 1$), small changes in the gap length δ or the area A will be accompanied by significant variations of the flux and, therefore, the speed. Two constructional designs, based upon *the* foregoing *principle of varying the reluctance to control the speed*, are embodied in the *Stowe* and *Lincoln* motors; neither of them has been generally accepted by industry because of their mechanical complications and expense.

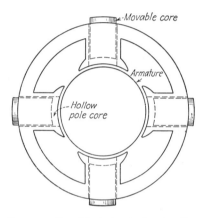

FIG. 151. Simplified sketch showing the construction of the variable magnetic-circuit type of the *Stowe* adjustable-speed motor.

In the Stowe motor the pole cores have large cylindrical holes that are bored radially, and into which soft iron cores are carefully fitted; the latter, fastened to a handwheel by a system of bevel gears and screw-threaded shafts, may be moved in or out to change the magnetic reluctance. When the inner surfaces of the movable cores are flush with the stationary part of the hollowed pole core, the reluctance is a minimum, the flux is a maximum, and the motor speed is low; conversely, with the movable cores withdrawn, the reluctance is a maximum, the flux is a minimum, and the motor speed is high. Figure 151 illustrates the construction of this type of machine.

In the Lincoln motor, manufactured by the Reliance Electric and Engineering Company, the armature core is slightly conical and fits into a pole-core structure whose inner pole shoes are conically shaped to provide a uniform air gap. A handwheel is geared to the armature so that the latter may be moved axially to change both the length and effective area of the air gap. A strong spring is provided which tends to push the armature core out of the magnetic field to balance the inward pull created by the magnetic field. With the armature drawn *in*, the magnetic reluctance is a minimum, the flux is a maximum, and the lowest motor speed is attained; as the armature is withdrawn, the reluctance increases, with a consequent reduction in flux and a rise in the speed. The construction of this motor is shown in Fig. 152.

Both types of motor are generally equipped with interpoles and provide good commutation over a speed range that may be as high as 10 to 1. Moreover, a stepless control is achieved, sometimes an important requirement in an application.

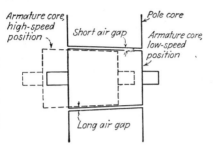

FIG. 152. Simplified sketch showing the construction of the variable magnetic-circuit type of *Lincoln* adjustable-speed motor.

Rototrol (Regulex) System of Control

An extremely interesting method that makes use of a rotating machine—a multifield generator—to control the speed of a motor is a system developed by the Westinghouse Electric Corporation called the *Rototrol* (a trade name which is formed by the first and last syllables of the words ROTating and conTROL). There is also one designed by the Allis-Chalmers Manufacturing Company called the *Regulex*. In the first of these, a d-c series (or self-excited shunt) generator is equipped with two or more *additional separately excited* field windings, the combined action of which is to adjust accurately the current delivered to the field of a separately excited generator which, in turn, controls the speed of a motor. In the actual Rototrol machine the several fields are so proportioned on the basis of mmf, and connected with regard to magnetic polarity, that small changes occurring in the motor circuit are amplified and reflected in the output of the control unit. Thus, for example, if the controlled motor is set to operate at a given speed when delivering a certain load, any tendency on the part of that machine to speed up or slow down is immediately accompanied by a change in the mmf of the Rototrol unit, which responds by strengthening or weakening the field of the motor; the speed of the latter can, therefore, be kept constant for a definite load and rheostat adjustment.

The principal advantage of this unique method of control is based upon the fact that a generator that is made to operate on the straight-line portion of the magnetization curve is subject to considerable output-voltage changes for relatively small variations in excitation. This is clearly seen in Fig. 153 where the slope of the magnetization curve is greatest, and constant, below the knee. Thus, for operating point P_1, 30 volts are generated when the net excitation is 26 amp-turns, whereas an increase in excitation to 88 amp-turns causes the terminal emf to rise to 110 volts; this means a gain of 80 volts for an increase of only 62 amp-turns. The curve represents the characteristic of a three-field Rototrol exciter in which the so-called *pattern* and *pilot fields* are separately excited and oppositely directed with respect to each other, while the *self-energizing field* is connected in

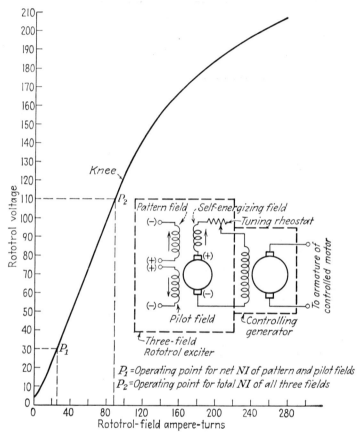

FIG. 153. Wiring diagram of a three-field Rototrol exciter, and its magnetization curve, used to control the speed of a motor.

series with the field of the generator that controls the speed of a motor. In the customary control system the tuning rheostat is adjusted so that the self-excited voltage is on the straight-line portion of the magnetization curve. The pilot field, which obtains its excitation from a small pilot generator coupled to the motor, is then made to neutralize the separately excited pattern field for the desired motor speed. Now then, if the controlled motor speed should increase momentarily, (1) the mmf of the pilot fie'd will do likewise, (2) the balance between pilot field and pattern field w.ll be upset, (3) the total mmf and the voltage of the Rototrol exciter will *decrease*, (4) the field strength and the voltage of the controlling generator will drop, and (5) the speed of the controlled motor will be corrected. A momentary reduction in the motor speed will be followed by an opposite set of reactions that will cause the speed to rise to its original value.

Figure 154 is a wiring diagram illustrating how a Rototrol system is connected to control a motor so that its speed will be maintained constant for varying values of output torque. In addition to the self-energizing and pattern fields, which are always used, there are two additional fields,

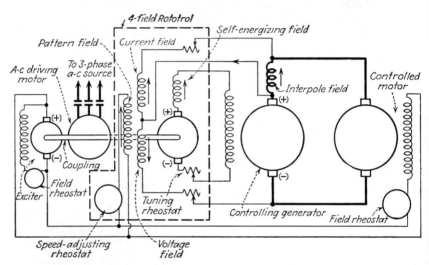

FIG. 154. Wiring diagram of a four-field Rototrol exciter to control the speed of a constant-field, separately excited d-c motor.

i.e., so-called *current and voltage fields;* the latter are required because the controlled d-c motor is provided with a constant separately excited field. Since the speed of a motor is rpm = $(V - I_A R_A)/k\phi$ and, in this case, the flux is constant, it follows that rpm = $k_1 V - k_2 I_A$. As a result this quantity can be measured by the combined effect of two properly adjusted Rototrol fields connected differentially, one of them across the brush terminals to register the voltage factor V and the other across the interpole field to signal variations in the current factor I_A.

To understand how the system operates, assume that the speed-adjusting rheostat is adjusted to give a desired motor speed for a given torque. Now then, if the load torque should increase, the armature current I_A must do likewise since $T = kI_A$, the flux being constant; this is followed by a drop of the generator voltage V and a momentary slowdown of the motor. These reactions then proceed to reduce the flux of the differential-voltage field and to raise the flux of the aiding current field, so that the *total effective flux is increased.* The net result is a boost of the Rototrol voltage, strengthening of the generator field, an increase in the generator emf, and finally

FIG. 155. Three-unit Rototrol set, consisting of a center a-c driving motor, an exciter on the left, and a four-field Rototrol machine on the right. (*Westinghouse Electric Corp.*)

a correction of the motor speed to its original setting. A momentary drop in the speed of the motor will, of course, be accompanied by an oppositely directed set of reactions and cause the speed to be returned to normal.

Figure 155 illustrates a three-unit set consisting of a driving motor in the center, a small exciter on the left, and a four-field Rototrol on the right, arranged exactly like that shown in the wiring diagram of Fig. 154. Note particularly the neat, compact arrangement of the construction.

A cutaway view of one of the composite field coils of a Rototrol unit is depicted in Fig. 156. The four independent fields are clearly seen, labeled 1, 2, 3, and 4, as are the interfield insulation 5, and the over-all insulation 6.

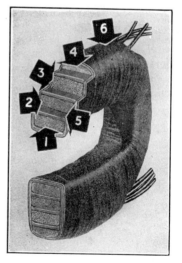

FIG. 156. Cutaway view of one of the composite coils of a four-field Rototrol. (*Westinghouse Electric Corp.*)

Braking

An electric motor is frequently brought to a quick stop by a mechanical, *i.e.*, friction, brake that is magnetically operated. Such a device is designed so that friction shoes are held against a brake drum by springs or weights and are released when an electromagnet is energized; the latter is generally connected to the same d-c source that serves the d-c motor. Mechanically operated brakes are, however, open to the objection that smooth, controlled stops are difficult because such action depends upon the condition of the braking surfaces and the skill of the operator. More desirable braking practices, requiring no rubbing surfaces, are entirely electrical; in these the motor is brought to a quick stop by permitting it to function as a generator during the period of retardation, under which condition the energy is either consumed in a resistor or returned to the supply source. The three widely employed methods—purely electrical—are known as *plugging, dynamic braking,* and *regenerative braking;* they are discussed in the following articles.

Plugging

Plugging is generally used when it is necessary to bring a motor to a quick stop so that it may be reversed, as in certain rolling-mill applications; with the field undisturbed, power is applied to the armature in the reverse direction, which quickly causes the machine to stop and then start up with the opposite rotation. In other installations the main switch is opened at the instant the armature comes to rest, *i.e.,* just before the motor

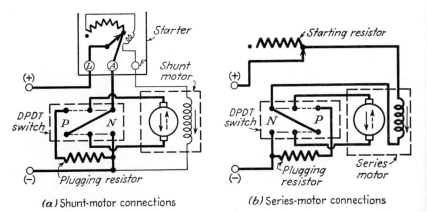

(a) Shunt-motor connections   (b) Series-motor connections

Fig. 157. Simple sketches illustrating the *plugging* method of stopping a shunt and series motor. N and P are, respectively, the normal and plugging positions of the DPDT switches.

starts to reverse. At the very moment the motor is "plugged," the armature impressed voltage and its counter emf are nearly equal and *in the same direction, i.e.,* additive. Therefore, to limit the initial rush of armature current to a reasonable value, it is necessary to insert a resistor in this circuit when the power is reversed; this usually means having a plugging resistor that is about 85 per cent more than the normal starting resistor. When a manual or automatic controller is provided with a plugging position, connections are often made so that the plugging resistor consists of the starting resistance and an additional unit; in normal operation the plugging resistor is, of course, short-circuited when the motor is started from rest.

Simplified wiring diagrams illustrating the plugging method of stopping shunt and series motors are given in Fig. 157. In the operation of these circuits it is assumed that the DPDT switches are opened at the instant the motors come to rest. The connections for a compound motor are essentially similar to those given with the exception that the series field might be reversed with the armature in the plugging position; this differential action of the two fields reduces the plugging current.

EXAMPLE 6. A starter limits the starting current in the armature circuit of a 5-hp 115-volt shunt motor to 150 per cent of its normal 38-amp rating. (a) Calculate the resistance of a plugging resistor (see Fig. 157a) if its value is to be 85 per cent more than the starter resistance, assuming a 3-volt brush drop. (b) Determine the maximum instantaneous armature current in the plugging position, assuming a counter emf of 102 volts.

Solution

(a) $$R = 1.85 \times \frac{115 - 3}{1.5 \times 38} = 3.64 \text{ ohms}$$

(b) $$I = \frac{(115 - 3) + 102}{3.64} = 58.8 \text{ amp}$$

Dynamic Braking

Dynamic braking makes use of the generator action in a motor (see Fig. 51) to bring it to rest quickly. If the armature terminals are disconnected from the source *while the field is kept energized*, the motor will *coast* to a stop; the time it will take to come to rest will depend upon the kinetic energy stored in the rotating system. However, if the armature terminals are disconnected from the source and immediately connected across a resistor of comparatively low value, *the field being kept energized*, the retardation rate will be greatly increased. The reason for this braking action is that the counter emf sends a current into the resistor, the kinetic energy of the rotating parts being rapidly expended in heat. The ohmic value of the braking resistor will determine the rate at which the mechanical energy is expended and, therefore, the time required for the motor to stop; in practice it is customary to design the resistor for an initial braking current of about 150 per cent of rated value, although quicker stops may be obtained if higher currents (lower ohmic resistances) and objectionable commutator sparking can be tolerated. The current obviously falls off with the countervoltage as the motor slows down, which means that the braking action is a maximum at first and diminishes to zero when the machine comes to rest; if it is necessary to hold the load in a stationary position when the motor stops, a mechanical brake must also be employed.

The principle of dynamic braking may be applied to a series motor in either of two ways. In one of these the series field is connected directly across the line in series with a current-limiting resistance, the armature being permitted to dissipate its energy in a resistor. With this scheme of connections the machine operates temporarily as a shunt motor, although in doing so the series-field circuit must be supplied with an ex-

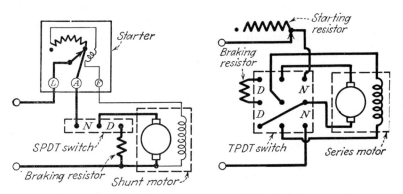

(a) Shunt-motor connections   (b) Series-motor connections

FIG. 158. Simple sketches illustrating the dynamic-braking method of stopping a shunt and series motor. N and D are, respectively, the normal and dynamic-braking positions of the switches.

tremely high current; the method is, therefore, wasteful of energy. A second, more common arrangement is to disconnect the motor from the line completely; the armature is then permitted to expend its kinetic energy in a resistor *and the series field, the latter being connected to carry current in the original direction.* Figure 158 shows two simplified sketches illustrating the dynamic-braking method applied to a shunt motor and a series motor. Similar connections may be used for the compound motor, although in doing so only the shunt field remains energized during the braking period.

EXAMPLE 7. The rated current of a 15-hp 230-volt series motor is 58 amp, and the total armature and series-field resistance is 0.28 ohm. If it is desired to limit the initial instantaneous dynamic-braking current to 1.75 times the motor's rating, calculate the value of the dynamic-braking resistor (see Fig. 158b). Assume a counter emf of 94 per cent of rated voltage and a brush drop of 3 volts.

Solution

$$R = \frac{(0.94 \times 230) - 3}{1.75 \times 58} - 0.28 = 1.82 \text{ ohms}$$

Regenerative Braking

Unlike the foregoing two methods wherein the motor is brought to a complete stop, the term *regenerative braking* is applied to a system in which the load *exerts a negative torque* on the motor, driving it as a generator so that power is returned to the supply lines. The braking action of regeneration, which is a modified form of dynamic braking, requires that the induced voltage in the motor, the counter emf, be greater than the line voltage; this means that the operating speed must be greater than the normal speed, a condition that can be brought about only if the load is of an overhauling character as in a railroad train going downgrade or in the cage of a hoist being lowered. In addition to overspeeding, shunt motors may be made to regenerate if, at reduced speed, the field strength is increased sufficiently to cause the counter emf to exceed the line potential; in other cases, where several motors drive a common load, they may be connected in various series or parallel combinations. Regenerative braking may also be used where it is desired to limit the speed of a given load to a certain maximum value.

Dynamos Operated Interchangeably as Motors and Generators

Motors are sometimes required to perform as generators during a part of their duty cycle; this, as was pointed out in the previous article, is necessary if a dynamo that normally develops torque while rotating in a given direction must regenerate, *i.e.*, deliver power to the electric system during some period of its operation, *while rotating in the same direction.* To understand how a machine can do this satisfactorily, it is necessary to recognize the following fundamental facts: (1) an operating motor is, at the same time, a generator, in which the counter emf E_c is oppositely directed with respect to the impressed voltage V; (2) as a motor, E_c is *less* than V; (3) as a generator, E_c is *more* than V; (4) as a motor, the positive brush terminal is the one *into which* the current passes into the armature; (5) as a generator, the positive brush terminal is the one *out of which* the current passes to the line; (6) for a given direction of rotation, the positive and negative brush polarities of a generator are determined only by the direction of the current through the field; (7) in a motor the armature current I_A and the counter emf E_c are *oppositely directed;* (8) in a generator the armature current I_A and the generated voltage E_G are in the *same direction.*

1. *Shunt-dynamo Operation.*   Referring to Fig. 159, it will be seen that all the foregoing conditions are fulfilled for a shunt dynamo, operating either as a motor or generator *without changes in wiring connections.*   In Fig. 159a the conditions are indicated for motor action, wherein E_c is less than V, and E_c is oppositely directed with respect to the normal current flow of I_A.   When the dynamo changes to generator action (Fig. 159b), E_c becomes E_G and is now more than V; moreover, the armature current

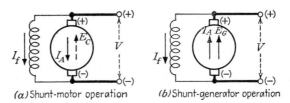

(*a*) Shunt-motor operation   (*b*) Shunt-generator operation

Fig. 159. Sketches illustrating currents, voltages, and polarities for motor and generator operation of a shunt dynamo.

reverses as is necessary, and the brush polarity properly matches the line polarity.   Note particularly that the direction of the current through the shunt field remains the same for motor and generator action.   Obviously, the speed of rotation, or the field strength, is increased when the machine is operating as a generator.

2. *Series-dynamo Operation.*   Referring to Fig 160a, it will be observed that the conditions are indicated for motor action, with E_c oppositely

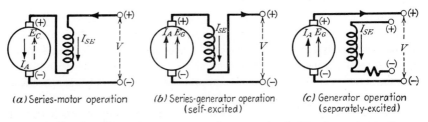

(*a*) Series-motor operation   (*b*) Series-generator operation   (*c*) Generator operation
                                        (self-excited)   (separately-excited)

Fig. 160. Sketches illustrating currents, voltages, and polarities for motor and generator operation of a series dynamo.

directed with respect to I_A.   However, when the machine changes to generator operation, *the field connections must be interchanged* as shown in Fig. 160b, if the proper brush polarity is to exist with respect to the line terminals.   The reason for the latter requirement is the fact that the field-current direction must *not* change even though the armature current does when conversion takes place from motor to generator; this is in accordance with the principles previously outlined.   In practice, as when a train is coasting downgrade, it is generally customary to excite the series field separately under the condition of regeneration; this is illustrated by Fig. 160c.

3. *Compound-dynamo Operation.* Since a compound dynamo (cumulative only) is a combination of a shunt and series machine, its two fields, shunt and series, must be properly connected when operating either way. As indicated previously, the shunt field remains undisturbed and the series-field terminals are interchanged when the operation changes from motor to generator; it is only in this way that the fields are prevented from acting differentially with respect to each other.

In this connection it should be mentioned that compound generators must not be used to charge storage batteries because a failure on the part of the prime mover will cause the battery to drive the generator as a differential-compound motor, with a tendency of the latter to become unstable and run away; it also represents a particularly heavy drain on the battery, which discharges under this condition.

Load Division between Rigidly Coupled Motors

Two shunt or series motors that are *rigidly coupled* to drive a common load will operate most satisfactorily *in parallel* if their characteristic *speed* vs. *current* curves are similar; this implies that, for all points on the curves, the *per cent full-load speed with respect to the per cent full-load current* will be the same for both machines. Under this condition a 25-hp load will, for example, be divided very nearly in the ratio of 15 to 10 between a pair of 15-hp—10-hp motors. Obviously, when the machines are exactly alike, the load division will be equal.

Series motors of identical design and rating may also be connected *in series* when coupled together; they will then carry the same current and, of course, develop the same torque and horsepower ($T = k\phi I_A$ and hp = $kT \times$ rpm). In the *series-parallel method of control* (page 213 and Figs. 149 and 150), the multiple use of motors, connected in several series and parallel combinations, is particularly advantageous in railway service.

It is important to understand that the rigid coupling of series motors is an essential requirement of satisfactory operation when they are connected in series. If this is not done, it is possible for one of the machines to run faster than the other; this comes about when a belt or clutch slips, or equal traction is not applied to the forward and rear wheels of a streetcar. Such a condition causes the faster motor (or motors) to develop a higher counter emf (the current and flux are the same in all), with the result that its impressed voltage will increase at the expense of the slower motor. When this happens the faster machine continues to speed up by slipping still more, while the slower motor tends to go into a stall with diminishing values of voltage. This is particularly significant in the case of a streetcar attempting to negotiate a hill on slippery rails; as indicated above the least tractive motors spin faster while those which are over-worked proceed to slow down and stall. The situation is remedied by preventing the wheels from slipping.

1. A 20-hp 230-volt shunt motor has a shunt-field resistance of 69.7 ohms. With a 1.4-ohm resistor in the armature circuit, the motor takes 74.3 amp when developing full-load torque. Calculate (*a*) power taken by the field; (*b*) the power loss in the inserted armature resistor.

2. A 50-ohm rheostat is placed in the field circuit of a 115-volt shunt motor. If the voltage drop across the rheostat is 38 volts, calculate (*a*) the resistance of the field winding; (*b*) the power taken by the field; (*c*) the power loss in the rheostat.

3. A 50-hp 550-volt 1,400-rpm shunt motor has an armature resistance of 0.26 ohm and a shunt-field resistance of 220 ohms. If the full-load efficiency is 89.4 per cent and the no-load line current is 4 amp, calculate (*a*) the per cent regulation of the motor, assuming brush drops of 5 volts and 2 volts at full load and no load, respectively; (*b*) the total power loss in the armature circuit at full load; (*c*) the power taken by the field.

4. A resistance of 1.74 ohms is placed in the armature circuit of the motor of Prob. 3 to reduce the speed. Calculate the speed and the per cent regulation when the motor is developing (*a*) rated torque; (*b*) one-half of rated torque. Assume brush drops of 5 and 4 volts, respectively, for rated and one-half rated armature currents.

5. Determine horsepower output for each of the conditions in Prob. 4.

6. What will be the power loss in the inserted armature resistor for each of the conditions of Prob. 4?

7. A 40-hp 250-volt 1,500-rpm shunt motor has a field winding whose resistance is 62.5 ohms. What is the ohmic value of a field rheostat that raises the motor speed to 2,500 rpm, if, under this condition, the field current is 2.78 amp?

8. A 100-hp 230-volt 1,750-rpm shunt motor has a full-load efficiency of 92.2 per cent; its armature and shunt-field resistances are 0.02 ohms and 32.8 ohms, respectively. If a field rheostat of 20 ohms is inserted, and this reduces the flux to 75 per cent of its original value, calculate (*a*) the speed of the motor when it develops rated torque, assuming a brush drop of 3 volts; (*b*) the power loss in the rheostat.

9. Calculate the speed and the horsepower output of the motor of Prob. 9 when the armature carries rated current.

10. A 50-hp 460-volt 1,200-rpm shunt motor has an armature resistance of 0.31 ohm. If the field is connected to a 460-volt source and the armature to a 230-volt supply, determine the motor speed when the armature takes the rated current of 89 amp. Assume a 4-volt brush drop.

11. Two identical coupled 50-hp 550-volt 1,500-rpm series motors are connected in series to a 600-volt source and develop rated torque. The total armature- and series-field resistance of each motor is 0.25 ohm and the full-load efficiency is 89.3 per cent. At what speed will the combination operate? (Assume a 5-volt brush drop.)

12. At what speed will the motors of Prob. 11 operate if they develop rated torque when connected in parallel?

13. A 60-hp 230-volt shunt motor has an armature resistance of 0.04 ohm and a field resistance of 38.3 ohms. At the moment it is developing rated torque it is plugged. Determine the value of the plugging resistor if the latter limits the instantaneous armature current to 200 per cent of its rated value. Assume a motor efficiency of 88.5 per cent and a brush drop of 3 volts.

14. For the motor of Prob. 13, what should be the value of a resistor for dynamic braking, for the same maximum instantaneous armature current?

15. A 200-hp 550-volt series motor has a total armature-circuit resistance of 0.06 ohm and operates at full load at an efficiency of 90 per cent. Calculate the value of a dynamic-braking res'stor that will limit the instantaneous maximum current to 580 amp, assuming a brush drop of 5 volts.

CHAPTER 11

EFFICIENCY, HEATING, AND RATINGS
OF DYNAMOS

Power Losses in Dynamos

When a dynamo converts energy from one form to another—mechanical to electrical in a generator, and electrical to mechanical in a motor—it does so at an efficiency that is always less than 100 per cent. This means, of course, that the input to the machine is greater than the output of the machine by the internal power losses. In other words, some of the power input to the machine is used to perform functions that do not show up as useful power output; understand that they are all necessary functions, but not *useful* in the sense that they represent electrical (generator) or mechanical (motor) loads.

Since the power losses are unavailable to drive the mechanical load in a motor or to supply electric power in a generator, they are obviously converted to heat that tends to raise the temperature of the dynamo; therefore, the greater the power losses, as a percentage of the total power input, the hotter will the machine become. Moreover, should such losses become unusually high, on the basis of the machine's ability to dissipate the heat that is produced, the temperature may rise sufficiently high to cause failure.

Power losses in electrical machines may be divided into two general classifications, namely, (1) those which are caused by the *rotation of the armature* and (2) those which result from a *current flow* in the various parts of the machine. The former are usually designated *rotational losses* (sometimes called *stray-power losses*), while the latter are termed *copper losses*. The rotational losses will, generally, vary with speed changes, while the electrical losses are affected by the current values in the various parts of the machine as well as the respective ohmic resistances.

Rotational Losses

Rotational losses occur in the rotating part of the dynamo and are made up of the following five components: (1) bearing friction, (2) wind friction, usually called *windage*, (3) brush friction, (4) hysteresis, and (5) eddy currents.

Bearing and windage losses are purely mechanical and result from the rotation of the armature. They may be determined by using a calibrated

228

motor to drive the armature of the machine at the proper speed, with the brushes lifted; the desired losses are represented by the known output of the calibrated motor for a measured input to the latter.

Brush-friction loss varies considerably with the kind of brushes and the nature of the rubbing surfaces. It may be determined by using a calibrated motor, as above, and noting the difference in power required for the armature turning free and the armature turning with the brushes in contact with the commutator. The loss may also be *estimated* by using the following values of *watts per square inch of brush-contact surface for each 1,000 ft per min (fpm) of peripheral speed:* (*a*) 8 watts for carbon and graphite brushes, (*b*) 5 watts for graphite brushes.

EXAMPLE 1. The following information is given in connection with a 320-hp 6-pole 800-rpm shunt motor: commutator diameter = 22 in., brushes per stud = 6, dimensions per brush = 0.75 by 1.625 in., brush arc = 0.777 in., type of brush = medium carbon. Assuming 8 watts per sq in. of brush-contact surface per 1,000 fpm of peripheral speed, calculate the brush-friction loss.

Solution

$$\text{Commutator velocity} = \frac{\pi \times 22 \times 800}{12} = 4{,}600 \text{ fpm}$$

Total brush area = 6 × (0.777 × 1.625) × 6 = 45.5 sq in.

$$\text{Brush-friction loss} = 8 \times \frac{4{,}600}{1{,}000} \times 45.5 = 1{,}675 \text{ watts}$$

Hysteresis loss takes place in the revolving armature core because the magnetic polarity in every element of the iron changes in step with the changing positions of the magnetic material under the various poles. Thus, when an armature-core tooth is passing under a *north* pole, its polarity will be south, *i.e.*, the iron particles are orientated with their north ends pointing inward. When this same tooth moves under a *south* pole, its polarity will be *north*, and the iron particles will then be directed so that their north ends point outward. The rapid "jerking" around of the tiny magnetic particles in the armature-core iron as it revolves rapidly causes a sort of magnetic-particle friction and produces heating. This hysteresis loss is magnetic in character but results only because the armature core is turning; it is for this reason that it may be properly regarded as a rotational loss. In the modern dynamo, it depends upon four factors, namely, (1) the quality of the magnetic iron, (2) the frequency of the alternating current in the armature conductors, which in turn is a function of the speed of rotation and the number of poles, (3) the flux density in the armature-core iron, and (4) the weight of iron. In equation form hysteresis loss P_h may be represented by the following equation:

$$P_h = k_h f B^{1.6} W \qquad (36)$$

where k_h = a constant, depending upon the core material and the units used

f = frequency, cps [Eq. (8)]

B = maximum flux density in the iron core

W = weight of the core

For the usual grades of iron used, $k_h = 6.2 \times 10^{-10}$, where B and W are expressed in lines per square inch and pounds, respectively.

EXAMPLE 2. If the armature core of Example 1 weighs 820 lb, calculate the hysteresis loss, assuming a maximum flux density of 92,000 lines per sq in.

Solution

$$P_h = (6.2 \times 10^{-10}) \times \frac{6 \times 800}{120} \times (92,000)^{1.6} \times 820$$

$$= (6.2 \times 10^{-10}) \times 40 \times (8.75 \times 10^7) \times 820 = 1,780 \text{ watts}$$

Note particularly that Eq. (36) is based upon a uniform flux density in the entire volume of iron, an assumption that is, strictly speaking, not correct. It should also be noted that the hysteresis loss is unaffected by whether or not the core is laminated.

Eddy-current Loss. As the armature revolves, voltages are generated in the iron exactly as they are in the copper wires. Such voltages are objectionable, however, because they create a flow of current in the core in "eddies." The *eddy currents*, as they are called, result because the generated emfs in the filaments of iron that run parallel to the shaft are greater near the outside surface than those closer to the center of the shaft; voltage differences exist because the *flux-cutting rate* is more in the outer filaments of iron than in those closer to the center. Since these eddy currents have paths that are, for the most part, parallel to the shaft, the logical way to minimize them is to introduce high resistances in the form of air spaces in direct line to such paths. This is readily accomplished by "slicing" or "laminating" the armature core and then coating each lamination with a high-resistance varnish. Note especially that this practice does *not* disturb the normal magnetic flux paths, since the latter are approximately radial, *i.e.*, along the laminations and not across them. Figure 161 illustrates how the eddy currents are set up before and after laminating. In the unlaminated core the current path is roughly represented by the length $(2l + 2w)$ and an area that is proportional to l; in the laminated core the current path has a length of about $(2l/3 + 2w)$ and an area that is proportional to $l/3$. This means that the magnitude of the current in each of the paths of the laminated core will be approximately one-ninth as much as in the solid core because the generated emf is about one-third as much and the resistance is nearly three times as much. However, since there are three such paths, the effect is as though the total eddy currents are reduced to one-third of their original value. Or, stating it in general terms, the eddy currents may be said to be pro-

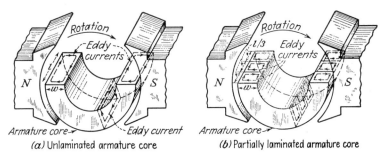

(a) Unlaminated armature core   *(b)* Partially laminated armature core

Fig. 161. Sketches illustrating eddy currents in an armature core, before and after laminating.

portional to the *thickness* of the laminations, while the power loss is proportional to the *square* of the lamination thickness.

In addition to lamination thickness, eddy-current loss depends upon the frequency of the currents, the flux density in the core, and the volume of iron. In equation form the eddy current loss P_e may be represented by the following equation:

$$P_e = k_e f^2 t^2 B^2 V \qquad (37)$$

where k_e = a constant depending upon the resistivity of the iron and the dimensions employed for other factors
f = frequency, cps
t = thickness of the laminations
B = maximum flux density in the core
V = volume of iron in the core

Eddy currents are electromagnetic in character but result only because of the rotation of the armature core; these, too, may therefore be regarded primarily as a rotational loss.

Copper Losses

Copper losses occur in the various parts of the machine that carry electric currents. One of the most important losses is the armature-winding copper loss $I_A{}^2R_A$. Then there are the field copper losses, one or more of which may be present in a given dynamo, depending upon its type. These are (1) the shunt-field copper loss $I_f{}^2R_f$, or, if the field rheostat is included, VI_f; (2) the series-field copper loss $I_{SE}{}^2R_{SE}$; (3) the interpole-field copper loss $I_A{}^2R_I$; (4) the compensating-field copper loss $I_A{}^2R_C$. (Since the interpole and compensating field windings are always in the armature circuit and depend upon the armature current, they are often combined with the armature-winding loss and designated as the *armature-circuit* copper loss.) Still another loss takes place at the brush contacts where arcing generally occurs. Although not, strictly speaking, a copper loss, it is usually included in this classification; the brush-contact loss is a function of the brush drop E_B and the armature current I_A and is equal to E_BI_A.

The *armature-winding copper loss* $I_A{}^2R_A$ is, in general, the largest of the individual losses in the d-c machine. Since it varies as the *square* of the armature current, and the latter is determined by the magnitude of the load, this loss is almost directly proportional to the square of the load. In the design of d-c machines, the cross-sectional area of the armature copper is made as large as practicable so that the winding resistance may be kept low.

The *shunt-field copper loss* $I_f{}^2R_f$ is usually considered constant over the normal operating range of the machine. In most cases the rheostat loss is included in this computation under which condition it becomes VI_f. For varying-field dynamos this loss will change somewhat with different field-rheostat settings.

The *series-field, interpole-field,* and *compensating-field losses,* like the armature-winding loss, vary almost directly as the square of the load; as previously noted, these fields are always in the armature circuit and carry the current I_A. These losses are generally the smallest of the individual components.

The *brush-contact loss* does not follow a clearly defined law, as do the other losses, but depends upon empirical relationships. Experiments have shown that the contact drop E_B of a particular grade of brush rises slightly with increases of current at the lower values but is generally an almost constant value over the range of current densities (amperes per square inch) used in common practice. Brush manufacturers publish figures of contact drop for each quality of brush, and it is to these that reference must be made for the calculation of E_BI_A. Except for the small changes in E_B, this loss is almost directly proportional to the load.

Stray-load Loss

Stray-load loss is a rather difficult loss to determine since it results from such indefinite factors as (1) the distortion of the flux because of armature reaction, (2) the lack of uniform division of the current in the armature winding through the various paths and through the individual, large-cross-sectional-area conductors, and (3) short-circuit currents in the coils undergoing commutation. The indeterminate nature of the stray-load loss makes it necessary to assign it a reasonable value arbitrarily; it is usually assumed to be about 1 per cent of the output of the machine when the rating is about 150 kw (200 hp) or more; for small ratings, the stray-load loss is generally neglected when efficiency calculations are made, without much loss of accuracy.

Table of Dynamo Losses

In order to summarize the various points made in connection with dynamo losses, Table 1 has been prepared. Note particularly how the individual components are determined and what changes affect them.

TABLE 1

DYNAMO LOSSES

Losses			Affected by	How determined
Rotational or stray power	Friction	Bearing	Speed changes	Usually by test
		Windage		
		Brush		
	Armature core	Hysteresis	Speed and flux changes	
		Eddy current		
Copper		Armature winding	Load	$I_A{}^2 \times R_A$
		Series field		$I_A{}^2 \times R_{SE}$
		Interpole field		$I_A{}^2 \times R_I$
		Compensating winding		$I_A{}^2 \times R_C$
		Brush contact		$E_B \times I_A$
		Shunt field		$I_f{}^2 \times R_f$ or $V \times I_f$
Stray load			Flux distortion and commutation	1 per cent of output for machines 150 kw (200 hp) and over

Efficiency of D-C Generators

The efficiency of a machine is defined as the ratio of its useful power output to the total power input, the units for both quantities being, of course, similar. In the electric generator this is the ratio of the electrical-power output $P_0(= V \times I_L)$ to the mechanical-power input P_I, converted to watts. As a percentage, this may be represented in equation form by the expression

$$\text{Per cent efficiency} = \eta = \frac{P_0}{P_I} \times 100 \tag{38}$$

Since $P_0 = P_I - P_L$ (where P_L = total losses for the given value of P_0), and $P_I = P_0 + P_L$, Eq. (38) may be written in the form

$$\eta = \left(1 - \frac{P_L}{P_0 + P_L}\right) \times 100 \tag{39}$$

Equation (39) makes use of quantities that are readily determined and yields more accurate slide-rule results when comparatively high efficiencies are anticipated.

EXAMPLE 3. Calculations indicate that the total losses in a 250-kw generator, operating at full load, are 19.5 kw. Calculate the efficiency.

Solution

$$\eta_{FL} = \left(1 - \frac{19.5}{250 + 19.5}\right) \times 100 = 92.77$$

EXAMPLE 4. The machine of Example 3 has an efficiency of 89.4 per cent when delivering one-half of rated load. Determine the losses under this condition.

Solution

$$P_L = \left(\frac{P_0 \times 100}{\eta}\right) - P_0 = \left(\frac{125 \times 100}{89.4}\right) - 125 = 15 \text{ kw}$$

Engineering practice recognizes two distinct methods for determining the efficiency of a generator. These are (1) the *conventional efficiency* method, based upon accurately evaluated losses, and (2) the *directly measured* efficiency method, based upon directly measured output and input quantities. In the latter method an actual test is performed upon the generator in which electrical instruments measure the output, while a *calibrated motor* drives the machine under test. A calibrated motor is one whose outputs (representing the inputs to the tested generator) are known for all values of measured inputs. Ordinarily, directly measured efficiency tests are difficult to perform, somewhat inaccurate, and very wasteful of energy when the machines are comparatively large. The inaccuracy results because efficiencies of such generators are comparatively high, which means that the input and output quantities do not differ greatly; small numerical errors in making measurements can, therefore, result in relatively large percentage errors. For small machines, however, the directly measured efficiency method is both simple and inexpensive and is, therefore, preferred to the conventional (losses) procedure; it is, moreover, fairly accurate because efficiencies are rather low, so that a considerable measurable difference exists between power input and power output.

Efficiency of D-C Motors

The efficiency of an electric motor is the ratio of the mechanical-power output, converted to watts, to the electrical-power input P_I ($= V \times I_L$). As a percentage, this may be represented in equation form by the expression

$$\eta = \frac{\text{hp} \times 746}{P_I} \times 100 \tag{40}$$

or, following the same arrangement of terms as in Eq. (39), it may be written

$$\eta = \left(1 - \frac{P_L}{(\text{hp} \times 746) + P_L} \right) \times 100 \tag{41}$$

EXAMPLE 5. A 20-hp 230-volt motor takes 73.7 amp when operating at rated load. Calculate the losses in the motor and its efficiency.

Solution

$$\text{Losses} = (230 \times 73.7) - (20 \times 746) = 2{,}031 \text{ watts}$$

$$\eta = \left(1 - \frac{2{,}031}{14{,}920 + 2{,}031} \right) \times 100 = 88.0 \text{ per cent}$$

As in the case of generators, the efficiency of a motor may be determined in either of two ways, *i.e.*, by the losses (conventional) method or the directly measured method.

Determining Losses in Dynamos

As previously explained, there are two general kinds of losses that must be determined for the calculation of the conventional efficiency of a generator or motor. These are (1) electrical losses that depend upon resistances, currents, and voltage drops, and (2) stray-power losses that are associated with the rotation of the armature. The first of these involves a group of resistance measurements, which may then be used with their respective currents to yield the proper copper losses; for the second set of losses it is necessary to operate the machine without load in accordance with carefully controlled procedures.

Armature- and Interpole-winding Resistance Measurements. Since the armature and interpole-winding resistances are low, a Kelvin bridge should be used for these measurements if a high degree of precision is desired. The drop-of-potential method may, however, be employed with reasonably good accuracy. Figure 162a illustrates the latter procedure, in which the armature circuit is connected in series with a current-limiting rheostat of sufficient current-carrying capacity to a d-c source. Several sets of readings are taken for current adjustments in the normal operating range of the machine; a record is made of I_A, E_A, and E_I, and resistances are

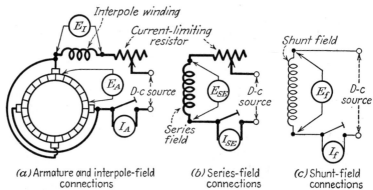

(a) Armature and interpole-field connections   (b) Series-field connections   (c) Shunt-field connections

Fig. 162. Connections for determining the resistances of the various parts of a dynamo.

calculated for R_A ($= E_A/I_A$) and R_I ($= E_I/I_A$). Average values are then used in making losses computations. Note particularly that the armature-winding voltage drop E_A is obtained by touching the voltmeter leads to commutator segments directly below two adjacent plus and minus brushes. (If there is a compensating winding, it will be in series with the interpole field; under this condition E_{I+C} is measured, which then gives the value of R_{I+C} ($= E_{I+C}/I_A$).)

Series-field Winding Resistance Measurement. Series-field winding resistance measurement is carried out in exactly the same way as for R_A and R_I, as indicated by Fig. 162b. The leads are merely shifted from the armature circuit to the series-field terminals. This resistance, R_{SE} ($= E_{SE}/I_{SE}$), which has a value considerably less than the armature winding, should be determined by performing the test very carefully.

Shunt-field Winding Resistance Measurement. Since the shunt-field winding has a comparatively high resistance, it is connected directly across the d-c source in series with a low-reading ammeter. A voltage measurement E_f must be made while the field is energized, and the voltmeter leads must be disconnected from the shunt-field terminals *before the switch is opened;* because the shunt field is highly inductive, an "inductive kick" is developed when the switch is *opened,* and this high voltage will damage the voltmeter if it is not disconnected. Figure 162c illustrates the wiring connections, from which $R_f = E_f / I_f$.

Stray-power-loss Measurement. Either of two procedures may be followed to determine the stray-power loss, *i.e.,* the sum of the frictional and core losses. In the so-called *no-load test,* the tested machine is operated as a shunt motor, free of mechanical load. In the *separate-motor test,* use is made of another motor to drive the dynamo whose losses are desired.

In the *no-load test* the machine, whether generator or motor, is operated free of any load as a shunt motor at *rated speed* and with a voltage across the armature circuit equal to the normal *generated emf;* the latter is equal to $E_A = V + E_B + I_A R_A$ for a generator and $E_A = V - E_B - I_A R_A$ for a motor, the drops being full-load values. Figure 163 illustrates the connections to be used. The power input to the *armature* then equals the friction and windage plus core losses and a very small armature copper loss. The fact that the machine runs at rated speed means that the frictional losses (bearing, brush, and windage) are duplicated; also, since the core loss and the

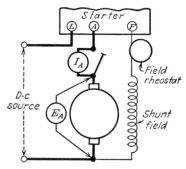

Fig. 163. Wiring connections for measuring the stray-power losses of a dynamo.

generated emf are both proportional to the flux (or flux density), the core loss will be correctly included in the measurement when the flux is adjusted to give the required generated voltage at rated speed.

EXAMPLE 6. A no-load test is to be made upon a 10-kw 250-volt 1,200-rpm long-shunt compound generator to determine the total friction, windage, and core losses. Armature and interpole resistance = 0.4 ohm, series-field resistance = 0.05 ohm, shunt-field resistance = 125 ohms. Find the required armature voltage for the test, and from the measured values calculate the stray-power loss. Assume a brush drop of 3 volts.

Solution

$$I_A \text{ at full load} = \frac{10,000}{250} + \frac{250}{125} = 42 \text{ amp}$$

$$E_A = 250 + 3 + (42 \times 0.45) = 271.9 \text{ volts}$$

With 272 volts impressed across the armature (brush) terminals, an armature current of 2.1 amp is measured when the machine is operated as a shunt motor at 1,200 rpm.

Stray-power loss = $[272 \times 2.1] - [(2.1)^2 \times 0.45] = 569$ watts

In the *separate-motor* test the machine whose stray-power losses are to be determined is operated as a separately excited generator, being coupled to and driven at rated speed by a comparatively small shunt motor; the size of the latter should be of about the same order of magnitude as the losses to be measured, and its normal speed nearly the same as the tested machine. Two sets of data must be taken, namely, (1) with the driving

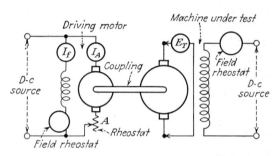

FIG. 164. Wiring connections to determine the stray-power losses by the *separate-motor* test.

motor running free and (2) with the machines coupled together. With the small driving motor *uncoupled* and instruments inserted as indicated in Fig. 164, the speed is adjusted so that it is the same as the normal rating of the machine under test; readings are then taken of I_f, I_A, and E_A. The two units are next coupled together, after which the following adjustments are made: (1) the speed is brought to the correct value by armature-resistance control A; (2) the field of the tested machine is separately excited and adjusted to give rated voltage E_T; (3) the field I_f is readjusted to exactly the value it had in the first test, this being necessary to prevent any change in the core losses of the driving motor. A second set of readings may now be taken of I_f, I_A, and E_A. Finally, the armature resistance of the separate motor is measured as in Fig. 162a. From the results obtained, the stray-power losses SPL may be calculated as follows:

$$SPL = (E_A I_A - I_A^2 R_A)_{\text{coupled}} - (E_A I_A - I_A^2 R_A)_{\text{uncoupled}}$$

This method of determining the indicated losses assumes, of course, that the input to the armature of the driving motor at no load is its constant losses, *i.e.*, friction, windage, and core losses, and that these remain unchanged when it is coupled to its load. An example will now be given to illustrate the procedure.

EXAMPLE 7. A 1-hp 230-volt 1,500-rpm shunt motor is available to drive a 10-kw 250-volt 1,200-rpm generator for the purpose of determining the stray-power loss of the latter machine. With the driving motor free and operating at 1,200 rpm, $E_A = 206$ volts, $I_A = 1.2$ amp, and $I_f = 0.6$ amp. With the machines coupled together and the terminal emf of the separately excited generator E_T adjusted to 250 volts, and the speed, as before, 1,200 rpm, the readings are $E_A = 207$ volts, $I_A = 4.0$ amp, and $I_f = 0.6$ amp. The armature resistance of the driving motor was found to be 0.8 ohm. Calculate the stray-power losses.

Solution

$$\text{SPL} = [(207 \times 4) - (4)^2 \times 0.8] - [(206 \times 1.2) - (1.2)^2 \times 0.8]$$
$$= 569 \text{ watts}$$

Maximum Efficiency

If a test is performed upon a dynamo, or calculations are made by the conventional method, to determine its performance, it will be found that the efficiency increases with increasing values of load, reaches a maximum,

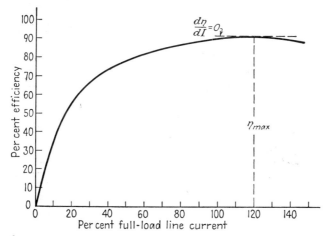

FIG. 165. Typical *efficiency* vs. *load-current* characteristic of a dynamo.

and then proceeds to drop; Fig. 165 illustrates a typical *efficiency* vs. *per cent current output* curve for a generator or motor. An analysis of the test data reveals that, for the rising position of the curve, the output rises more rapidly than the losses, and for the falling section of the curve, the losses increase faster than the output. Moreover, as will be shown, maximum efficiency occurs when the constant losses, *i.e.*, SPL, and VI_f, if present, are equal to those which vary as the square of the load.

Considering a shunt generator, the efficiency

$$\eta = \frac{\text{power output} (= P_0)}{P_0 + \text{total losses}} = \frac{VI_L}{VI_L + (\text{SPL} + VI_f) + I_A{}^2 R_A}$$

where R_A is the total armature-circuit resistance, including all windings *and an assumed constant brush-contact resistance*. Since I_A is larger than I_L by a rather small percentage, the two values may be considered equal for the purposes of analysis. Thus

$$\eta = \frac{VI_L}{VI_L + (\text{SPL} + VI_f) + I_L{}^2 R_A}$$

Maximum efficiency will occur when the slope of the *efficiency* vs. *current curve* is zero, *i.e.*, $\eta_{\max}$ occurs when $d\eta/dI_L = 0$. Differentiating the above equation and setting its result equal to zero

$$\frac{d\eta}{dI_L} = \frac{(VI_L + \text{SPL} + VI_f + I_L{}^2 R_A)(V) - (VI_L)(V + 2I_L R_A)}{(VI_L + \text{SPL} + VI_f + I_L{}^2 R_A)^2} = 0$$

from which

$$\text{SPL} + VI_f = I_L{}^2 R_A \cong I_A{}^2 R_A \tag{42}$$

Equation (42) indicates that the maximum efficiency of a shunt generator, assuming a constant line potential, occurs when the constant losses—the stray-power and field losses—are equal to those losses which vary as the square of the load—the armature-circuit copper losses.

Similarly for a shunt motor

$$\eta = \frac{P_I - \text{total losses}}{\text{power input} (= P_I)} = \frac{VI_L - (\text{SPL} + VI_f) - I_L{}^2 R_A}{VI_L}$$

Differentiating as before

$$\frac{d\eta}{dI_L} = \frac{VI_L(V - 2I_L R_A) - (VI_L - \text{SPL} - VI_f - I_L{}^2 R_A)V}{(VI_L)^2} = 0$$

from which $\text{SPL} + VI_f = I_L{}^2 R_A \cong I_A{}^2 R_A$. Thus, the maximum efficiency $\eta_{\max}$ for a shunt generator or motor is

$$\eta_{\max} \cong \frac{P_0}{P_0 + 2(\text{SPL} + VI_f)} \cong \frac{P_0}{P_0 + (2I_L{}^2 R_A)} \tag{43}$$

EXAMPLE 8. A 60-kw 250-volt shunt generator has an armature-circuit resistance of 0.05 ohm, a field resistance of 50 ohms, and a maximum efficiency of 91 per cent. Calculate (a) the load for which the efficiency is approximately a maximum; (b) the stray-power losses.

Solution

(a) $$0.91 = \frac{250 I_L}{250 I_L + 2(I_L{}^2 \times 0.05)} = \frac{250}{(250 + 0.1 I_L)}$$

$$I_L = 247.2 \text{ amp}$$

and

$$P_0 \text{ for maximum efficiency} = 0.25 \times 247.2 = 61.8 \text{ kw}$$

(b) $$\text{SPL} \cong [(247.2)^2 \times 0.05] - 1{,}250 \cong 1{,}800 \text{ watts}$$

EXAMPLE 9. A 75-hp 230-volt shunt motor has an armature-circuit resistance of 0.035 ohm. If tests indicate that the shunt-field and stray-power losses are 2,940 watts, calculate the approximate line current, horsepower output, and maximum efficiency for the operating condition of maximum efficiency.

Solution

$$\text{SPL} + V I_f = I_L{}^2 R_A \qquad 2{,}940 = I_L{}^2 \times 0.035$$

$$I_L = \sqrt{\frac{2{,}940}{0.035}} = 290 \text{ amp}$$

$$\text{hp} = \frac{P_I - \text{total losses}}{746} = \frac{(230 \times 290) - (2 \times 2{,}940)}{746} = \frac{60{,}820}{746} = 81.5$$

$$\eta_{\max} = \left(1 - \frac{5{,}880}{66{,}700}\right) \times 100 = 91.2 \text{ per cent}$$

The foregoing analysis is not completely rigorous but is sufficiently accurate for most practical purposes. Also, when calculations must be made for compound and series machines, due account must be taken of speed and voltage changes as they affect the stray-power losses, series-field voltage drop and losses, and the way the connections are made.

Conventional-efficiency Calculations

After preliminary tests have been made upon a dynamo to determine the so-called constants, *i.e.*, resistances and stray-power losses, a systematic table should be prepared for the calculation of performance data. Curves can then be plotted of the conventional efficiency with respect to the output. Two examples will now be worked out in detail illustrating a suggested procedure.

EXAMPLE 10. The following information is given in connection with a flat-compound generator: kw = 65, V = 250, rpm = 1,200, $R_{(A+I)}$ = 0.036 ohm, R_{SE} = 0.008 ohm, R_f = 41.7 ohms, SPL = 2,060 watts, E_B = 2 volts. Calculate the efficiency of the machine for loads represented by 25, 50, 75, 100, and 125 per cent of rated output. (Assume SPL and E_B to be constant for all loads; these quantities vary slightly with load but are sufficiently accurate for practical calculations.) Also determine the maximum efficiency and the power output at which this occurs. All resistances were measured at room temperature but were corrected to 75°C.

Solution

	Line volts	250	250	250	250	250
Amperes	Line	65	130	195	260	325
	Shunt field	6	6	6	6	6
	Armature	71	136	201	266	331
Losses	Stray power	2,060	2,060	2,060	2,060	2,060
	Shunt field	1,500	1,500	1,500	1,500	1,500
	Armature	182	665	1,455	2,550	3,940
	Series field	40	148	323	565	875
	Brush contact	142	272	402	532	662
	Total	3,924	4,645	5,740	7,207	9,037
Output		16,250	32,500	48,750	65,000	81,250
Input		20,174	37,145	54,490	72,207	90,287
Per cent efficiency		80.5	87.5	89.5	90.1	90.0

Since the maximum efficiency occurs when the constant losses equal the armature-circuit copper losses, that is, $SPL + VI_f = I_A^2 R_{(A+I)}$,

$$2{,}060 + 1{,}500 = I_A^2 \times 0.044$$

so that

$$I_A = \sqrt{\frac{3{,}560}{0.044}} = 284 \qquad \text{and} \qquad I_L = 284 - 6 = 278$$

Therefore $P_0 = 250 \times 278 = 69{,}500$ watts, at maximum efficiency, and

$$\eta_{\max} = \left(1 - \frac{7{,}120}{76{,}620}\right) \times 100 = 90.7$$

An *efficiency* vs. *kilowatt-output* curve is given in Fig. 166.

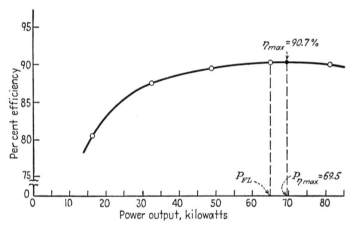

FIG. 166. *Efficiency* vs. *kilowatt-output* curve for Example 10.

EXAMPLE 11. A 10-hp 550-volt 1,750-rpm compound motor, long-shunt, has the following constants: $R_{(A+I)} = 2.1$ ohms, $R_{SE} = 0.3$ ohm, $R_f = 1{,}100$ ohms, $SPL = 360$ watts, $E_B = 5$ volts. Assume reasonable values of line current from about 25 to 125 per cent of rated value, and make all necessary calculations to determine points for the *efficiency* vs. *horsepower-output* curve. From the curve, find the efficiency for a load of 10 hp and the load and efficiency when the latter is a maximum. All resistances were measured at room temperature but were corrected to 75°C.

Solution

Since the rated full-load line current is unknown, a preliminary calculation for an approximate value is based on an assumed efficiency of 85.0 per cent.

$$I_{FL} = \frac{10 \times 746}{550 \times 0.85} = 16 \text{ amp}$$

The following table is, therefore, prepared for arbitrarily assumed line current of 4, 8, 12, 16, and 20 amp, with a constant brush drop and a constant stray-power loss.

	Line volts	550	550	550	550	550
	Line	4.0	8.0	12.0	16.0	20.0
Amperes	Shunt field	0.5	0.5	0.5	0.5	0.5
	Armature	3.5	7.5	11.5	15.5	19.5
	Stray power	360	360	360	360	360
	Shunt field	275	275	275	275	275
	Armature	26	118	278	505	798
Losses	Series field	4	17	40	72	114
	Brush contact	18	38	58	78	98
	Total	683	808	1,011	1,290	1,645
Watts input		2,200	4,400	6,600	8,800	11,000
Watts output		1,517	3,592	5,589	7,510	9,355
Horsepower output		2.03	4.95	7.50	10.05	12.55
Per cent efficiency		69.0	81.6	84.7	85.3	85.0

An *efficiency* vs. *horsepower* curve is given in Fig. 167.

The curve indicates that the 10-hp-output efficiency is 85.3 per cent, and that a maximum efficiency of 85.5 per cent occurs when the horsepower output is 10.7 hp.

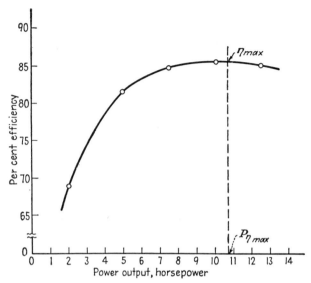

FIG. 167. *Efficiency* vs. *horsepower-output* curve for Example 11.

Directly Measured Efficiency of Motors

Two important procedures are generally employed to determine the efficiency of a motor by the directly measured method; these involve the use of a *prony brake* or an *electrodynamometer*. In the directly measured method, a hollow cast-steel pulley is placed on the shaft extension of the motor and a set of brake shoes, fitted to a lever that acts on a scale, is made to ride on the flat cylindrical surface of the brake drum. Provision is made for tightening the shoes against the drum by a pair of knurled adjusting thumbscrews and, with the motor rotating in the proper direction, the force is registered on the scale. To prevent vibration of the latter, a dashpot is sometimes placed near the end of the brake arm. While the testing proceeds, sufficient water is poured into the hollow drum to keep it reasonably cool. Figure 168 illustrates the arrangement of a typical brake equipment. Before the testing begins it is necessary to obtain the *tare* or "dead" weight of the brake and to see that the latter is perfectly horizontal; it is also desirable to know in advance the approximate range of scale readings that will yield a suitable set of horsepower-output values. Accurate speed measurements must, of course, be taken for all settings.

Since hp $= (T \times \text{rpm})/5{,}250$ and $T = F \times L$, it follows that

$$\text{hp output} = \frac{F \times L \times \text{rpm}}{5{,}250} \qquad (44)$$

where $F = net$ force on scale, lb
$L = $ length of brake arm

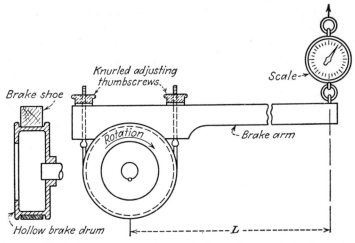

Fig. 168. Typical arrangement of prony-brake equipment for testing motors.

EXAMPLE 12. Calculate the force that will be exerted on the scale in a prony-brake test when a 20-hp 1,400-rpm motor is operating at full load. The length of the brake arm is 3 ft, and the tare weight of the brake is 3.75 lb.

Solution

$$F = \frac{20 \times 5,250}{3 \times 1,400} = 25 \text{ lb net}$$

Force on scale $= 25 + 3.75 = 28.75$ lb

To determine the efficiency of the motor under test, electrical-input values must be measured; this is done by recording the voltage and the total current for each of the output quantities.

EXAMPLE 13. The following information is given in connection with one set of readings in a prony test on a 25-hp 230-volt 1,750-rpm shunt motor: force on scale $= 20.25$ lb, $L = 4$ ft, rpm $= 1,760$, tare weight $= 4.5$ lb, $E = 232$ volts, $I_L = 77.8$ amps. Calculate the efficiency of the motor for this condition of loading.

Solution

$$\text{hp} = \frac{15.75 \times 4 \times 1,760}{5,250} = 21.1$$

$$\eta = \frac{21.1 \times 746}{232 \times 77.8} = 87.3 \text{ per cent}$$

One of the most satisfactory pieces of equipment used to test motors, conveniently and accurately, is the *electrodynamometer*. Built in a wide range of sizes for small and large machines, it is now generally preferred for commercial and laboratory testing. Having none of the disadvantages of the prony brake, it completely eliminates such objectionable features as grabbing and vibrating brakes and the need for cooling a braking device to dissipate the heat energy of the load; moreover, energy represented by the load on the tested motor need not be wasted but may be "fed" back into the supply lines. The electrodynamometer is essentially a dynamo whose frame, *i.e.*, field structure, instead of being rigidly fastened

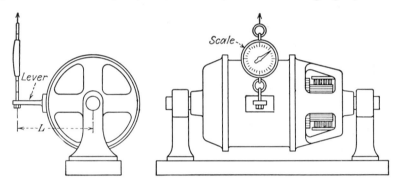

Fig. 169. General construction arrangement of electrodynamometer equipment.

to a solid stationary base, is cradled in a set of bearings. Thus, if permitted to do so, the frame is free to revolve as is the armature; however, a lever that is fastened to one side of the yoke acts upon a scale and permits the frame to rotate just enough to register the thrust of the countertorque. The latter may be adjusted to any desired value merely by causing the electrodynamometer to act as a d-c generator, preferably separately excited, and to develop electric energy as it is driven by the tested motor. Since the *output of the motor is exactly equal to the input to the electrodynamometer*, the torque and speed measurement will be an accurate measure, for a given setting, of the horsepower output; Eq. (44) is applicable to this equipment as for the prony brake. The efficiency can, of course, be determined if the electrical input to the motor under test is measured. Figure 169 illustrates the general construction of this type of equipment.

Importance of Efficiency

Modern dynamos are, in general, well-designed, well-constructed, and manufactured in accordance with certain recognized standards. (The National Electrical Manufacturers Association, NEMA, has set up standards of manufacture and performance that have been universally adopted.)

Moreover, machines are continually being improved so that, with the use of better materials, as well as the better *use* of materials, they are becoming more efficient, are able to withstand higher temperatures, and give more trouble-free continuous service under the most severe conditions of service.

Efficiency has an extremely important influence upon the operating characteristics of a dynamo since it affects such factors as temperature rise, continuity of service, and cost of electric energy. A machine that operates at a comparatively high efficiency loses little power; conversely, one that operates at a low efficiency loses much power. Since all power losses are converted into heat, it should be clear that the temperature rise of a machine is, in great part, affected by the efficiency. If the temperature rise of a generator or motor exceeds well-established practices, in most cases 40 and 50°C, it tends to cause insulation failure and eventual breakdown. Obviously then, from the standpoint of heating, it is very desirable to minimize the losses as much as possible so that efficiencies will be comparatively high. Furthermore, if a machine has a low efficiency and the temperature rise exceeds accepted standards, it usually becomes necessary to use a cooling fan mounted on the shaft, which in turn requires additional power to lower the efficiency still more.

Another important consideration, especially in industrial plants where large numbers of motors are used, is the cost of operation. The energy cost of the losses in a dynamo, as a percentage of the total operating cost, rises as the efficiency drops; therefore, in machines of a given output the energy charge is more for the less efficient units than for those which are more efficient. It is true, as a rule, that the first cost of the highly efficient dynamos is somewhat above their poorer counterparts, but on the other hand, it is significant that, in addition to the saving in energy charges, they are likely to be more reliable and less subject to breakdown; the latter point is particularly important where continuity of service must be maintained. An example will now be given illustrating how efficiency affects the cost of operation.

EXAMPLE 14. Two 10-hp motors *A* and *B* operate identical pumping installations on the average of 8 hr a day and 5 days a week. Assuming continuous rated output for both machines and efficiencies of 90 and 85 per cent, respectively, calculate the difference in the cost of operation for a period of 1 year, if the energy rate is 2 cents per kilowatt-hour.

Solution

$$\text{kw input for } A = \frac{10 \times 0.746}{0.90} = 8.29$$

$$\text{kw input for } B = \frac{10 \times 0.746}{0.85} = 8.78$$

Energy cost for $A = 8.29 \times 8 \times 5 \times 52 \times 0.02 = \$344.86$

Energy cost for $B = 8.78 \times 8 \times 5 \times 52 \times 0.02 = \$365.25$

Difference in operating cost $= \$20.39$

A well-designed machine in which high-grade materials are used and high standards of manufacturing are employed is likely to perform well. To produce such a dynamo requires careful planning, from the moment design calculations are begun and the selection of raw materials are made to the various steps in production, inspection, and testing.

It is generally true that the larger machines are more efficient than the smaller ones; also, high-speed dynamos are more likely to perform satisfactorily, from the standpoint of efficiency, than low-speed ones. Such conditions result from the fact that the losses, as a *percentage* of the total input, tend to become less for the higher capacity, high-speed generators and motors. These are, of course, broad statements and must be understood to imply that differences may exist between individual machines and those of the many manufacturers. Still another point that should be mentioned is that mass-production methods have made it possible to produce uniformly high-efficiency dynamos at costs that are much lower than they would be for production requiring a considerable amount of handwork. This is particularly applicable to the manufacture of very small motors, *i.e.*, in the fractional-horsepower sizes.

Heating and Temperature Rise

When dynamos are placed in service they are expected to perform within certain ranges of voltage (generators) and speed (motors) for designated load variations between zero and the name-plate rating; outputs in excess of the latter will usually mean a departure from the recorded full-load voltage and speed. Furthermore, if considerable overloading exists for comparatively long periods of time, commutation may become objectionable, and heating, due to increased losses, may cause the temperature to rise above acceptable standards. To protect machines and equipment against the difficulties indicated, and possible breakdowns, it is, therefore, customary to provide them with protective devices such as fuses, circuit breakers, thermal relays, and the like.

The most important limitation of electrical-machine output is heating and its tendency to raise the temperature. When properly designed and operated, a dynamo will dissipate heat at the same *rate* as is developed by the losses, after the temperature has leveled off to a certain acceptable maximum. However, under certain conditions of overloading the machine is incapable of getting rid of heat rapidly enough, in which event the temperature may rise sufficiently to cause the insulating materials to carbonize and become brittle; in such cases the insulation soon fails to fulfill its mission of keeping the winding from touching the iron or of maintaining complete electrical separation between the individual wires. This soon leads to *grounds* and *short circuits* and eventual breakdown.

Three general kinds of insulating materials are used in the construction of d-c electrical machines; these are designated by the three classes *O*, *A*, and *B*. *Class O* insulation consists of cotton, silk, paper, and similar *organic* materials when neither impregnated nor immersed in a liquid dielectric. (Impregnation implies that a suitable substance is used to replace the air between fibers, even if this substance does not completely fill the voids between the insulated conductors themselves.) *Class A* insulation consists of (1) cotton, silk, paper, and similar *organic* materials when impregnated with a liquid dielectric; (2) molded or laminated materials with cellulose filler, phenolic resins, and other resins of similar properties; (3) films and sheets of cellulose acetate and other cellulose derivatives of similar properties; and (4) varnishes (enamel) as applied to conductors. *Class B* insulation consists of mica, asbestos, fiberglass, and similar *inorganic* materials in built-up form with organic binding substances; a small proportion of Class A materials may be used for structural purposes only.

When Class A insulating materials are employed for generators and general-purpose motors, the temperature rise in the armature and unexposed field windings must not be more than 40°C above the surrounding air (ambient) temperature under normal operating conditions, or more than 55°C when operated for 2 hr at 125 per cent of its nominal rating. When machines are totally enclosed, the temperature rise must not exceed 55°C when rated load is being delivered. The temperature rise of commutators is permitted to be 55°C in normal operation and 65°C where 125 per cent load is delivered for 2 hr, or in the case of totally enclosed machines. Series-field windings that are completely bare of insulation, with copper exposed, are permitted a temperature rise of 50°C under full-load conditions, and 65°C when the load is 25 per cent above the name-plate rating, or in machines that are totally enclosed.

Class B insulations can withstand somewhat higher temperatures than the organic materials. They are frequently used in totally enclosed machines or where the dynamos must operate under extremely high ambient-temperature conditions. The armature and field windings of machines employing these materials are permitted to have a temperature rise of 75°; commutators and exposed series-field windings have 85°C allowable temperature-rise limits.

The Class O materials are used sparingly in modern d-c generators and motors, and only where the conditions of operation are particularly mild. Permissible temperature-rise limits are consistently 15°C below the Class A insulations.

Since cooling of a large mass such as an armature or field structure does not take place uniformly, all parts of a given winding are not at the same temperature; surface temperatures are, in general, lower than embedded sections. For example, in a field winding that may have many layers of wire, built up to perhaps 2 or 3 in., the lowest temperature will usually be on the air-cooled surface, somewhat higher near the heated iron core and greatest somewhere close to the center of the section. Obviously, it is the highest or "hot-spot" temperature that imposes a limiting condition on the output of the machine because insulation failure and possible breakdown will usually occur where the effect of the heating is most severe. In the use of Class A insulations whose maximum temperature must not be permitted to exceed 105°C for reasons of safety, the maximum *surface temperature rise* of any winding is limited to 50°C; this provision allows for a possible ambient temperature of 40°C and a differential of 15°C between the surface and hot-spot temperatures, *i.e.*, 105 − 40 − 15 = 50. As a result of these limitations, Class A-insulated machines must not have temperature-rise ratings greater than 50°C; they are, in fact, more often given 40°C ratings to provide an additional factor of safety. Applying similar operating conditions to Class B insulations, which have an ultimate safe temperature of 125°C, machines using these materials must not have temperature-rise ratings greater than 65°C.

Temperature Measurements

Before actual measurements are made to determine the heating effect upon the various parts of a machine, the dynamo must be operated for a sufficiently long period at *full load* to make sure that a constant or leveling-off temperature has been reached; such a test is usually called a *heat run*. Since the time required for such leveling off is often entirely too long, the heat run may be accelerated by overloading the machine for an hour or so and then lowering the load to rated value; this practice generally reduces the testing period considerably. Where occasional tests are performed on small machines and the wasted energy is not substantial, it is common to "feed" a generator load into a rheostat of sufficient carrying capacity or to use prony brakes or electrodynamometers for motor loads. However, in commercial testing, where energy losses must be reduced to a minimum, heat runs are conducted by circulating rated currents through the windings to duplicate the normal losses, without requiring the machines to "deliver" actual electrical or mechanical loads; this is accomplished by the feedback circuit, generally referred to as the *Kapp opposition method*. Figure 170 illustrates the arrangement of *two similar machines* that must be available for such a temperature-rise test; the dynamos are coupled together and connected as shown.

Referring to the diagram, the M-G set is started, *with switch S open,* by bringing machine M (and the coupled unit) up to speed in the usual way. With the polarity (plus and minus terminals) of the separately excited generator G matching the source, the field of that machine is adjusted until its voltage is exactly equal to the line potential; switch S may now be closed. Under this condition both units acting as motors will be supplied by the source. If the excitation of machine G is next increased, it will begin to function as a generator and supply electrical power to motor M, while the latter will, in turn, act as the prime mover for the generator G.

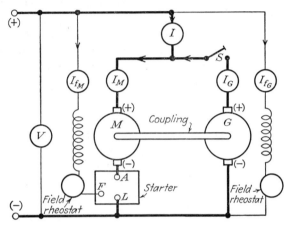

Fig. 170. Wiring connections of the Kapp feed-back circuit, in which two identical shunt machines are used.

To make the heat run on generator G, the motor-field rheostat is manipulated to give the correct speed, while the generator-field rheostat is adjusted until I_G is rated value. Since the armature of the motor receives power from *both* the line I and the generator I_G, it should be clear that the only power delivered to the set is $VI = V(I_M - I_G)$; this, of course, is the power required to take care of the *losses* of the two machines and does *not* involve wasted power in a load rheostat. After the temperature of the generator has leveled off, temperature measurements can be made as explained below. A heat run can be made upon machine M by making it act as a generator; this is done by increasing the field strength of M and properly decreasing that of G; under this condition the two machines interchange their functions.

Three methods may be employed in making temperature measurements. These are (1) by the use of thermometers, (2) by the use of thermocouples embedded in the stationary windings or on other parts of the machine, and (3) by computations from cold and hot winding-resistance values. When thermometers are used, usually mercury type, the glass bulbs are placed in direct contact with the machine parts, covered by felt pads, and cemented with cotton waste and oil putty or other tape; the felt pads should be $1\frac{1}{2}$ by 2 in. and $\frac{1}{8}$ in. thick. Temperature measurements are taken several times during the test run and immediately after the set is shut down, the highest reading being the accepted value. A similar procedure is followed when thermocouples are employed; these devices have the added advantage that they may be placed in any stationary part *within* the machine and may even be made to yield the hot-spot temperature if embedded in the winding. When resistance measurements are taken of the several windings of the machine to determine the temperature, it is necessary to do so before the set is started, *i.e.*, after the machine parts have assumed the ambient temperature, and immediately after the heated machine is shut down. The average final temperature, in degrees centigrade, is calculated from the equation

$$\frac{R_f}{R_{rt}} = \frac{234.5 + t_f}{234.5 + t_{rt}} \tag{45}$$

where the subscripts f and rt refer to $f$inal and $r$oom-$t$emperature values.

EXAMPLE 15. The resistance of an armature winding was measured when its temperature (the ambient temperature) was 77°F and was found to be 0.26 ohm. A repetition of this measurement gave 0.296 ohm after a heat run. Calculate the temperature rise of the winding.

Solution

$$t_f = \frac{R_f}{R_{rt}} (234.5 + t_{rt}) - 234.5 = \frac{0.296}{0.260} (234.5 + 25) - 234.5 = 61°C$$

Temperature rise $= 61 - 25 = 36°C$

Operating Conditions and Ratings of Dynamos

Electrical machines are constructed in a variety of ways to serve under conditions that permit self-ventilation (self-cooling) as well as those requiring separate ventilation. They are, moreover, expected to fulfill many kinds of duty concerned with the *degree of regularity of the load*. Recognizing these varying demands, the electrical industry has set up standards of construction and operation, and these are carefully defined and approved by the *American Standards Association.**

Ventilation. Where the ambient conditions are reasonably free of contamination, *self-ventilated machines* are generally employed. These permit the free circulation of air by means integral with the rotating element. They

---

* AIEE, Standard Definitions of Electrical Terms.

are of the completely *open type* and have no restriction to ventilation other than that necessitated by mechanical construction. On the other hand, surrounding conditions that may be injurious to insulating materials or commutation require types that are *enclosed;* these constructions may permit self-ventilation or require separate ventilation. In the *enclosed self-ventilated machine* there are openings for the admission and discharge of ventilating air, which is circulated by means integral with the rotor, the machine being otherwise enclosed. These openings are so arranged

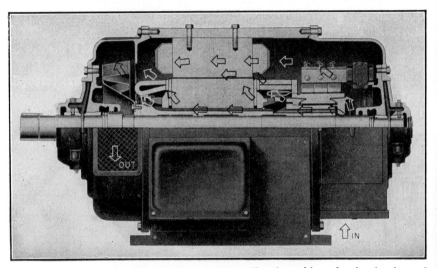

FIG. 171. Cutaway view of an enclosed self-ventilated machine, showing intake and outlet ducts and the general air paths. (*General Electric Co.*)

that inlet and outlet ducts or pipes may be connected to them. Figure 171 illustrates this type of construction and clearly indicates how the air is drawn in on the right, passes through unobstructed passages, and is emitted on the left. The *enclosed separately ventilated machine* has openings for the admission and discharge of the ventilating air, which is circulated by a fan or blower external to and not a part of the machine, the latter being otherwise totally enclosed. The term *totally enclosed* refers to a construction that is so enclosed as to prevent exchange of air between the inside and the outside of the case, but not sufficiently enclosed to be airtight. It should be clear, of course, that, whether open or closed, self- or separately ventilated, the essential requirement is to maintain a well-regulated balance between heat losses and heat transfer; the temperature rise must not be permitted to exceed accepted standards.

Service Conditions. The degree of load regularity applied to electrical equipment, *i.e.*, the *duty*, varies considerably in industrial practice. At one extreme are the desirable applications requiring *continuous-duty* generators or motors. Such installations demand operation at substantially constant loads for an indefinitely long time; they are fulfilled by machines having *continuous ratings* whose designated loads are known and whose operating characteristics are based on definite conditions. At the other extreme are *varying-duty* requirements of service that demand operation at loads, and for intervals of time, both of which are subject to wide variation; it is extremely difficult to provide proper power equipment for such loads because the latter are generally indefinite and often unknown. Another type of service is the *short-time duty* which refers to operation at a substantially constant load for a short and definitely specified time; machines powering such loads are for the most part physically smaller than equally rated units that supply continuous loads. Where the load conditions are intermittent but recur with regularity, machines must be installed that have a *periodic-duty* rating; many such applications appear in practice and, since the load requirements are known, are readily provided for. A final type of service involves an *intermittent-duty* load that demands operation for alternate intervals of (1) load and no load, (2) load and rest, or (3) load, no load, and rest; such alternate intervals are definitely specified, which means that power equipment for such installations can be properly selected.

Rating. Several kinds of rating are recognized by the electrical industry; these are (1) continuous rating, (2) short-time rating, (3) nominal rating, and (4) continuous with 2-hr 25 per cent overload rating. Where the load conditions are steady, *continuous-rating* machines are used; these carry specified loads for indefinitely long periods of time. *Short-time rating* refers to load conditions which are of short duration and definitely specified periods of time; machines for such requirements must be at approximately room temperature at the time the loads are applied. *Nominal rating* defines the constant load that, having brought the machine to a constant temperature, may have the current increased by 50 per cent at the specified voltage for a period of 2 hr without causing the temperature to exceed the maximum permissible value. *Continuous with 2-hr 25 per cent overload rating* defines the load that can be carried continuously, immediately followed by a 25 per cent overload for 2 hr without causing the temperature to rise above the maximum permissible limits. Practically speaking, however, it is customary to apply the continuous-rating specification to an installation if no definite loading conditions are indicated.

When machines are conservatively designed and constructed, manufacturers are authorized to apply a so-called *service factor* to the name-plate rating. Always properly specified on the name plate, it permits the use of an electrical machine at a continuous load greater than rated load determined by the established service factor, assuming that operation is at rated voltage and that the ambient temperature does not exceed 40°C. The following service factors are permitted for motors: $\frac{1}{20}$ to $\frac{1}{8}$ hp,

1.4; $\frac{1}{6}$ to $\frac{1}{3}$ hp, 1.35; $\frac{1}{2}$ to 1, 1.25; $1\frac{1}{2}$ to 2, 1.2; 3 and larger, 1.15. A service factor of 1.15 is generally applied to generators since these are built in the larger sizes.

The foregoing discussion of industrial demands and standards of performance should make it clear that d-c machines must be designed and constructed to provide varying degrees of trouble-free service. This generally implies that commutation must be sparkless, or virtually so, and that temperature rises must be held within the safe limits of insulations employed.

Standard and Conventional Designs

Present-day d-c generators and motors are manufactured in a variety of types, for many kinds of general purpose and special services. These include the conventional shunt, series, and compound machines in their many operating combinations of voltage, speed, torque, overload, and control. They also involve constructions for different styles of mounting, enclosures, ventilation, shaft extensions, couplings, and gearings. Such varying industrial demands are met by groups of designs that, within certain ratings, are considered standard and others that must provide the needs of special installations. The manufacturing costs of expensive dies, jigs, fixtures, machine tools, and other equipment are kept at a minimum by the use of interchangeable parts and laminations. Finally, mass-production methods of planning, fabricating, assembling, inspecting, and testing have been so highly developed that modern electrical machines fulfill exacting requirements reliably and well.

The author has, for many years, been privileged to gather actual design data and information of modern dynamos from several of the more prominent manufacturers. Some of this material has been summarized in Tables 2 and 3 and is presented with the hope that the student will study it carefully in the light of the discussions throughout the book. Note particularly the organized arrangement under logical and readily identified headings.

PROBLEMS

1. Calculate the brush-friction loss in a d-c generator, given the following particulars: commutator diameter = 7.5 in., number of brush studs = 4, brushes per stud = 3, area per brush in contact with commutator = 0.75 by 1.0 in., type of brush = carbon and graphite, speed = 1,750 rpm.

2. A certain motor has a core loss of 840 watts, of which one-third is eddy-current loss, when operated at a speed of 1,200 rpm. Assuming the flux to remain unchanged, what will be the core loss when the speed (a) is increased to 1,600 rpm? (b) is decreased to 900 rpm?

3. What will be the core loss in the armature of Prob. 2 if the speed remains unchanged and the flux density (a) is increased by 15 per cent? (b) is decreased by 20 per cent?

4. The armature core of a 4-pole generator weighs 120 lbs and operates at a speed of 1,800 rpm. Calculate the hysteresis loss for a maximum flux density of 88,000 lines per sq in.

5. A 75-hp motor has a full-load efficiency of 88.4 per cent. What are the total losses?

6. What should be the full-load horsepower rating of a motor that drives a 150-kw generator whose efficiency is 89.3 per cent?

7. Calculate the losses in a 150-kw generator when operating at 50 per cent of rated load, if the efficiency under this condition is 86.2 per cent.

8. The following information is given in connection with a 10-kw 250-volt flat-compound generator: $R_f = 125$ ohms, $R_A = 0.4$ ohm, $R_{SE} = 0.05$ ohm, SPL $= 452$ watts, E_B (assumed constant) $= 3$ volts. Calculate the efficiency (a) at full load; (b) at 50 per cent load.

9. Using the given data of Prob. 8, calculate (a) the power output of the generator when the efficiency is a maximum; (b) the maximum efficiency.

10. Referring to Example 10, page 242, calculate the efficiency of the generator for a load of 150 per cent of rated output.

11. Referring to Example 11, page 243, calculate the efficiency of the motor for a load requiring an input current of 24 amp, and the horsepower output under this condition.

12. A 10-kw 220-volt 1,400-rpm shunt generator is operated at rated speed as a motor. The armature takes 2.95 amp from a 232-volt source. The total armature resistance including brushes is 0.26 ohm, and the shunt-field resistance is 146.5 ohms. Determine (a) the stray-power losses; (b) the full-load efficiency when the machine is operating as a generator.

13. The following information is given in connection with a prony-brake test upon a motor: $F = 37$ lb, tare weight of brake $= 3.5$ lb, $L = 3$ ft, rpm $= 1,160$. Calculate the horsepower output of the motor under this condition.

14. Determine the force that will be exerted on the scale in a prony-brake test when a 5-hp 2,200-rpm motor is operating at full load. The length of the brake arm is 2.5 ft and the tare weight of the brake is 3.25 lb.

15. If the motor of Prob. 14 takes 18.9 amp at 228 volts, calculate its full-load efficiency.

16. Calculate the cost of operating the motor of Prob. 15 for a period of 1 year if the machine runs continuously at rated output for 8 hr a day and 5 days a week. Energy costs 2½ cents per kilowatt hour.

17. If the motor of Prob. 16 is replaced by one having an efficiency of 91 per cent, what saving in energy cost can be expected?

18. The shunt-field winding of a motor has a resistance of 48 ohms at a room temperature of 86°F. What is the temperature rise of the winding if, after a heat run, its resistance increases to 55.1 ohms?

TABLE 2

SPECIFICATIONS AND DESIGN DATA FOR D-C GENERATORS

	SPECIFICATIONS							ARMATURE CORE					COMMUTATOR			ARMATURE WINDING							
No.	Kw rating	Volts	Full-load amperes	Rpm	No. of main poles	No. of comm. poles	Type of machine	Diameter, in.	Length, in.	No. of slots	No. and size of vent. ducts	Peripheral velocity, fpm	Diameter, in.	No. of segments	Peripheral velocity, fpm	Type	No. of circuits	Total no. of conductors	Frequency, cps	Current density, amp/sq in.	Back pitch Y_s	Comm. pitch Y_c	No. of equalizer connections
1	5	125	40	1,750	4	2	Shunt	7	4	27	None	3,210	4¼	107	1,145	Wave	2	648	57.3	3,510	6	53	
2	5	125	40	1,750	4	2	Comp.	7¼	4¼	31	None	3,320	5⅛	61	2,350	Wave	2	496	57.3	3,110	8	31	
3	30	125	240	1,750	4	2	Shunt	12	4½	33	1, ⅜″	5,490	8½	99	3,890	Wave	2	198	57.3	3,430	8	49	
4	38	125	304	900	4	2	Comp.	15	5¾	35	1, ⅜″	3,540	9½	105	2,240	Wave	2	210	30	2,570	9	53	
5	40	250	160	1,500	4	2	Comp.	14	5½	45	1, ⅜″	5,490	9	135	3,520	Wave	2	270	50	2,050	11	68	
6	40	250	160	1,200	4	4	Comp.	12	7	31	3, ⅜″	3,770	8	93	2,520	Wave	2	372	40	3,200	8	47	
7	60	250	240	1,200	4	4	Comp.	13	8¼	37	3, ⅜″	4,080	9	147	2,820	Wave	2	296	40	3,075	9	73	
8	65	250	260	1,200	4	2	Comp.	14½	7¼	43	2, ⅜″	4,560	10	129	3,140	Wave	2	258	40	2,410	10	64	
9	85	125	680	870	6	6	Comp.	19	6¼	66	1, ⅜″	4,330	11½	198	2,620	Lap	6	396	43.5	2,930	11	1	33
10	100	250	400	1,200	4	4	Comp.	14½	10¼	55	3, ⅜″	4,560	10¼	109	3,220	Wave	2	220	40	2,900	14	54	
11	100	250	400	1,200	6	6	Shunt	18	7½	48	4, ⅜″	5,650	12	144	3,770	F-L*	12	1,152	60	2,620	8	$L = 1$ $W = 47$	
12	200	250	800	1,200	6	6	Comp.	20¼	10¼	63	4, ⅜″	6,360	14	189	4,400	Lap	6	378	60	3,010	10	1	63
13	200	250	800	1,200	6	6	Shunt	21	8	72	4, ⅜″	6,600	16	216	5,030	F-L	12	864	60	2,235	12	$L = 1$ $W = 71$	
14	250	250	1,000	1,200	6	6	Comp.	21	10	90	5, ⅜″	6,600	16	180	5,030	F-L	12	720	60	2,800	15	$L = 1$ $W = 59$	
15	300	250	1,200	1,200	6	6	Comp.	22	11½	75	5, ⅜″	6,910	15	150	4,720	Lap	6	300	60	3,075	12	1	50

No.																						
16	300	250	1,200	1,200	6	6	Comp.	25	8	81	3, ½"	7,860	16½	162	5,180	F-L	12	648	60	3,610	L=13 W=14	L=1 W=53	
17	400	250	1,600	1,200	6	6	Comp.	25	10½	117	4, ⅜"	7,860	16½	117	5,180	Lap	6	234	60	2,980	19	L=1 W=41	39
18	500	250	2,000	900	6	6	Comp.	28	14½	126	5, ½"	6,600	21	126	4,950	F-L	12	504	45	2,915	20	1	
19	500	460	1,088	900	6	6	Comp.	28	14½	108	5, ½"	6,600	21	216	4,950	Lap	6	432	45	2,950	18	1	72
20	600	500	1,200	900	6	6	Shunt	34	10½	120	4, ½"	8,000	21	240	4,950	Lap	6	480	45	2,780	20	1	80
21	700	250	2,800	750	8	8	Comp.	40	12	160	6, ⅜"	7,870	26½	160	5,200	F-L	16	640	50	2,610	19	L=1 W=39	
22	1,000	250	4,000	750	8	8	Comp.	40	16	120	8, ⅜"	7,870	26½	120	5,200	F-L	16	480	50	2,310	14	L=1 W=29	74
23	1,000	600	1,667	750	8	8	Shunt	40	16	148	8, ⅜"	7,870	26½	296	5,200	Lap	8	592	50	2,920	18	1	
24	1,250	250	5,000	750	8	8	Comp.	45	14	120	6, ⅜"	8,840	26½	120	5,200	F-L	16	480	50	2,755	15	1	
25	1,250	600	2,083	750	8	8	Comp.	45	14	148	6, ⅜"	8,840	26½	296	5,200	Lap	8	592	50	2,065	18	L=1 W=29	74
26	1,500	250	6,000	500	12	12	Comp.	66	13	210	7, ⅜"	8,650	41	210	5,370	F-L	24	840	50	1,985	L=17 W=18	L=1 W=34	
27	1,500	600	2,500	500	12	12	Comp.	66	13	222	7, ⅜"	8,650	41	444	5,370	Lap	12	888	50	2,170	18	1	74
28	2,000	250	8,000	375	14	14	Comp.	78	15	259	8, ⅜"	7,670	55	259	5,400	F-L	28	518	43.7	2,385	L=18 W=19	L=1 W=36	82
29	2,000	600	3,333	500	14	14	Comp.	78	11	287	6, ⅜"	10,200	41	574	5,370	Lap	14	1,148	58.3	2,480	20	1	
30	2,500	250	10,000	375	20	20	Comp.	90	13½	300	7, ⅜"	8,840	62	300	6,080	F-L	40	1,200	62.5	2,605	14	L=1 W=29	
31	2,500	600	4,163	500	14	14	Comp.	78	13	259	7, ⅜"	10,200	41	518	5,370	F-L	28	2,072	58.3	2,760	L=18 W=19	L=1 W=73	
32	3,000	300	10,000	300	16	16	Comp.	96	18	288	9, ⅜"	7,550	62	288	4,870	F-L	32	1,152	40	2,025	17	L=1 W=35	
33	3,000	600	5,000	375	16	16	Comp.	90	14½	296	7, ⅜"	8,840	55	592	5,400	F-L	32	2,368	50	1,745	L=18 W=19	L=1 W=73	
34	5,000	600	8,333	240	24	24	Comp.	144	12½	420	6, ⅝"	9,040	82	840	3,090	F-L	48	3,360	48	1,830	L=17 W=18	L=1 W=69	

* F-L = Frog leg.

TABLE 3

SPECIFICATIONS AND DESIGN DATA FOR D-C MOTORS

	SPECIFICATIONS							ARMATURE CORE					COMMUTATOR			ARMATURE WINDING							
No.	Hp output	Volts	Full-load amperes	Rpm	No. of main poles	No. of comm. poles	Type of machine	Diameter, in.	Length, in.	No. of slots	No. and size of vent. ducts	Peripheral velocity, fpm	Diameter, in.	No. of segments	Peripheral velocity, fpm	Type	No. of circuits	Total no. of conductors	Frequency, cps	Current density, amp/sq in.	Back pitch Y_s	Comm. pitch Y_c	No. of equalizer connections
1	1	230	4.6	1,750	4	2	Shunt	4⅛	3	25	None	1,880	2¾	75	1,265	Wave	2	1,800	58.3	5,650	6	37	
2	1½	230	6.7	1,160	4	2	Shunt	4¾	3	25	None	1,445	2¾	75	837	Wave	2	1,800	38.7	5,270	6	37	
3	2	230	8.9	1,150	4	2	Shunt	5	3½	31	None	1,510	3	61	904	Wave	2	1,240	38.3	4,410	8	31	
4	3	230	12.3	1,750	4	2	Shunt	5	3½	31	None	2,295	3	61	1,360	Wave	2	992	58.3	4,810	8	31	
5	3	230	12.0	1,150	4	2	Shunt	6	3½	31	None	1,815	4	93	1,190	Wave	2	1,116	38.3	3,730	8	47	
6	5	230	19.5	1,750	4	2	Shunt	6	3½	31	None	2,755	4	93	1,810	Wave	2	744	58.3	4,800	8	47	
7	5	115	41.5	1,750	4	2	Shunt	6½	3½	23	None	2,980	4¾	69	2,180	Wave	2	828	58.3	4,070	6	35	
8	5	230	19.5	1,150	4	2	Shunt	7⅛	3¾	37	None	2,150	4¾	111	1,430	Wave	2	888	38.3	4,060	9	55	
9	5	115	39.0	1,700	4	2	Series	6½	3½	23	None	2,900	4¾	69	2,120	Wave	2	828	56.7	3,830	6	35	
10	7½	230	29.0	1,750	4	2	Shunt	7¾	3	33	None	3,550	4¾	99	2,180	Wave	2	792	58.3	3,560	8	49	

11	7½	230	29.4	1,750	4	2	Shunt	7¼	4¼	35	None	3,330	5⅛	105	2,350	Wave	2	1,260	58.3	2,880	9	53	
12	7½	230	28.5	1,700	4	2	Series	7¼	4¼	35	None	3,230	5⅛	105	2,280	Wave	2	1,260	56.7	2,800	9	53	
13	10	230	38.5	1,750	4	2	Shunt	7¾	4¼	33	None	3,550	4¾	99	2,180	Wave	2	594	58.3	3,760	8	49	
14	10	550	15.6	1,750	4	2	Shunt	7¾	4¾	35	None	3,550	5¾	139	2,640	Wave	2	1,400	58.3	2,290	9	70	
15	10	230	37.7	1,150	4	2	Shunt	8½	4½	32	1, ⅜″	2,565	5	95	1,510	Wave	2	768	38.3	3,430	8	47	
16	15	230	58.0	1,750	4	2	Shunt	9¼	3¾	31	None	4,230	5¾	93	2,640	Wave	2	558	58.3	3,110	8	47	
17	20	230	74.3	3,450	4	2	Shunt	7¾	4¾	35	None	8,400	5¾	69	5,140	Wave	2	280	115	2,530	9	35	
18	20	250	80.0	1,450	4	2	Series	10½	5	37	2, ⅜″	4,000	7	111	2,660	Wave	2	444	48.3	3,150	9	56	
19	20	230	73.7	1,150	4	2	Shunt	9¾	5½	40	1, ⅜″	2,940	6¾	119	2,035	Wave	2	480	38.3	3,070	10	59	
20	20	230	75.0	1,750	4	2	Comp.	10½	4	45	1, ⅜″	4,820	7	89	3,210	Wave	2	360	58.3	1,795	11	44	
21	20	115	150	1,750	4	2	Shunt	10½	4	33	1, ⅜′	4,820	7	99	3,210	Wave	2	198	58.3	2,720	8	50	
22	25	230	92	1,500	4	2	Comp.	13	6½	37	1, ⅜″	5,100	9½	17	3,730	Wave	2	592	50	3,070	9	73	
23	30	230	115	1,200	4	4	Shunt	15	5¾	53	1, ¼″	4,720	9½	159	2,980	Wave	2	636	40	1,440	13	80	
24	30	230	108	1,750	4	2	Shunt	10½	5	37	2, ⅜″	4,820	7	73	3,210	Wave	2	296	58.3	2,680	9	37	
25	35	100	285	1,200	4	2	Series	12	5	39	1, ¼″	3,770	7½	77	2,355	Wave	2	156	40	3,300	10	39	
26	40	250	130	3,000	4	2	Shunt	10	5¾	57	None	7,850	6	57	4,720	Wave	2	228	100	4,980	14	28	
27	40	230	146	1,750	4	2	Shunt	12	4¼	29	1, ¼″	5,500	7½	145	3,460	Wave	2	290	58.3	3,750	7	73	
28	50	230	181	1,750	4	2	Shunt	12	5	29	1, ¼″	5,500	7½	115	3,440	Wave	2	232	58.3	3,090	7	58	
29	50	550	76	1,750	4	2	Shunt	12	5	35	1, ¼″	5,500	7½	139	3,440	Wave	2	560	58.3	3,020	9	70	
30	60	230	222	1,200	6	6	Comp.	21	8¾	76	2, ⅜″	6,600	16	227	5,030	Wave	2	456	60	2,055	12	76	
31	60	230	215	1,750	4	2	Shunt	13	5	37	1, ¼″	5,960	8¼	111	3,790	Wave	2	444	58.3	2,890	9	56	
32	75	230	274	500	4	4	Shunt	15	13	54	1, ⅜″	1,960	9½	216	1,240	Lap	4	432	16.7	2,925	13	1	54
33	100	230	350	500	4	4	Shunt	16½	14½	62	1, ⅜″	2,160	10½	186	1,370	Lap	4	372	16.7	2,245	15	1	31
34	200	230	650	800	6	6	Shunt	25	10⅝	72	2, ⅜″	5,230	16	288	3,350	F-L*	12	1,152	40	2,260	12	$L = 1$	
																						$W = 95$	

* F-L = Frog leg.

CHAPTER 12

SPECIAL MACHINES, CIRCUITS
AND APPLICATIONS

Third-brush Generators

Generators are usually installed in permanent, stationary locations and are driven at constant speed; under such conditions of operation, control of voltage and current is simple and accurate. In some special applications, however, they are expected to operate over a considerable range of speed and, at the same time, maintain substantially constant voltage; the small generator, used in an automobile to supply power to the various appliances and to charge a storage battery, is an excellent example of such an installation. It will be recalled that wide variations in speed of *ordinary* shunt and compound generators have a marked effect upon the terminal voltage ($E = k\phi \times$ rpm), and if used for the type of service indicated, these generators would cause the voltage and charging current to change greatly between the low and high automobile speeds. Moreover, at high speed, the generator emf would rise sufficiently to burn out low-voltage lights, small motors, radios, and other devices. To overcome the varying-voltage difficulty described, special generator and electromagnet designs may be employed, in the first of which the effect of armature reaction is utilized to offset the objectionable tendency of the emf to rise at high speed and drop at low speed.

The *third-brush* type of generator was widely used in automobiles (now generally superseded by electromagnetic regulators) to maintain the electrical-system voltage fairly constant and to keep the storage battery in a charged condition. In construction it is a simple *shunt* type of machine with the exception that the field is connected to the ungrounded brush and an auxiliary brush (the *third brush*), the latter being located between the main power brushes; note particularly that the field voltage is *less* than that between plus and minus brushes and tends to decrease with increasing values of load because, as explained below, the effect of armature reaction is to alter the distribution of voltages between commutator segments. In fact, if the field flux and car speed are inversely proportional to each other, the terminal emf will be almost constant. In practice, the generator is designed for low-voltage service (6 to 8, or 12 to 16 volts) and is equipped with a so-called *cutout relay* so that electrical connection between it and

262

the battery is made after the automobile reaches a speed of about 10 mph· When the armature current is low, *i.e.*, at light load (Fig. 172*a*), the cross-magnetizing flux has little effect upon the main field. Under this condition the voltage between positive and negative brushes will be determined primarily by the number of series conductors in the angle between these two brushes; also, since the voltage distribution at the commutator is quite uniform, the field voltage, current, and flux will be a maximum.

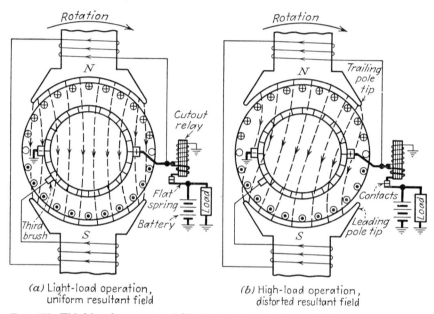

(*a*) Light-load operation, uniform resultant field

(*b*) High-load operation, distorted resultant field

FIG. 172. Third-brush generator-field distributions for low and high values of load.

On the other hand, for high values of armature current, *i.e.*, at high speed and heavy load (Fig. 172*b*), the armature-reaction flux greatly distorts the main field, shifting the latter in the direction of rotation; the result is that the leading pole tips—those which subtend the field brushes—are weakened, whereas the trailing pole tips are strengthened. Moreover, since the voltage distribution at the commutator is no longer uniform, being progressively less from grounded brush to ungrounded brush, the field voltage suffers a drop, which in turn reduces the field mmf and its flux. Still another condition that mitigates the influence of higher car speeds is the fact that the effect of armature reaction is correspondingly greater as the field becomes weaker, so that the actual *resultant* flux decreases more rapidly with respect to cross-magnetization than does the rise in armature speed. This means, therefore, that the battery-charging current of a third-brush generator reaches a maximum at some intermediate speed and then tends to drop off with further increase in speed. Figure 173 shows a typical *output-current* vs. *speed* curve for this type of machine for a battery-charging load.

A serious objection to the use of these generators in automobiles is that they actually charge batteries at higher rates when the latter are in a fully charged condition than when discharged; this is, of course, contrary to the desired action. The reason for this is that a full-charged battery has a higher terminal voltage than one in a discharged condition; as a

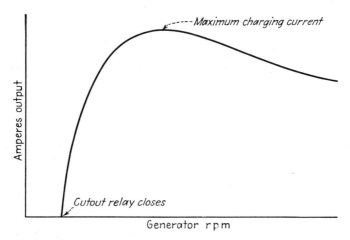

Fig. 173. Characteristic *output-current* vs. *speed* curve for a third-brush generator charging a battery.

result the voltage at the generator and field terminals will be higher, which in turn will mean a further rise in terminal emf and charging current. Conversely, when a battery is discharged, its voltage will be low; this implies a reduced generator emf and a correspondingly weak field, which in turn means a lower battery-charging current.

Third-brush generators are generally designed to create a weak shunt field (few ampere-turns) and a strong armature-reaction field. In this way the latter may be made to exert a substantial influence on the main-field flux, since the armature mmf can distort a weak field more readily than one that is strong.

Regulator-controlled Generators

The early attempts to improve the operating performance of the third-brush generator involved the use of an electromagnet that was adjusted to open a pair of normally closed contacts when the voltage reached a predetermined value; when this happened a resistance was automatically inserted in the field circuit. This so-called lockout relay—a voltage relay—

provided a desired degree of voltage control, permitting the generator to charge an uncharged battery at a high rate and a charged battery at a low rate. However, since the arrangement did not limit the current output of the generator, which, under certain conditions, became excessive, it was found necessary to redesign the relay (using a short air gap and a second winding in series with the field) to cause the contacts to make and break many times a second; the rapid vibration of the contacts, alternately inserting and removing resistance in the generator field, resulted in a better stabilized voltage control because the contacts were held open a greater percentage of the time when the load was heavy and held closed a relatively longer period when the load was light. Thus, when the battery was low and many accessories were turned on, the voltage was high enough so that the third-brush generator limited the current output.

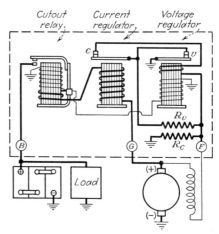

Following the early experiences in which the performance of the third-brush generator was improved by adding a supplementary control relay, present practice dispenses entirely with the third brush and utilizes two separate relays for regulation purposes; one of them

FIG. 174. Wiring diagram showing a three-unit regulator connected to a shunt generator and its load, in an automobile electrical system.

—the voltage regulator—maintains constant voltage in the electrical system, and the other—the current regulator—limits the maximum current output.   Figure 174 is a wiring diagram of this type of three-unit *regulator* (all parts are mounted on a common base), in which the functions of a simple shunt generator are controlled by cutout, current and voltage relays.

In operation, the current and voltage regulators are designed and adjusted so that only one of them can operate at one time to *open* its contacts, *i.e.*, in no case can both sets of contacts c and v be open at the same time.   Moreover, the current regulator functions when the load requirements are high and the battery is in a discharged condition; this prevents the generator from exceeding its safe maximum current output.   Also, the voltage regulator operates when the load requirements are reduced or the battery comes up to charge.   Note particularly, in studying the circuit diagram, that when contacts c open—current regulator operated—the two resistors R_c and R_v are in parallel and connected in series with the field winding; furthermore, when contacts v open—voltage regulator operated—only R_c is in series with the field.

Now then, when the generator is delivering normal output, both sets of contacts c and v are closed; under this condition the field is connected directly across the line. Should the load requirements increase sufficiently, a limit is placed on the current output of the generator because the current regulator will function to open its contacts c; this places R_c and R_v in parallel, and in series with the field, and reduces the field mmf by just the proper amount. Furthermore, if the load is reduced, or if the battery, in an improved-charge condition, develops a higher voltage, the voltage regulator will operate, and this action disconnects R_v, to leave R_c only in series with the field; this further reduces the field mmf, lowers the generator current, and instantly causes the current regulator to drop out.

The Rosenberg Generator

Another type of shunt generator, in addition to the three-brush machine previously discussed, that takes advantage of the effect of armature reaction to regulate for constant current was first developed about 1905 for use in train-lighting service. Embodying several unique design and constructional innovations, this so-called *Rosenberg generator* develops a voltage whose brush polarity is, moreover, independent of the direction of rotation of the armature; this means, of course, that the polarity of the battery, always used in conjunction with the generator, will be correct for either direction of motion of the train. A simplified diagram showing the general arrangement and connections for a bipolar machine is given in Fig. 175, although the following analysis of its operation applies equally to those having many poles. Note particularly that (1) there are two sets of brushes, namely, the power brushes P connected to the load, and the short-circuited brushes S; (2) the pole shoes are extremely heavy and notched at the center, the purpose being to provide, respectively, a low-reluctance magnetic path for the cross field and to aid commutation; (3) the pole cores are rather small because the flux density in these parts is low; (4) the cutout between generator and battery which operates to prevent the battery from discharging through the low-resistance armature when the latter is at rest or running too slowly to supply load current.

Referring to Fig. 175, assume first that the armature is rotating clockwise and that the short circuit between the S brushes is removed. Under this condition the main field winding, excited by the battery, will create the magnetic field M_F that will be directed vertically downward; no voltage will appear at the power brushes P because, being in a vertical plane, they gather conductor emfs on the left or right of the P axis that add up to zero; maximum voltage will, however, appear at the S brushes. If the S brushes are next connected by a low-resistance wire, an extremely high current will be "fed" into this short circuit, and the currents in the various conductors will be as indicated by the crosses and dots *within the small circles*. As soon as this happens, a *cross field* M_C will be created—an armature-reaction field—that will have a direction from right to left, as may be verified by applying the right-hand rule to the armature-conductor currents; observe also that this field finds a very low-reluctance path in the

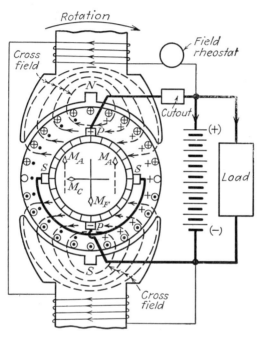

FIG. 175. Wiring diagram showing the simplified connections of the Rosenberg train-lighting generator, supplying current to a battery and load.

heavy pole shoes. The next step in the analysis is to recognize the fact that the two fields M_F and M_C combine vectorially to produce a *resultant* field whose general direction is from northeast to southwest; this means, therefore, that the voltage between the power brushes E_{PP} is no longer zero because the conductor emfs are now determined by an *oblique* field instead of one that is vertical. Now then, when E_{PP} reaches a value that is sufficient to operate the cutout, and this happens when the train speed is high enough and the field rheostat is properly adjusted, the generator is ready to deliver current to the battery and the load.

Still another factor that must be considered is the rotation of the armature conductors through the component of flux previously identified as M_C. Thinking of this as an independent generator action, it is seen that a set of voltages will be developed that have directions indicated by the *inner crosses and dots* (not within the conductors). Applying the right-hand rule to these emfs, it is obvious that an mmf will be established that *directly opposes the main field* M_F; this is represented by M_A in the diagram. The result is that the main field is weakened considerably and becomes secondary in importance to the cross field. Moreover, since the main field is weak under the center of the poles where commutation takes place, sparking is not objectionable; a still further improvement in commutation is made by notching the pole faces as shown, this construction helping to reduce the reactance voltage in the coils short-circuited by the power brushes PP.

The Rosenberg generator functions to regulate for constant current because any tendency on the part of the machine to deliver more current is immediately accompanied by the demagnetizing action of M_A; this in turn reduces the short-circuit current and the cross field M_C. The weakened cross field then lowers the voltage E_{PP}, which, therefore, keeps the load and charging currents at their original values. Furthermore, the main current cannot increase above a certain maximum, whose adjustment is made with the field rheostat; the limit is reached when the demagnetizing mmf M_A completely neutralizes the main field M_F, under which condition no emf exists at the power brushes PP.

If the direction of rotation of the armature is reversed, *i.e.*, if counterclockwise, the emfs in the conductors under the main *north* and *south* poles will be changed. This reverses the short-circuit current, as a consequence of which the cross field M_C will be directed from left to right. Combining the two fields M_F and M_C vectorially as before yields an oblique field whose general direction is now northwest to southeast. Still having a *vertical component that is downward*, the brush polarity will not be altered. It follows, therefore, that the polarity of the machine remains the same for either direction of motion of the train.

Constant-potential System with Rosenberg Generator

As in automobile electrical systems, previously described, it is desirable to have generating equipment for train-lighting service that develops a *constant-potential* characteristic for varying loads. One such system makes use of a modified Rosenberg generator, a compound machine, and an auxiliary control unit; it is illustrated schematically in Fig. 176. Referring to the diagram, it will be noted that the series field is connected directly into the load circuit, while the shunt field is "fed" by the battery through a Wheatstone bridge. The latter has two *fixed* resistances RR in one pair of opposite arms and two iron *ballast* resistances BB in the other opposite pair of arms; the unique property of the ballast resistors is that, operating at a dull red heat, small changes in current result in large resist-ance changes. The circuit conditions are adjusted initially so that the ohmic values of R and B are practically equal when the generator voltage matches that of the battery; under this condition the bridge will be bal-anced, no current will pass through the shunt field, and the machine will operate as a series generator. Should the generator emf increase above the

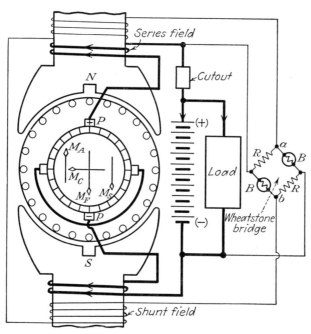

Fig. 176. Wiring diagram showing a modified Rosenberg generator equipped with a control unit to provide a constant-potential train-lighting system.

desired value, more current will pass through the B resistors than through the R resistors; this unbalances the bridge, makes the potential of a rise above that of b, and causes a current to pass through the shunt field. The direction of the latter being such as to create an mmf that *opposes* the series-field mmf, the machine operates as a differential-compound generator, and the terminal voltage tends to drop. Conversely, if the generator emf should drop, less current will pass through B than through R; this causes the potential of b to rise above a, makes the shunt-field mmf *aid* the series-field mmf, in which case the machine operates as a cumulative-compound generator, and raises the terminal voltage to its original value. The mmfs in the middle of the sketch follow those given in Fig. 175, with the ex-ception that M_S, the series-field mmf, has been added, and with the under-standing that the shunt-field mmf M_F may aid or oppose M_S as explained.

The Amplidyne *

Although the Rosenberg generator, originally developed for train-lighting service, is little used in present-day practice, its theory of operation has been applied to the design of a remarkably versatile type of *control generator* called the *Amplidyne*. Differing greatly in construction and function from its original counterpart, it does, nevertheless, belong to the class of machines known as *armature-reaction* generators. Like its predecessor it has two sets of brushes; one short-circuited set occupies the same relative positions as do the brushes in the conventional generator, while a second set is located along an axis that is displaced 90 electrical degrees with respect to the former and is connected to the load. The field structure is rather complex, consisting of a stack of slotted one-piece laminations of high-grade silicon steel, similar to an induction-motor stator, that is energized by one or more *distributed control-field* windings, and three additional *distributed* windings that serve to create compensating and corrective mmfs. Always used as an auxiliary with other electrical equipment, a comparatively low value of excitation watts, applied to the control winding, is capable of controlling a large amount of output power with extreme rapidity.

The principle of operation of the Amplidyne, closely following that already given for the Rosenberg generator, may be explained by first considering the actions of the two basic fields, the control field and the compensating field. Referring to Fig. 177, assume that the control field (also called the voltage control field) is energized by some function of the final output, and in such a manner as to respond to the voltage conditions in the controlled unit. For the current direction shown, the main field M_F will be directed downward so that the upper and lower poles will be north and south, respectively. With the armature rotating clockwise, emfs will be generated in the conductors, the directions of which are indicated by the *outer set* of crosses and dots; moreover, if the C brushes, located along the quadrature axis (the dividing line between the upper and lower halves of armature conductors), are short-circuited, current will flow from brush to brush in the external connector, and in the armature conductors in the same directions as the emfs. Thus far the machine behaves exactly like a conventional separately excited shunt generator under short-circuit conditions. As soon as current is established in the armature conductors, the armature will create a cross-magnetizing mmf directed from right to left, represented in the diagram of vectors by M_C. Next, if a second set of brushes P are located along the main-pole (direct) axis to "feed" current into a load, and a low-reluctance magnetic circuit is provided so that the armature-reaction mmf can establish a strong field, the machine begins to develop characteristics that are quite different from the usual; this is

* See references 18, 19, and 22 in Bibliography.

especially so because the armature-reaction flux is encouraged in the Amplidyne, whereas measures are generally taken to suppress this flux in the usual d-c generator. Assuming that the cross-magnetizing mmf creates an independent field that is directed to the left, the same conductors that cut the main control field (vertically downward) will develop emfs that are indicated by the *inner set* of crosses and dots; moreover, if the P brushes are connected to a load, currents will flow in the same directions as the emfs. Remembering that M_C is regi rded as an inde-

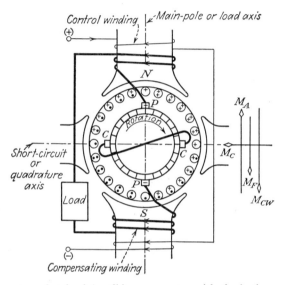

Fig. 177. Elementary sketch of Amplidyne generator with the basic control and compensating fields.

pendent mmf, the inner set of crosses and dots may likewise be considered as developing a separate mmf M_A *that is directed upward to oppose the main control field*. If the machine were left in this condition, M_A would create a third component of flux, which in turn would establish a new set of emfs, the result of which would be that a new current would flow in the quadrature axis to nullify the original short-circuit current; under this condition, the main field M_F would lose control and the machine would operate as a constant-current generator. To alter the situation described so that the generator may be made to display amplifier characteristics, a second field—a *compensating field*—must be placed on the main poles so that, carrying load current, it develops an mmf M_{CW} that is equal and opposite to the armature mmf M_A. Thus, the *net mmf existing in the direct axis is* M_F, which, therefore, assumes complete control over the output voltage.

The fact that the Amplidyne has the ability of increasing the input watts, represented by the power input to the control field, to a much larger value of output watts gives the machine amplification properties, the *amplification being defined as the ratio of watts output to excitation watts input to any single control field, the other fields being deenergized.* Furthermore, since such amplification takes place in two stages, one stage from control field to quadrature field and the second stage from quadrature

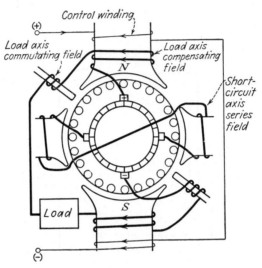

FIG. 178. Sketch of Amplidyne generator showing one control field and three auxiliary fields.

back to the direct axis, the Amplidyne is generally recognized as a two-stage amplifier.

To improve both the operating performance and the degree of amplification, Amplidynes are frequently equipped with commutating poles, whose windings are energized by the load current, and a series field that is connected in the short-circuit path; this is illustrated by Fig. 178. With such field additions commutation is exceptionally good and amplifications as high as 10,000 may be attained. Moreover, extremely rapid response obtains under transient conditions because, as previously mentioned, the windings are *distributed* in a slotted, laminated core of high-grade magnetic steel (shown in Figs. 177 and 178 as salient poles, for convenience).

In some Amplidyne applications that require a number of control functions, several control fields, independently excited by signal devices, are placed on the same core structure; under such conditions the machine will respond to their resultant mmf and will act to amplify the latter as though it were a single control field. Since each of the control windings occupies an extremely small space, it is often possible to employ as many as four such fields, thus permitting many independent signals to control the Amplidyne output. Each of these fields is readily adjusted or controlled by a small resistor and, because current requirements are low, fast-response devices can be used. Also, rectifiers may be utilized to block these fields until specified operating conditions or limits are reached. Figure 179 is a photograph of a disassembled Amplidyne having an output

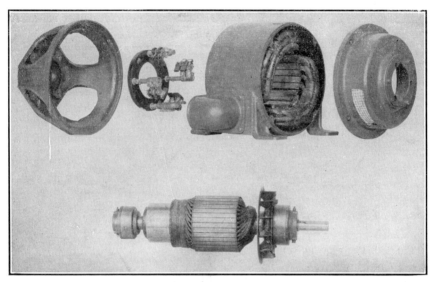

Fig. 179. Disassembled view of a 5-kw 250-volt 1,750-rpm Amplidyne. (*General Electric Co.*)

rating of 5 kw at 1,750 rpm and 250 volts; the stator clearly shows the slotted core and the distributed windings.

Amplidynes are used in a great variety of applications where extremely accurate control is required. Once the system is properly adjusted, any slight deviation from a preset standard gives rise to electrical signals which, applied to one or more control fields, results in a considerable increase in the Amplidyne's power output to prevent the change. The following practical applications illustrate several important uses of this control unit. (1) An Amplidyne may be employed to "couple electrically" two or more d-c motors so that their speeds are perfectly matched; the arrangement has been applied to a flying shear in a steel mill. (2) In a power shovel perfect control is maintained over the voltage of the generators that supply power to the operating motors; a unique scheme has been developed that provides maximum rates of acceleration and deceleration and protection of electrical and mechanical equipment during stalling and plugging periods and eliminates overshooting and consequent load peaks. (3) In an electric furnace the electrical characteristics are adjusted by mechanical means, *i.e.*, by the smooth positioning, up or down, of the individual electrodes; such control maintains uniform heat. (4) In a large-reel motor, operating over a wide speed range, the current and tension are held constant throughout the reel build-up. (5) In a multiroll paper machine a single-motor drive maintains accurate speed control. (6) On a boring mill an Amplidyne may be coupled to accurate positioning controls. (7) The Amplidyne may be employed in a large paper rewinder

Fig. 180. Photograph of an Amplidyne motor-generator set. (*General Electric Co.*)

to maintain extreme accuracy in positioning the edge of the paper as it speeds through the machine.

A photograph of an Amplidyne motor-generator set is illustrated in Fig. 180; the set consists of a 3-kw 1,750-rpm 250-volt Amplidyne driven by a 5-hp 220-volt 3-phase induction motor.

Diverter-pole Generators *

Shunt and compound generators, although excellent for most power applications, have certain limitations for battery-charging service. A shunt generator, for example, having a drooping *voltage* vs. *load* characteristic (see Fig. 86), acts to charge a battery at a constant rate, rather than at a high rate when the battery is in a discharged condition, and a low rate as it comes up to charge. When the battery is low, its terminal emf is also low; thus, as the generator attempts to deliver a high-current charge, its voltage drops, which, in turn, exerts a limiting effect upon the delivered current. Conversely, when the battery is coming up to full charge, its voltage rises; the generator now tries to charge the battery at a low rate, and this action, being accompanied by a rise in the generator emf, causes

* See reference 24 in Bibliography.

the charging current to increase. As previously indicated, it is better, for practical reasons, to start the charging cycle at a high rate and taper down to a low value as the battery approaches a "full" condition; this prevents "gassing."

A flat-compound generator, obviously, has a better external characteristic than a shunt machine for this kind of service because, having a terminal emf that is virtually constant throughout its operating range, it delivers the desired tapering charge. It is, however, open to the objection that it

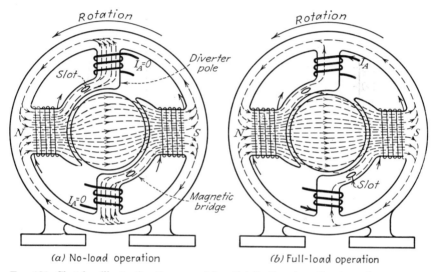

(a) No-load operation   (b) Full-load operation

Fig. 181. Sketches illustrating the general flux distributions in a diverter-pole generator.

can accidentally become a motor, should the battery emf exceed the generator voltage; under this condition the negative current (with respect to generator operation) will reverse the series field (though not the shunt field) and cause the differential-compound motor to become unstable. It would, in fact, attempt to "run away" unless a reverse-current relay were installed to prevent the motor action.

A new type of generator, having the desired flat external characteristic of a compound machine, but one that cannot "motor," is the so-called *diverter-pole generator*. In construction, it is quite similar to the standard generator with interpoles (see Fig. 69), with the exception that each of the interpoles is joined to the *succeeding main pole* (in the direction of rotation) by a magnetic bridge. The heavy winding on the so-called *diverter poles* (which are actually interpoles) is connected in series in the armature circuit and tends to magnetize the interpoles so that the latter have the same polarity as the main poles to which they are bridged.

Figure 181 is a sketch representing a two-pole diverter-pole generator, in which the flux distributions are shown for two degrees of loading.

Note particularly the narrow slots cut lengthwise into the bridges, their purpose being to cause saturation in the restricted area as the load increases. Since the armature current is zero at no load (Fig. 181a), the diverter poles produce no mmf to "buck" the main poles to which they are joined by their respective bridges; under this condition, a good part of the main-pole flux is diverted through the magnetic shunts to the diverter poles. The extent of this diversion is limited by the degree of saturation of the bridges, the areas of which are reduced by the longi-

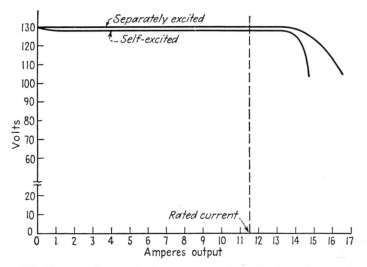

Fig. 182. Typical *voltage* vs. *load-current* curves for a diverter-pole generator.

tudinal slots. As the load increases, however, the armature current, no longer zero, passes through the diverter-field windings to create mmfs that oppose the main-field mmfs; hence, less leakage flux is diverted through the bridges, with the result that a larger proportion of the main-field flux enters the armature where the emf is developed. The generator, therefore, tends to maintain a constant terminal voltage for all load conditions because increasing values of armature flux compensate for the $I_A R_A$ drop and the effect of armature reaction. Figure 181b illustrates the general flux distribution at full load and clearly indicates how the action of the diverter poles restricts the leakage flux.

Another advantage of this type of machine is that the flux that does enter the armature from the bridges in the interpolar zones is in the correct direction to aid commutation; in this respect the diverter poles function like interpoles that inject flux into the armature to neutralize the reactance voltage in the armature coils undergoing commutation. Moreover, the generator is self-protecting at heavy overloads because the diverter-pole mmf cannot reverse the shunt-field mmf; the small cross-sectional areas of the bridges become saturated at heavy loads and thus prevent the passage of flux from the diverter poles into the main poles. The machine does, however, have a maximum current output, at which point the voltage falls abruptly to zero; this occurs when the total flux entering the armature is reduced to a very low value, at comparatively high overloads, by the opposing shunt-field and diverter-pole mmfs.

A typical *voltage* vs. *load* characteristic for such a machine is given in Fig. 182. Note particularly how the terminal emf remains practically constant throughout its operating range and falls off sharply at a load somewhat above rated value. As previously mentioned, diverter-pole generators are especially suitable in battery-charging service, and are often used in powerhouses and substations for this purpose, where batteries operate the circuit breakers. They may be arranged for separate as well as self-excitation.

Arc-welding Generators *

The application of electric arc welders for the purpose of strongly bonding metals together has become extremely important in recent years. Two general types of equipment are employed, namely, (1) that requiring an a-c source, in which case the weld is made with an a-c arc, and (2) machines that deliver direct current to the arc for the welding function. The early welders were almost exclusively the d-c types, primarily because standard welding rod did not have a proper kind of *coating* that is required when the operation is performed with alternating current. However, since practically all arc welding is now done with *coated rod*, a-c equipment seems to be gaining favor because, involving fewer service and maintenance problems, the quality and speed of the job is considered equally as good as with d-c machines. To elaborate briefly, it should be pointed out that an uncoated rod loses heat very rapidly and, moreover, goes through changing periods of heating and cooling with the variations of current in each half cycle of an alternating current; the latter condition does not exist with the fairly steady d-c arc. Also, when coated rod is used, a slag is formed over the bead, and this, together with a gas that shields the arc, maintains a uniformly high temperature with either kind of current.

Most welders are "single-operator" units, although some larger multiple-operator machines have been built. Furthermore, d-c welders are self-regulating, in the sense that voltage and current changes take place automatically with the rapidly changing load conditions. Still another important point that should be recognized is that, unlike the conventional constant-flux type of shunt generator which cannot be used for such service, the d-c welding generator is a specially designed machine in which

* See reference 21 in Bibliography.

the flux changes greatly with load variations. In operation it must function to deliver an extremely high current to a stable arc, under which condition the molten metal and the arc represent a virtual short circuit; also it must quickly regain its open-circuit emf when the arc is extinguished. The voltage drop across the arc is usually between 20 and 25 volts (40

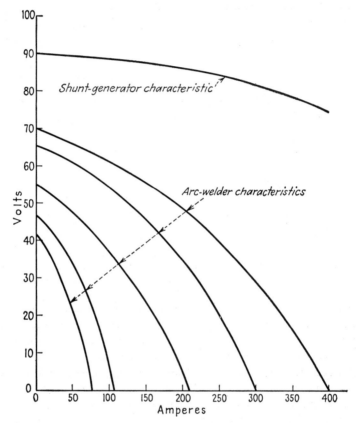

FIG. 183. Characteristic *volts* vs. *amperes* curves for an arc welder and a conventional shunt generator.

volts in some recent high-speed machines) and remains substantially constant under all transient conditions of arc length, current, and voltage. To fulfill these important requirements, the external *voltage* vs. *current* characteristics for given generator adjustments must *droop* considerably as indicated by the family of curves in the lower part of Fig. 183; they must not have the conventional shape of the standard shunt generator, represented by the upper curve.

One of the first d-c welding generator designs made use of a differential-compound machine, with interpoles, whose shunt field was separately excited by a small exciter mounted on the same shaft as the coupled M-G set; an a-c motor was generally used for mechanical power. A wiring diagram of such a system is shown in Fig. 184. Since all flux changes are met by the "bucking" series field (the shunt field is adjusted to a given value for a desired welding current), all iron portions of the magnetic circuit must be carefully laminated; this practice greatly reduces the time lag between flux and current. The fact that the series field opposes the action of the shunt field means that any rise or fall in arc current is instantly accompanied by an inverse change in the arc drop; this character-

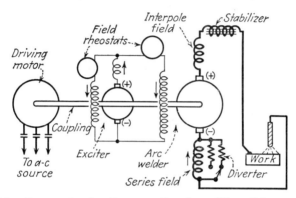

Fig. 184. Wiring diagram showing the connections for a differential-compound type of arc-welding generator and its auxiliary equipment.

istic of the generator results in an approximately constant power input to the arc as well as a tendency to stabilize the arc. Further stabilization is provided by an inductance coil, a stabilizer, in series with the welding circuit for the purpose of smoothing out transient series-field changes; also, additional control is possible by the use of diverters across the series field, as indicated.

The more recent designs of arc welders are radically different from the original modified conventional generators and operate much more effectively under all conditions of transient and steady-state loading. The dynamic curves (the E vs. I curves) have been made *steeper* with the result that arc-welder performance is much improved in several ways. As the slope of the curve becomes steeper, (1) the welding current remains more nearly constant because large changes in arc voltage produce small changes in welding current, (2) the smaller becomes the transient short-circuit current because this peak current approaches the steady-state short-circuit current, and (3) the smaller becomes the time lag between the welding current and the flux, and this results in a greater recovery voltage because the latter depends upon the flux in the machine at that instant.

The so-called *split-pole* type of arc-welding generator combines the foregoing advantages in a single machine, eliminating the need for an exciter, an external stabilizer, and diverters. A wiring diagram of such a design is given in Fig. 185. In construction it has four main poles and two commutating poles, with the main-pole windings connected so that the polarities are *N-N-S-S* (not *N-S-N-S*); the effect is to *split* each large main pole into two parts, and hence the term *split-pole*. Observe that (1) the axis of the main brushes lines up with neutral axis between the main *north*

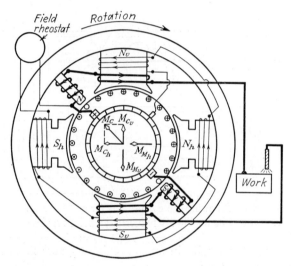

Fig. 185. General constructional details, and polarity and mmf relations, in a special type of split-pole arc-welding generator.

and *south* poles; (2) two of the split sections of main poles have constricted areas; (3) the differential series-field windings are placed over the full-sized main poles; (4) the shunt field is connected to one power brush and a third brush between the two main brushes.

When the generator is in operation, assuming a clockwise rotation and the indicated magnetic and brush polarities, the main poles will tend to set up two mmfs, M_{M_v} vertically downward and M_{M_h} horizontally from right to left; the armature conductors will then carry currents shown with their proper in $(+)$ and out $(\cdot)$ symbols. Applying the right-hand rule to the armature mmf, it is seen that the cross field M_C will have a northwesterly direction and that this latter field may be divided into two quadrature components M_{C_h} and M_{C_v}. Now then, if the individual components of mmf are properly paired, it is seen that M_{M_h} and M_{C_h} are in the *same* direction, while M_{M_v} and M_{C_v} *oppose* one another. Furthermore.

since the horizontal poles have constricted areas and are *not* acted upon by a series field, they will be *highly saturated* and will produce a field that is substantially constant at all loads; armature reaction does not affect the strength of the horizontal field. Also, the vertical poles have large cross-sectional areas and *are* acted upon by an opposing series field; this results in an *unsaturated* magnetic circuit whose flux changes considerably and rapidly as the load current and its accompanying vertically directed

Fig. 186. Cutaway view of portable d-c welder. (*The Lincoln Electric Co.*)

cross field changes.   Finally, since the shunt field is connected to the positive and third brushes which subtend conductors in the rapidly varying vertical field, the shunt-field voltage, current, and flux will rise and fall with the rapidly varying load.   The result of all these reactions, therefore, is to contribute to the desired *steeply drooping E* vs. *I external characteristic*.   Load-current control is usually obtained by field-rheostat adjustment and by using all or part of the "bucking" series field.

A cutaway view of a modern d-c welder, mounted on a portable truck, is shown in Fig. 186.   Note particularly that the exciter armature, the squirrel cage of the driving a-c motor, and the armature of the welding generator are assembled from left to right on a common shaft; also clearly seen are the controls directly above the unit and the cooling blower at the extreme right.

Series Boosters

The term *booster* is applied to a d-c electrical system in which a generator is used to raise the voltage at some point in a transmission line to compensate for excessive IR drop in feeders. A machine used for this purpose may be any of the three general types, *i.e.*, series, shunt, or compound, but the armature is always connected in series in the circuit so that its voltage *adds to*, or *boosts*, the line potential. Moreover, since the line drop is directly proportional to the load current, it should be clear that the generated emf in the armature of the booster must vary in the same way; this means that, for such service, the external characteristic of the generator, that is, E vs. I, must be a straight line that passes through the origin.

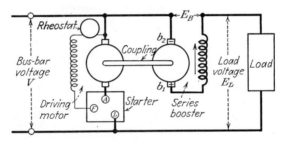

Fig. 187. Wiring diagram of a series-booster system.

A series booster is a series generator properly connected in a transmission line; its voltage depends upon the current passing through it, *i.e.*, its load, because the same load current energizes the series field. Figure 85 represents a typical external characteristic for such a machine. Thus, when correctly designed for the particular installation, any IR drop in the line wires is immediately accompanied by a rise in the booster emf, which, in turn, provides the needed compensation. Correct design means, of course, that the booster generator is operated at low flux densities so that the voltage is directly proportional to the load current ($E = k\phi \times$ rpm, where rpm is constant), and that the booster emf is, for all load currents, equal to the line drop. Series boosters may, therefore, be made to function so that the voltage at the far end of a transmission system is practically constant regardless of the load. Figure 187 shows a wiring diagram of the system described and simply illustrates how a shunt motor, connected to the bus bars, drives a series generator; note especially that the polarity of the booster is such as to raise the line voltage at the load end of the line. In operation, such a motor-generator set must be protected against the possibility that the driving motor might accidentally be disconnected from its source of power. Should this happen, the series generator would immediately become a series motor *rotating at runaway speed in the reverse direction*. A study of the wiring diagram indicates why this will happen.

When the booster is acting normally as a *generator*, the booster voltage E_B adds to V to become E_L; under this condition, brush b_1 is positive and br ush b_2 is negative. However, when the booster accidentally becomes a *motor* because it has lost its motive power, the brush polarities reverse (that is, b_2 and b_1 become positive and negative, respectively), but the current through the series field does not; this means that the booster changes its direction of rotation and, because it has no mechanical load, attempts to "run away." The obvious protection for such a possibility is to provide the booster with a relay that will trip its circuit in case of a power failure.

Series boosters are seldom used at present for the purpose described, and then only when such an installation is cheaper than larger line wires

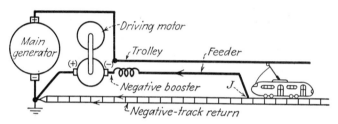

FIG. 188. Wiring diagram of a negative feeder-booster system.

and feeders. A more frequent application of such equipment is to prevent electrolysis of water and gas mains and lead-covered telephone and telegraph cables. In street-railway systems the negative or *return* circuit consists of the tracks, the surrounding earth, and any metallic structure capable of carrying current back to the *grounded* negative bus of the main generator. Even if the tracks are carefully and properly bonded together at their joints, some of the current will always "leak" from the rails and enter gas and water mains and metallic sheath cables. Eventually, when the current leaves the underground structures to return through the earth to the tracks to complete its journey back to the negative bus of the generator, electrolysis, *i.e.*, "eating away" of metal, takes place. Series boosters connected in series between rails and a negative feeder have proved very successful in preventing the damage indicated; when used in this way, they are called *negative-feeder* or *track-return boosters*.

A wiring diagram showing a negative-feeder circuit is given in Fig. 188. Note particularly that the polarity of the booster is such as to provide an emf of the proper direction so that the return current will attempt to avoid the tracks and follow the low ohmic-resistance feeder. In fact, if the booster voltage exactly equals the negative-feeder voltage drop, no current will flow in the track system out to the point of juncture J, because point J will then have exactly the same potential as the generator ground.

In the actual installation, however, the negative-booster voltage is made only large enough to keep the leakage current from doing minor damage to the underground metallic structures.

Shunt Boosters

Small self-contained d-c systems that must supply *gradually changing loads that vary over a considerable range* are frequently equipped with an auxiliary storage battery and a small booster; the function of the battery is to take care of normally light loads when a large generator would be operating inefficiently, while the booster provides the necessary additional

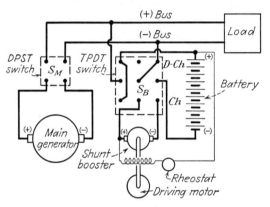

Fig. 189. Wiring diagram of a shunt-booster system.

emf which, together with the constant generator voltage, is required for battery-charging purposes. Figure 189 represents a wiring diagram, in simplified form, of such a *shunt-booster system*. Note particularly the DPST main switch S_M that is used in the main-generator circuit, and TPDT battery-balancer switch S_B that is provided so that the battery may serve as a source of power or be charged. When S_M is open and S_B is closed in the *up* position, the *discharge* side, the battery alone energizes the bus when the load is light; if, on the other hand, S_B is open and S_M is closed, the main generator supplies power to a moderately heavy or heavy load. During battery-charging periods, however, the main switch S_M should be closed, and the booster generator must be started; then, after the emf of the booster unit is adjusted so that its value, together with the line potential, is sufficiently higher than the battery emf to charge the latter at the required current, S_B is closed in the down position, the *charge* side. A zero-center type of ammeter is generally placed in the battery circuit to indicate the charge or discharge current. Observe also that the shunt field of the booster is connected directly across the bus terminals when that machine is in service; in this respect, the machine, therefore, acts as a separately excited shunt generator, with the field being energized from a reasonably constant bus potential.

In a 120-volt system, there will usually be about 66 cells in the battery, each of which has an open-circuit emf of approximately 2.2 and 1.85 volts when respectively charged and discharged. If it is assumed that each cell will require about 2.65 volts during the charging period, the impressed voltage across the battery under this condition must be $66 \times 2.65 = 175$ volts. Since the armature of the booster is in series with a line potential of 120, the booster must develop a maximum of $175 - 120 = 55$ volts. It is, moreover, customary in practice to provide the battery with an *end-cell switch* (not shown in the diagram) so that one or more cells may be cut in or out at will; this permits the battery to deliver load at the required line voltage even though the emf per cell changes with its condition of charge.

Constant-current Boosters

When generators must supply power to both constant-current lighting loads and rapidly fluctuating motor loads that are repeatedly starting and stopping, the line voltage will vary sufficiently to cause objectionable flickering of lights. This condition is particularly aggravating in office

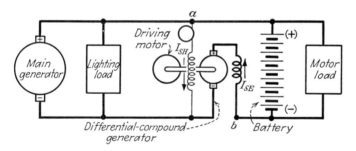

Fig. 190. Wiring diagram of a constant-current booster system.

buildings and hotels having elevators, where individual power plants provide the electric service. To prevent the lights from flickering when elevators are started, it is generally necessary to use a storage battery in conjunction with a booster to smooth out the wide-current fluctuations on the main generator. A satisfactory scheme is illustrated in Fig. 190 and consists of a differential-compound generator booster and a storage battery. In operation, the main generator serves the lighting load directly, while the motor load may receive power from the battery as well as the main generator. When the elevator load is comparatively light or zero, the current I_{SE} through the series field, the ampere-turns of which oppose the shunt-field ampere-turns, is small or zero. Under this condition the line potential between a and b, being higher than the battery emf, causes the battery to charge; the main generator, therefore, supplies power to the lighting load, the small elevator load, and the battery. However, when the elevator load is heavy, the series-field current I_{SE} increases sufficiently to cause the differential-compound generator to lose voltage to such an extent that the battery voltage exceeds the emf between points a and b; under this condition the battery discharges into the motor load, aiding the main generator in this respect. If adjustments are carefully made in the system, it is quite possible to maintain a fairly constant voltage across the main generator and also have the latter deliver a substantially uniform load current to lights, motors, and battery. This method of control is known as a *constant-current booster system.*

Dynamotors

Certain d-c applications require voltages that are quite different from available standard sources of supply. When this becomes necessary, it is possible to do one of several things. For rather large amounts of power a motor-generator (M-G) set may be employed, in which the voltage rating of the motor matches the line emf, and the generator delivers the required potential to the load. Batteries, although expensive as a primary source of power, may also be used. An extremely desirable construction, for comparatively small amounts of power, is a single unit that functions both as a d-c motor and generator. Called a *dynamotor,* from the words *dynamo* and *motor*, it is a machine that combines both motor and generator actions in *one magnetic field*, either with two independent armatures and commutators arranged lengthwise with the shaft, or with a single armature core having two armature windings and commutators. The more common procedure is to place the two properly proportioned windings in the same slots, one on top of the other, so that both may be acted upon by the same flux. The motor winding must, obviously, be designed so that the speed will be correct, while the generator winding design must be concerned with developing the desired voltage. Special dynamotors have been built with as many as four windings and four commutators, three of them designed to generate different voltages, with the fourth serving for motor action. This type of machine is less expensive and more efficient than two-unit motor-generator sets, because it involves the stray-power losses, *i.e.*, friction, windage, and core losses, of only one rotating structure. The dynamotor is, however, open to the objection that, for a given design, the generated emf is fixed by the voltage impressed on the "motor end," *i.e.*, voltage control is not possible, as is the case with generators operating in their own magnetic fields.

The operation of the dynamotor may be analyzed by considering the counter emf E_C in the motor winding with respect to the generated emf E

In the generator winding. Since both windings cut the same flux at the same speed, the respective *generated voltages will be directly proportional to the number of turns per path in the corresponding motor and generator windings.* This implies that any change in flux, occasioned by a rheostat adjustment or variation in speed, or both, affects the two windings similarly. Therefore, neglecting the armature-resistance drops, the $I_A R_A$ drops, it should be clear that there will always be a definite ratio of input voltage (to the motor) to output voltage (from the generator). That is,

$$\frac{E_{C_m}}{E} \cong \frac{V_m}{E} = \frac{N_m/a_m}{N_g/a_g} = \text{constant} \qquad (46)$$

To put it another way, assume that the field is strengthened. This slows down the motor so that the generator winding cuts *more flux* at a correspondingly *lower rate* of speed, *i.e.*, since the rate of flux cutting $N(d\phi/dt)$ remains constant, the value of E does likewise. Conversely, if the field is weakened, the motor speeds up; however, the generator winding

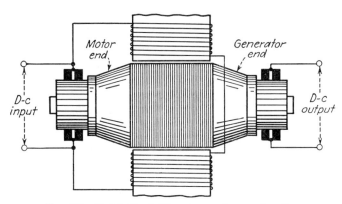

Fig. 191. Sketch illustrating dynamotor construction.

cuts less flux at a correspondingly *higher rate*, so the flux-cutting rate and the generated voltage E remain constant.

Commutation in dynamotors is usually excellent, because the effects of armature reaction result from two sets of ampere-turns that are oppositely directed with respect to each other. Since the instantaneous generator and motor currents in conductors occupying the same slots are in opposite directions, their mmfs tend to neutralize; the net armature ampere-turns is, however, exactly that needed to provide sufficient torque for the rotational losses.

The dynamotor may be properly regarded as a *rotary converter* because, like the latter, it is a rotating machine that converts electric energy at one voltage to electric energy at another voltage; several important differ-ences do, however, exist in the larger rotary converters, these being that (1) a single winding is employed, (2) slip rings are placed at one end and a commutator at the other, with the single winding tapped to both, and (3) the current is changed from alternating current to direct current, and vice versa.

Figure 191 represents a sketch of a typical small dynamotor.

Universal Motors

When specially designed, a d-c *series* motor will operate satisfactorily from the standpoint of developed torque and commutation if connected

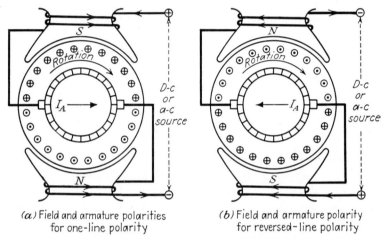

(a) Field and armature polarities for one-line polarity

(b) Field and armature polarity for reversed-line polarity

FIG. 192. Elementary sketches illustrating that the same direction of rotation results in a series motor for either line polarity.

to an a-c source of equal voltage. The reason for this is simply that both the magnetic polarity and the electrical brush polarity reverse simul-taneously with the positive and negative halves of the a-c cycle; *i.e.*, since the *same* current passes through the armature winding and the field, the two elements are affected similarly. Figure 192 is a sketch representing a two-pole series motor in which clockwise torque and rotation is developed for either line polarity; note particularly the reversed magnetic polarities and current directions in Figs. 192*a* and *b*.

In the case of series motors of comparatively large size, for example, in electric-railway service, the inductive effects of the field and armature tend to create serious commutation difficulties, which, if permitted to remain uncorrected, will cause the machines to perform unsatisfactorily when used on a-c circuits. Moreover, the field hysteresis and eddy-current losses, which are not present when connected to a d-c source, tend to become abnormally high. Such difficulties are, however, forestalled by designing these machines (1) with a well-laminated field; (2) for operation on the lower frequencies, such as 15 and 25 cycles, as well as on direct current; (3) with a comparatively low ratio of field mmf to armature mmf, consistent with good performance; (4) so that the field iron is worked at low flux densities; (5) with special compensating and interpole windings for improved commutation on alternating current; (6) with armatures having a comparatively large number of commutator bars, so that the reactance voltage of the short-circuited coils may be reduced to a minimum; and (7) with special, added resistance between armature-coil ends and the commutator segments to which these are connected and soldered. It should be clear that the foregoing special design treatment is given these machines in order to improve commutation when alternating current is used, and this generally means that extreme care must be taken to overcome the bad effects of armature reaction.

Small motors, *i.e.*, those having fractional-horsepower output ratings, do not generally receive the special attention indicated for their larger counterparts. They are, for the most part, plain series motors that are operated with a negative brush lead of about 30 to 50 electrical degrees; the latter is necessary to ensure satisfactory commutation when alternating current is used. However, if a particularly high grade of performance is desired, small universal motors are designed with distributed field windings, placed in slots as is the armature winding, and special compensating windings acting to nullify the cross-magnetizing action of the armature. The American Standards Association (ASA) has formally designated that a *universal* motor shall be ". . . a series motor that may be operated either on direct current or single-phase alternating current at approximately the same speed and output." It further specifies that ". . . these conditions must be met when direct-current and alternating-current voltages are approximately the same and the frequency of the alternating current is not greater than 60 cycles per second."

The term "small motors" is, of course, relative, but it generally refers to those two-pole fractional-horsepower machines that have ratings within the range of about $\frac{1}{500}$ to $\frac{3}{4}$ hp. They are employed in an unusually large number of applications, performing many kinds of service, and have power consumptions of about the same order of magnitude as home appliances such as incandescent lamps, flatirons, space heaters, and the like. Their widest fields of application are under the following conditions: (1) when they must be capable of performing equally well on standard d-c and a-c sources of supply; (2) when it is necessary that they operate at comparatively high speeds—since the horsepower output is almost directly proportional to the speed, the power per unit weight increases with the speed; (3) when it is desirable that the speed be capable of automatically adjusting itself to the magnitude of the load—the speed is high at light loads and low at heavy loads.

The field structure of the small universal type of motor is always a stack of laminations, riveted together and fitted with field windings; yoke and pole projections of the individual laminations are integral. The armature is similar to those of larger construction, with the exception that the stack of laminations is pressed on the shaft so that the slots are usually *skewed*, *i.e.*, set at an angle with respect to the shaft axis. The latter construction

FIG. 193. Field and armature-core laminations for small universal motors. (*Carnegie-Illinois Steel Corp.*)

helps to reduce magnetic noise and eliminates the tendency on the part of the armature to lock when started. Figure 193 illustrates several sets of field and armature laminations.

These motors display typical series-motor characteristics, having good starting and overload torques and considerable speed-load variations; Fig. 142 indicates the inverse relation between speed and torque. Speeds as high as 20,000 rpm, and more, are not uncommon, and because the armature diameters are about 1 to 2 in., their peripheral velocities are not excessive; even at no load the friction and windage is sufficient to limit their maximum speeds to values that are well below "runaway" speeds. Gears are frequently incorporated to reduce the load speeds to reasonably low values.

If tests are performed on a universal motor, it will usually be found that the d-c and a-c (60-cycle) *speed-load curves* do not coincide. In some motors, the a-c speeds will be higher than the d-c speeds for equivalent loads, while in others the reverse is true; in still other designs, the curves cross between no load and full load. Several factors are responsible for the differences indicated. When operated on direct current, the *armature-* and *field-resistance drops* tend to lower the speed as load is applied, while the effect of armature reaction is to raise the speed under similar loading conditions. In addition to the foregoing, a third factor, namely, *reactance-voltage drop*, acts to reduce the speed when the motor is connected to an a-c source. Note particularly that the effect of armature reaction is to reduce the air-gap flux, which, in turn, causes a rise in speed, while reactance voltage drop, appearing when alternating current is used, acts to lower the effective motor voltage and, therefore, the speed. Whether or not the actual speed for a given load is higher on alternating than on direct current depends upon which of the above two factors is changed more. If the reactance voltage drop increases more than the air-gap flux decreases, the motor will tend to operate at a lower speed when alternating current is used; otherwise, the reverse is true. Also, at the greater loads the iron is saturated, so that the effective flux per a-c ampere is less than that produced per d-c ampere; the result of this condition is that the motor tends to run faster with alternating current. In other words, the relative speeds on direct current and alternating current will depend upon the factors that predominate in a given machine, remembering that armature reaction and armature reactance act oppositely, and that the latter component is present only on alternating current. In a good design, the reactance-voltage drop is kept fairly low, and the difference in flux produced by direct and alternating current is reduced to a minimum by operating at low flux densities. Such improvement in operation is gained at the expense of good commutation, correction for which must be made by selecting the proper grade of brush.

In some special applications of universal motors, as in kitchen food mixers, it is desirable to incorporate a constant-speed governor, the function of which is to maintain a definite speed at a given setting of a dial. There are several designs of such governor devices, but they all operate on the principle that a spring-loaded contact mechanism, mounted on the rapidly rotating armature shaft, opens and closes contacts to control a line resistance or the flux, which, in turn, controls the speed. Figure 194*a* illustrates one scheme in which a comparatively high resistance is alternately inserted and short-circuited as the motor attempts to speed up or slow down, respectively, for a given spring-tension adjustment. A second method (Fig. 194*b*) makes use of an inductively coupled field that is alternately open-circuited or short-circuited by the spring-loaded contacts. If, with a given spring-tension adjustment, the contacts are closed and the motor speeds up slightly, the contacts will open; this will open the induc-

tively coupled field, with the result that the field strength will increase
and slow the motor down.   Conversely, should the motor speed tend to
drop below the set value, the contacts will close to short-circuit the inductively coupled field; the effect will be a reduction in flux and a corresponding increase in speed.   The small capacitors across the contacts are
for the purpose of absorbing rapidly dissipated energies to prevent arcing
at the contacts.   In practice the contacts are opening and closing very
rapidly (approximately 150 times a second), so that, in fact, the instan-

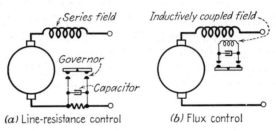

(a) Line-resistance control   (b) Flux control

Fig. 194. Sketches illustrating two types of constant-speed governor control.

taneous speeds are always changing between two rather narrow limits;
the average *speed* is, however, kept constant for a given spring tension
as adjusted by the operator.   While the speed is gradually increasing, the
contacts are held closed a relatively greater part of the time, whereas the
reverse is true when the speed is gradually decreasing.

These motors are used in considerable numbers in a great many kinds
of applications.   In some, the actual motor speed is the load speed, a good
example being a vacuum cleaner.   In others, the load speed is considerably
reduced through a gear train; good examples are drink mixers and portable
drills.   To illustrate the wide range of applications of universal motors,
Table 4 is given.

TABLE 4

COMMON APPLICATIONS OF UNIVERSAL MOTORS

1. Electric shavers	14. Food mixers	27. Sanders
2. Hair driers	15. Routers	28. Ventilating equipment
3. Sewing machines	16. Wood shapers	29. Planers
4. Vacuum machines	17. Nut setters	30. Valve grinders
5. Drink mixers	18. Saws	31. Surgical instruments
6. Small fans	19. Hedge trimmers	32. Vibrators
7. Clippers	20. Files	33. Grease guns
8. Dishwashers	21. Polishers	34. Hones
9. Motion-picture outfits	22. Sirens	35. Die sinkers
10. Portable drills	23. Advertising devices	36. Lock mortisers
11. Pipe threaders	24. Pumps	37. Nibblers
12. Calculating machines	25. Hammers	38. Cast cutters
13. Small grinders	26. Screw drivers	39. Compressors

A disassembled small universal motor is shown in Fig. 195. Note especially how one end of each field coil is connected to a brush holder.

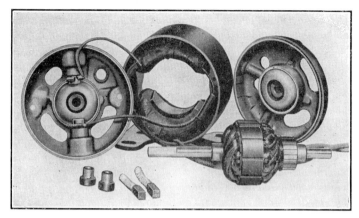

Fig. 195. A disassembled small universal motor. (*Redmond Mfg. Co.*)

PROBLEMS

1. A third-brush generator in an automobile delivers 35 amp at 6.8 volts. What portion of the engine horsepower is required for this load, assuming an efficiency of 64 per cent?

2. A diverter-pole generator is used to charge a battery whose open-circuit emf is 102 volts. If the total resistance of the battery and all connections is 2 ohms, calculate the charging current when the generator voltage is 128.

3. After a period of charge the emf of the battery in Prob. 2 rises to 121 volts, and the total circuit resistance drops to 1.4 ohms. Calculate the charging current if the generator voltage is 129 under this condition.

4. How much power is delivered to the arc in a welding operation that requires 220 amp at 25 volts?

5. A series booster, like that shown in Fig. 187, compensates for a 15-volt line drop when the current in the circuit is 635 amp. Calculate the horsepower rating of the driving motor if the efficiency of the generator is assumed to be 85 per cent.

6. The main generator in a shunt booster system (Fig. 189) has a rating of 75 kw at 125 volts. If the lighting and appliance load is 70 kw, what charging current can be delivered to the storage battery without overloading the generator?

7. A small two-pole dynamotor has a 24-volt motor winding and a 180-volt generator winding; the commutator at the motor end has 18 segments, while the generator-end commutator has 54 segments. Neglecting the

$I_A R_A$ drops, calculate the number of turns in each of the elements connected to adjacent segments at the generator end if 8 turns are used in each of the elements at the motor end.

8. Calculate the horsepower output of a universal motor that develops a torque of 18.7 oz-in. at a speed of 18,000 rpm.

9. The armature of a ¾-hp portable drill operates at 15,000 rpm and the gear ratio is 8 to 1. What torque in pound-feet and ounce-inches is delivered to the drill when the motor is operating at full load?

CHAPTER 13

COMMUTATION

The Commutation Problem

One of the most important functions of the d-c machine is that of commutation, briefly discussed in Chap. 3. The process involves the reversal of the emf and current in successive coils, as they are repeatedly short-circuited by the brushes, and the transfer of such coils from one electrical circuit to another. In the generator the *generated* emf and the armature current are alternating and are rectified by the commutating mechanism so that the load voltage and current are direct current; in the motor the *impressed* emf and current are unidirectional, and the commutation mechanism changes these to alternating current. It is during, and immediately following, the short-circuit period that the coils, commutator, and brushes undergo their severest strain, to minimize which proper corrective measures must be employed. Previous discussions, particularly Chaps. 5 and 6, dealt with armature reaction and armature reactance, the primary causes of faulty commutation, and the use of interpoles and compensating windings to neutralize and nullify the objectionable fields created by the armature mmfs.

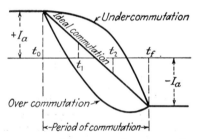

FIG. 196. *Current* vs. *time* curves for three kinds of commutation.

Under conditions of *ideal* commutation, the current in a given coil s has a value $+I_a$ (the current per path) in one direction just before commutation begins, diminishes *uniformly* and becomes zero at the instant the coil ends are directly under the center of the brush, increases *uniformly* in the opposite direction as the coil ends recede from the brush center, and reaches its full $-I_a$ value at the instant commutation is complete. When this happens commutation is said to be *linear* or *straight line*. However, when the current change during the commutation period, the short-circuit period, is not uniform—and this is generally the case—undercommutation or overcommutation is said to exist. Figure 196 illustrates graphically the three general kinds of commutation, although it should be pointed out that oscillograph records show that commutation does not

295

proceed along curves as smooth as those indicated; the current in the short-circuited coils is, in fact, quite irregular because electromagnetic disturbances and mechanical imperfections cause high-frequency ripples to appear. Undercommutation, a state of *retarded* commutation, implies that the current does not change as rapidly as it should, and this is, in general, brought about because each coil possesses self-inductance, a property that tends to oppose a current change. In undercommutated coils the current changes very slowly during the initial short-circuit period and then, as though to make up for lost time, proceeds to change very sharply as commutation approaches completion; this usually results in extremely high current densities under the brush tips and a considerable amount of localized heating. Moreover, if the current is not completely reversed at the end of commutation, an objectionable spark will appear at the trailing brush tip. In overcommutation, which is a state of *accelerated* commutation, the current changes so rapidly in the early stages that its value is too high near the end of the short-circuit period; in such cases a spark will also appear to correct the faulty commutation. Overcommutation is usually brought about by a commutating-pole field that is too strong, *i.e.*, one that overemphasizes its function to aid current reversal; it, too, causes high current densities under the brush tips with accompanying excess heating. It is important to recognize the latter point because unusually high temperatures in the brushes, commutator, and brush contacts have the effect of inducing chemical changes that may cause carbon brushes to disintegrate; these conditions may exist even if the sparking occurs under the brushes and is not actually visible.

Figure 197 represents four stages in the somewhat oversimplified ideal commutation of a coil. Starting with sketch (a), just before the short-circuit period, the current through coil s is $+I_a$; current passes through segment 2 from both directions, across the brush contact and out at the brush as $2I_a$. Under the assumed ideal conditions the current density at the brush contact will be uniform. In sketch (b) the armature has moved one-third of a segment to the right, and coil s is short-circuited by segments 1 and 2. The current $+I_a$ now divides into two parts, one-third of which continues to flow in coil s while two-thirds proceeds across the restricted brush-contact area; in Fig. 196 this is indicated by time t_1. When the coil ends are directly under the center of the brush, the coil current is reduced to zero; in this case the left and right halves of the brush, respectively, serve the $+I_a$ and $-I_a$ currents. Continuing, sketch (c) represents the condition when two-thirds of the commutation period has elapsed, and the coil now carries one-third of the $-I_a$ current while two-thirds passes into the brush through segment 2; this is indicated by time t_2 in Fig. 196. Finally, in sketch (d) commutation is complete, and coil c has been transferred into another path and now carries the full

$-I_a$ current. It is especially important to observe that the contact area between commutator bar 2 and the *left half* of the brush continues to diminish as the coil moves to the right; thus, the contact resistance increases, with a resulting reduction in current $+I_s$. Also, after the coil current passes through zero, the contact area between segment 1 and the right half of the brush continues to increase; this decreases the contact resistance and causes the current $-I_a$ to increase until, at t_f (Fig. 196), it reaches its full value $-I_a$. The contact resistance between segments

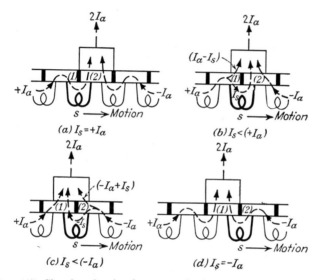

Fig. 197. Sketches showing four stages in the commutation of coil s.

and brush, therefore, provides a measure of help to the commutated coil because its ohmic value properly tends to increase as the current changes from $+I_a$ to zero and decreases as the current changes from zero to $-I_a$.

In connection with this matter of *contact resistance*, it should be stated that the early machines commutated badly because, among other things, they were fitted with copper or bronze brushes. Since the contact resistance with these materials is extremely low, there is no inducement for the current to alter its path *gradually* through the short-circuited coils; instead, rapid current changes take place at the brush contacts, with the result that there is much arcing and burning. Later, when it became clear that high contact resistance provides a measure of control over the commutation process, carbon brushes rapidly superseded metal brushes, then in general use.

What has been said concerning linear commutation when the brush covers only one segment applies equally to machines in which each brush is wider than one segment; in such cases, each of the several coils that are short-circuited simultaneously are in different stages of commutation. Figure 198 is a sketch showing a brush that overlaps four segments. Here, the current divisions indicate that coil c is halfway through commutation and carries no current; coils b and d carry equal currents that are each one-half of I_a; coils a and e, respectively, are just beginning and finishing

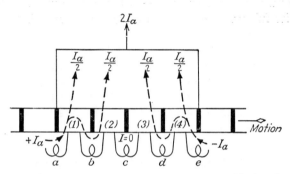

Fig. 198. Sketch showing a brush overlapping four segments during the commutation process.

commutation and, therefore, pass full-current values. Obviously, when the armature has moved one segment to the right, coils a, b, c, and d will successively take on current values now indicated for b, c, d, and e.

Carbon and Graphite Brushes

Good commutation, *i.e.*, sparkless commutation, requires, among other things, that brushes be properly selected and fitted to the machine on the basis of such operating conditions as peripheral velocity, current density, commutator wear due to abrasion, and others. Present-day brushes are manufactured in a variety of grades, but all consist of carbon, graphite, and, in some cases, mixtures of the latter with metals such as copper, tin, zinc, or lead. Four general classifications may be made of the materials listed, these being (1) carbon, (2) natural graphite, (3) electrographite, and (4) metal-mixture.

Carbon brushes were the original successors to the copper-gauze type and played an important role in the development of modern d-c machines. These are made of such materials as gas carbon, petroleum coke, or anthracite, which are pulverized and agglomerated with binders like pitch, tar, or resin. A baking process hardens the mixture and gives it desirable electrical properties. By mixing varying amounts of natural graphite with the hard carbon, brushes may be given several gradations of hardness. Current densities and peripheral velocities are limited to rather low values when this material is employed.

Natural-graphite brushes have superior properties when current densities and peripheral velocities are high. This is particularly true in interpole- and compensating-winding machines which are generally designed to take the fullest advantage of the materials of construction, *i.e.*, the weight per unit output is kept as low as possible, and this means comparatively high speeds and currents. Graphite is uniformly soft and has a natural tendency to cling to the commutator surface; as a result, these brushes show low friction losses, have a rather long life, and are extremely quiet. Moreover, because of their greater thermal conductivity, they are capable of supporting heavier currents without overheating. Graphite brushes are now produced with varying degrees of hardness so that contact drop may be suited to particular commutation problems.

Electrographitized brushes were developed to accommodate the needs of extremely high-speed and high-current-density designs. The material is almost pure carbon, very homogeneous, quite hard, possesses excellent mechanical stability at high temperatures, and has a low coefficient of friction when rubbing over a copper surface. Since they perform extremely well over a considerable range of operating conditions, requiring little if any "breaking in," they are not only widely used but often standardized in general service work.

Metal-mixture brushes consist of an intimate mixture of metallic "flour" and crushed graphite; in manufacture the materials are combined under extremely high pressures. Copper is the usual metal employed, although such materials as tin, zinc, and lead are often added. Used almost exclusively in low-voltage machines, such as automobile starting motors and electroplating generators, metalized-graphite brushes have very low contact resistances; the brush drop and the brush-contact loss are, therefore, low. Also, the fact that they have high thermal conductivity means that small surface areas may be kept reasonably cool even when the current densities are high.

Contact Drop

Mention has repeatedly been made, in many problems and in previous discussions, of the voltage drop across the brush contacts. This results, of course, because there is an actual current flow between brush and commutator surfaces, and is a necessary requirement of the commutation process if the current in a given coil must diminish from its $+I_a$ value to zero and again increase from zero to $-I_a$ as that coil passes from one electrical circuit into another during the commutation period. Such a contact drop is, therefore, a *corrective* voltage for commutation, whose value will determine, in great part, whether or not there will be sparking. The fact that there is a current flow in the short air gap between brush and commutator means that the space is ionized; the gap is, therefore, a fairly good conductor rather than an insulator, which it is in a normally un-ionized state.   Moreover, evidence seems to indicate that atoms of carbon and copper enter the air space further to improve its conductivity. These conditions give rise to contact drops that vary somewhat with current density, but more particularly with the *qualities* of the contact surfaces; Fig. 199 illustrates the relationship between these variables and

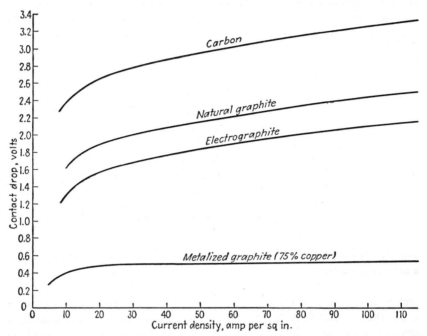

Fig. 199. Typical *contact-drop* vs. *current-density* curves for different kinds of brush materials.

indicates how the different types of brush differ from each other in this respect.   It is interesting to observe that the contact drops for the several brush grades do not change greatly within their usual current-density ranges, but that significant differences do exist among them.   Careful brush selection is, therefore, important to good commutation.

Actual contact drops are generally a little higher than those published by manufacturers because service conditions are rarely as good as those under which test data are obtained.   Surface contacts are often uneven because arcing burns away material, brushes chip, and gritty substances sometimes enter the contact spaces to roughen the commutator.   If the brushes have a slightly abrasive action, much of the unevenness may be worn down.

Interpolar Flux and Short-circuit EMF

The motion of the armature winding through the zone of commutation requires the complete reversal of the current in a succession of coils during extremely short periods of time. This commutation process, involving as it does the rapid transfer of coils from a circuit carrying current in one direction to another in which the current is oppositely directed, is complicated by the fact that the flux in the zone of commutation is, in noninterpole machines, not zero or in a direction to aid current reversal, but nearly constant in magnitude and *directed to prevent linear commutation.* Figure

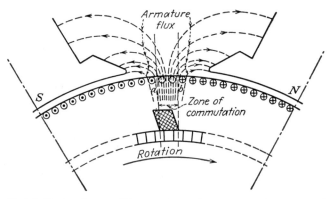

Fig. 200. Sketch illustrating conditions under which commutation must take place in a noninterpole generator.

200 illustrates why this is so. As conductor *a* approaches the commutation zone, the current flows in the same direction as the emf generated in it. When the coil, of which conductor *a* is a part, passes under the brush and is short-circuited, it is still cutting flux—armature flux—*of the same polarity.* The direction of the voltage generated in the coil is, therefore, unchanged and *tends to maintain the current* in the short-circuited coil *in the same direction;* the magnitude of the current will depend upon the short-circuit emf and the resistance of a path consisting of the ohmic value of the coil and brush contact. Finally, as the brush removes the short circuit when the coil moves out of the commutating zone, conductor *b* in Fig. 200, *the current is completely reversed but the direction of the emf developed by the armature flux remains unchanged.*

The armature mmf that sets up the objectionable *interpolar* flux has its maximum value at points on the armature winding that correspond to the brush positions on the commutator and is zero midway between such points; with zero brush lead, in a generator, these will be located, respectively, midway between pole tips and directly under the pole centers. The flux density in the commutating zone is, however, comparatively low, because the reluctance of the magnetic path is high, being due mainly to a long air space. Figure 59b illustrates this clearly.

Methods that combine basic magnetic-circuit theory and certain practical assumptions have been developed * to determine the total flux produced by the current-carrying armature winding in the *commutating zone.* Since the magnetic circuits are extremely complex, being influenced by a toothed armature core, irregularly shaped pole shoes, and conductors that occupy positions in a slotted core as well as free space, the total flux is conveniently divided into three principal parts. These are (1) the interpolar flux that passes from the armature surface to the neighboring pole shoes and pole cores; this is shown in Fig. 200; (2) the flux that passes across the slots between the teeth; (3) the flux that is created in the space occupied by the overhanging armature winding, beyond both ends of the core. As the short-circuited coils move across the three components of flux indicated, voltages are generated that oppose current reversal. Equations involving machine constants for the calculation of these fluxes are given below.

1. *Armature flux ϕ_a.* This flux, due to the armature mmf, passes between the field poles and the tops of the armature teeth in the zone of commutation. It may be calculated by the formula

$$\phi_a = \left[\frac{0.92 W_a l_a}{(1 + 2/P)(1 - \tau)D} \right] Z I_a \qquad (47)$$

2. *Slot flux ϕ_s.* This flux, due to the currents in the short-circuited coils, crosses the slots *above* the conductors and leaves the armature teeth which are *not* included between the two extreme positions of the short-circuited coils. It may be calculated by the formula

$$\phi_s = \left[\frac{2.1 d l_a}{s \times S} \right] Z I_a \qquad (48)$$

3. *End flux ϕ_e.* This flux exists in the end connections—in the two overhangs—beyond the influence of the armature-core iron and poles. It may be calculated by the formula

$$\phi_e = \frac{2.5 W_a}{P} Z I_a \qquad (49)$$

Combining formulas 47, 48, and 49 into a single equation for the *total interpolar-zone flux,*

$$\phi_t = \left[\frac{0.92 W_a l_a}{(1 + 2/P)(1 - \tau)D} + \frac{2.1 d l_a}{s \times S} + \frac{2.5 W_a}{P} \right] Z I_a \qquad (50)$$

* Alfred Still, "Elements of Electrical Design," McGraw-Hill Book Company, Inc.

where all dimensions are in inches, and the terms are defined as follows:

W_a = brush arc *referred to the armature periphery*

l_a = armature core length

P = number of poles

τ = ratio of pole arc to pole pitch

D = diameter of armature core

d = radial depth of slot

s = width of slot

Z = total number of armature conductors

I_a = armature current per path

An example will now be given to illustrate the procedure in calculating the value of the flux that is responsible for the voltage which opposes the reversal of current.

EXAMPLE 1. The following information is given in connection with a 300-kw 250-volt 1,200-rpm 6-pole compound generator: armature-core diameter D = 22 in., commutator diameter = 15 in., brush arc = 1.25 in., l_a = 11.5 in., τ = 0.63, d = 1.25 in., s = 0.39, Z = 300, S = 75, number of segments = 150, armature winding = simplex lap. Neglecting the shunt-field current, and assuming that there are no interpoles and that the brushes are located on the mechanical neutral, calculate (a) the total flux in the commutating zone due to the armature mmf; (b) the generated voltage in each short-circuited coil opposing reversal of current.

Solution

(a) $\quad W_a = \dfrac{22}{15} \times 1.25 = 1.835$ in. $\quad I_a = \dfrac{300,000}{250 \times 6} = 200$ amp

$$\phi_t = \left[\frac{0.92 \times 1.835 \times 11.5}{(1 + \frac{2}{6})(1 - 0.63)22} + \frac{2.1 \times 1.25 \times 11.5}{0.39 \times 75} \right.$$

$$\left. + \frac{2.5 \times 1.835}{6} \right] 300 \times 200$$

$$= (1.79 + 1.03 + 0.765)\,300 \times 200 = 215,000 \text{ maxwells}$$

(b) Since there are $\frac{300}{75}$ = 4 conductors per slot, and twice as many segments as slots, each short-circuited coil will have *one turn* connected between adjacent segments. Also

$$\text{Time of commutation} = t_c = \frac{W_a}{\text{peripheral velocity (in./sec)}}$$

Therefore

$$t_c = \frac{1.835}{(\pi \times 22 \times 1{,}200)/60} = 0.00133 \text{ sec}$$

Voltage generated in each conductor $= \dfrac{\phi_t \times \text{turns/coil}}{t_c \times 10^8}$

Therefore

Voltage generated/turn $= \dfrac{2 \times \phi_t \times \text{turns/coil}}{t \times 10^8}$

Hence

$$E_c = \frac{2 \times 215{,}000 \times 1}{0.00133 \times 10^8} = 3.24 \text{ volts}$$

In the well-designed machine, interpoles would be provided to annul the flux set up in the interpolar zone, and this construction would permit each coil to be commutated without the opposition that results from the cross-magnetizing mmf of the armature. Commutating-pole design is treated in several excellent texts dealing with such matters.

EXAMPLE 2. Each of six commutating poles in Example 1 develops 32 per cent more ampere-turns at full load than the armature cross-magnetizing NI/pole. Calculate the number of turns on each interpole.

Solution

$$NI/\text{interpole} = \frac{300 \times 200}{2 \times 6} \times 1.32 = 6{,}600$$

$$\text{Turns/interpole} = \frac{6{,}600}{1{,}200} = 5\tfrac{1}{2}$$

Noninterpole machines commutate better with full-pitch windings than with fractional-pitch windings. The reason for this is made clear by reference to Fig. 201. Assuming no brush lead, note that the full-pitch coil aa' will cut flux at the lowest parts of the flux-density distribution curve, while commutation will occur in a fractional-pitch coil where the flux density is somewhat higher.

It should also be pointed out that commutation will, in general, be more difficult as the brush is widened to cover more commutator bars. The reason for this is that the emfs of several coils that are short-circuited at the same instant add in series, while the total resistance of the path through which the short-circuit current passes is not much higher than for a single short-circuited coil; the latter condition obtains because the resistance lies mainly in the brush contact. It follows, therefore, that with no external assistance, the short-circuit current increases with brush width.

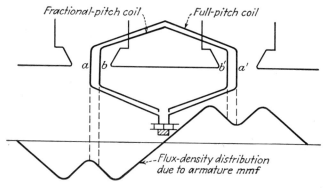

Fig. 201. Sketch showing that a full-pitch coil cuts slightly more flux than a fractional-pitch coil during the commutating period.

Brush and Commutator Adjustments

It is a significant fact that good commutation involves a number of important mechanical brush and commutator adjustments, in addition to the application of correct design procedures. Such adjustments are generally made by experienced craftsmen whose work is probably more dependent upon the human element than any other in the construction of the electrical machine. The selection of the proper grade of brush is, of course, the first essential; this requires a knowledge of such particular operating conditions as the magnitudes of the current and current density, the peripheral velocity, brush angles, *i.e.*, tilting, and the like. Brush arms must obviously be spaced very accurately with respect to each other on the commutator and must occupy correct magnetic-neutral positions. Moreover, individual brushes must be free to move radially in their holders, yet should not be loose enough to chatter. Finally, brush-tension adjustments must be made so that all brushes collect equal currents, and in accordance with recommended values furnished by manufacturers.

After a d-c machine has been in operation for some time, the condition of the commutator will usually indicate whether or not commutation is satisfactory. The surface should take on a burnished, somewhat darkened appearance. There must be no rough spots on the copper, nor must high mica or loosened segments be permitted to destroy intimate contact between brushes and a commutator that is not eccentric. Whether or not the mica between segments should be left flush with the copper surface or be recessed, *i.e.*, *undercut*, is debatable, although experience seems to indicate that undercutting is desirable in most cases. When the latter practice is employed, great care must be exercised to avoid sharp, razorlike edges on the commutator bars and the projecting of thin mica walls above the level of the commutator surface.

Locating the Brush Neutral

The position of the brush neutral on most modern machines is frequently indicated by a pointer on the brush rocker that matches with an etched line on the frame. In the absence of such markings, it may be necessary to reestablish the correct neutral by test. A simple, often satisfactory, method is to operate the machine at no load with the field partially excited and move the brushes forward beyond the neutral until they just begin to spark, then moving them backwards from the neutral until sparking is again visible; the neutral position will be halfway between the two extremes. Still another scheme is to operate the machine as before, as a generator, and contact two adjacent segments by means of pointers connected to a low-reading voltmeter; the neutral position is located where no deflection is indicated on the instrument. If the machine is stationary, the location of the neutral may be found with sufficient accuracy by connecting a low-reading voltmeter to the plus $(+)$ and minus $(-)$ brushes and moving the rocker arm to the position that gives no deflection when the field current is quickly varied by means of a rheostat.

Sparking at the Brushes

The real criterion of satisfactory commutation is whether or not the brushes are behaving properly. This generally applies to sparking that may be visible at the edges of the brush-contact surfaces, referred to as *fringe* or *pinpoint* sparking, or underbrush arcing which, although not clearly visible, may be dangerously destructive. Such sparking may be due to electrical overloading or mechanical defects and poor adjustments. Under such conditions it is well to check for high or low segments, loose brushes and rocker arms, worn-out or broken brushes, loose pigtails, commutator eccentricity, poor and uneven brush contacts, etc. Experience seems to indicate, however, that fringe sparking generally occurs on interpole machines only, and that some minor commutation defect is responsible for the difficulty. *Ring fire, i.e.,* streaks of fire that are continuous around the commutator, is frequently observed when a machine operates in a dusty atmosphere or when soft brushes release tiny particles of carbon that become incandescent. Although this kind of visible arcing is not a direct result of poor commutation, it may lead to flashover unless corrected; generally, it is merely necessary to clean the commutator thoroughly and, in some cases, change to a different grade of brush. A particularly serious kind of sparking results from such armature-winding failures as short circuits and open circuits. This important matter is treated in special texts * that deal with the causes, symptoms, and location of troubles in d-c machines.

* C. S. Siskind, "Direct-current Armature Windings," McGraw-Hill Book Company, Inc.

PROBLEMS

1. An armature, whose core diameter is 21 in., operates at a speed of 1,500 rpm. If the total interpolar flux in the zone of commutation, which is 1.6 in. wide, is 57,000 maxwells, calculate the short-circuit emf in each coil of 4 turns.

2. A 1,500-kw 600-volt 12-pole generator has a simplex-lap-wound armature with a total of 888 conductors. Calculate the cross-magnetizing ampere-turns per pole developed by the armature at full load. Neglect the exciting field current.

3. If each of 12 commutating poles develops 30 per cent more ampere-turns at full load than the cross-magnetizing NI/pole determined in Prob. 2, calculate the number of turns on each interpole.

4. The following machine constants are given for a 2,000-kw 600-volt 500-rpm 14-pole compound generator: $D = 78$ in., commutator diameter $= 41$ in., brush arc $= 1.375$ in., $l_a = 11$ in., $\tau = 0.64$, $d = 1.75$ in., $s = 0.47$ in., $Z = 1,148$, $S = 287$, number of segments $= 574$, armature winding $=$ simplex lap. Neglecting the shunt-field current and assuming that the machine has no interpoles, calculate (a) the cross magnetizing ampere-turns per pole; (b) the total flux in the commutating zone due to the armature mmf; (c) the generated emf in each short-circuited coil opposing the reversal of current.

5. If each of 14 commutating poles in Prob. 4 develops 35 per cent more ampere-turns at full load than the armature cross-magnetizing NI/pole, calculate the number of turns on each interpole.

BIBLIOGRAPHY

Books

1. SISKIND, "Direct-current Armature Windings," McGraw-Hill Book Company, Inc., 1949.
2. SISKIND, "Electrical Machines: Direct and Alternating Current," McGraw-Hill Book Company, Inc., 1950.
3. LANGSDORF, "Principles of Direct-current Machines," 5th ed., McGraw-Hill Book Company, Inc., 1940.
4. STILL, "Elements of Electrical Design," 2d ed., McGraw-Hill Book Company, Inc., 1932.
5. JAMES and MARKLE, "Controllers for Electric Motors," McGraw-Hill Book Company, Inc., 1945.
6. STAFFORD, "Troubles of Electrical Equipment—Their Symptoms, Causes, and Remedies," 3d ed., McGraw-Hill Book Company, Inc., 1947.
7. SHOULTS, RIFE, and JOHNSON, "Electric Motors in Industry," John Wiley & Sons, Inc., 1942.
8. HARWOOD, "Control of Electric Motors," John Wiley & Sons, Inc., 1944.
9. WALKER, "Design of Dynamo-electric Machinery," Longmans, Green & Co., Inc., 1915.
10. STIGENT and LACEY, "J. & P. Transformer Book," Johnson & Phillips, Ltd., London, 1941.
11. VEINOTT, "Fractional Horsepower Electric Motors," 2d ed., McGraw-Hill Book Company, Inc., 1948.
12. ANNETT and ROE, "Connecting and Testing Direct-current Machines," 2d ed., McGraw-Hill Book Company, Inc., 1937.
13. HAYES, "Current-collecting Brushes in Electrical Machines," Sir Isaac Pitman & Sons, Ltd., London, 1947.
14. CROUSE, "Automotive Electrical Equipment," 2d ed., McGraw-Hill Book Company, Inc., 1950.
15. LAMME, "Electrical Engineering Papers," Westinghouse Electric Corp., 1919.
16. KNOWLTON, "Standard Handbook for Electrical Engineers," 8th ed., McGraw-Hill Book Company, Inc., 1949.

Bulletins and Articles

17. NATIONAL ELECTRICAL MANUFACTURING ASSOCIATION, NEMA Motor Standards, *Bulletin*.
18. SAUNDERS, Dynamoelectric Amplifiers, *Electrical Engineering*, August, 1950, pp. 711–716.
19. GENERAL ELECTRIC Co., Amplidynes, *Bulletins GEM* 4053, 1420, 1421.
20. WESTINGHOUSE ELECTRIC CORP., Rototrol, *Bulletin B*–3649.
21. GENERAL ELECTRIC Co., Arc Welders, *Bulletin GEH* 1334.

22. Bower, Fundamentals of Amplidyne Generators, *Trans. AIEE*, Vol. 64, pp. 873–881, 1945.
23. Industrial Applications of Amplidyne Generators, *Trans. AIEE*, Vol. 59, pp. 944–949, 1940.
24. Smith, The Diverter-pole Generator, *J. AIEE*, January, 1929, p. 11.
25. General Electric Co., Diactor Generator-voltage Regulator Bulletins.

ANSWERS

Chapter 1

1. 59,000 lines per sq in. **2.** 4,070 amp-turns. **3.** 71,400 lines per sq in. **4.** 8 turns. **5.** 296. **6.** 216. **7.** 0.228 sq in. **8.** 2,583 cir mils or No. 16 B & S wire. **9.** 3,340 turns. **10.** 240 ohms. **11.** (a) 500 amp; (b) 50 amp; (c) 40 amp per sq in. **12.** 55,000 lines per sq in.

Chapter 2

1. (a) 10; (b) 2; (c) 6; (d) 8. **2.** (a) 100 amp; (b) 50 amp. **3.** (a) 8; (b) 8; (c) 16; (d) 23; (e) 17. **4.** 1, 2, 3, 4. **5.** (a) 26 or 27; (b) 29; (c) 95; (d) 140 or 142; (e) 98 or 100. **6.** (a) 1; (b) 2; (c) 1; (d) 1; (e) 3. **7.** (a) 1; (b) 1; (c) 1; (d) 1; (e) 2 for $Y_c = 98$ and 4 for $Y_c = 100$. **8.** Sketch. **9.** Sketch. **10.** Diagram. **11.** Diagram. **12.** Diagram. **13.** Diagram. **14.** Diagram. **15.** (a) 2; (b) 3; (c) 4; (d) 5; (e) 6. **16.** Tables. **17.** (a) Quadruplex-wave; (b) 16. **18.** (a) $Y_s = 12$, $Y_c = 1$; (b) $Y_s = 12$, $Y_c = 95$.

Chapter 3

1. 600 volts. **2.** 2 turns. **3.** 59,500 lines per sq in. **4.** (a) 43.5; (b) 50; (c) 75; (d) 60. **5.** 2.52 amp. **6.** 1,920 amp-turns. **7.** 84,700 lines per sq in. **8.** 1.13. **9.** (a) 92,000; (b) 81,700; (c) 79,300; (d) 112,500; (e) 52,500. **10.** 200 volts. **11.** 32.6 ohms. **12.** 48,500 lines per sq in. **13.** 259 amp. **14.** (a) 268 volts; (b) 191.5 volts. **15.** Describe methods.

Chapter 4

1. (a) 8.63 lb; (b) 0; (c) 6.1 lb. **2.** 347 lb-ft. **3.** 51,300 lines per sq in. **4.** 1,510 rpm. **5.** 5 hp. **6.** 0.443 ohm. **7.** 59.7 hp. **8.** 103 hp. **9.** 261 lb-ft. **10.** 517.5 amp. **11.** $T = 68.4$ lb-ft, hp = 19.5. **12.** $T = 92.4$ lb-ft, hp = 30. **13.** 2,155 rpm. **14.** 2,075 rpm. **15.** 803 rpm. **16.** 66.3 amp. **17.** 813 amp. **18.** 558 rpm.

Chapter 5

1. 3,960 amp-turns per pole. **2.** 5,130 amp-turns per pole. **3.** 1,740 amp-turns per pole. **4.** 3,260 amp-turns per pole. **5.** (a) 2,970 amp-turns per pole; (b) 5,330 amp-turns per pole. **6.** 5.76 volts. **7.** 2.15 volts. **8.** 32.7 amp.

Chapter 6

1. (a) 1,090 amp-turns; (b) 3,000 amp. **2.** 900 kw. **3.** (a) 9,690 amp-turns; (b) 14½ turns. **4.** 2.5 in. **5.** 12,800 lines per sq in. **6.** 6 conductors. **7.** 848 conductors.

Chapter 7

1. 6 per cent. **2.** 648 volts. **3.** 127.2 kw. **4.** 262 volts. **5.** 0.0208 ohm. **6.** (a) 7.62 per cent; (b) 454.8 volts, 68.2 kw. **7.** 229 kw. **8.** (a) Drawing; (b) 300 volts; (c) 252 volts, 19.1 per cent; (d) 60 amp, 15.1 kw; (e) 160 amp, 140 volts; (f) 12 amp. **9.** 225 volts, 33.3 per cent. **10.** 70 amp, 184 volts. **11.** 284 volts. **12.** 15 turns. **13.** 1,625 rpm.

14. 0.036 ohm.   **15.** 377 amp-turns per pole.   **16.** 2,720 amp-turns.   **17.** (a) 0.113 ohm; (b) 2,300 amp-turns; (c) 2,525 amp-turns.

Chapter 8

1. 61 amp, 7,010 watts.   **2.** 40 amp, 9,360 watts.   **3.** 60 amp, 226 volts.   **4.** 121 volts, 48.5 amp, 5,870 watts.   **5.** 50 amp.   **6.** (a) 115.5 volts; (b) 28.9 amp and 31 amp; (c) 6,920 watts.   **7.** (a) $I_A = 210$, $I_N = 40$, $I_B = 250$; (b) $P_T = 52.9$ kw; (c) $P_G = 2.3$ kw (lower unit), $P_M = 2.3$ (upper unit).   **8.** (a) 17.15 amp, 1.975 kw; (b) 22.85 amp, 2.625 kw; (c) 232.85 amp, 53.55 kw.   **9.** (a) $P_A = 80$ kw, $P_B = 120$ kw, $P_T = 200$ kw; (b) $V_t = 227$ volts, $P_A = 112$ kw, $P_B = 168$ kw.   **10.** (a) $V_t = 235$ volts, $P_A = 7.05$ kw; (b) $P_A = 20.25$ kw, $P_B = 18$ kw, $P_T = 38.25$ kw.   **11.** (a) $P_A = 75.3$ kw; (b) $P_A = 124$ kw, $P_B = 191$ kw, $P_T = 315$ kw.   **12.** $P_T = 19.12$ kw, $P_A = 10.28$ kw, $P_B = 8.84$ kw.   **13.** (a) 2 ohms; (b) $P_A = P_B = 12.1$ kw.   **14.** 260 and 240 volts.

Chapter 9

1. (a) 9.5 ohms; (b) 2.77 ohms.   **2.** 110.2 amp.   **3.** 376 rpm.   **4.** 0.693 ohm.   **5.** (a) 6.25 per cent; (b) 46.2 hp.   **6.** 13.3 per cent.   **7.** 657 rpm.   **8.** (a) 89.5 amp; (b) 5.3 mph.   **9.** (a) 2,000 rpm; (b) 25 per cent.   **10.** (a) 195 lb-ft; (b) 262 amp, 670 lb-ft; (c) 76.3 amp, 1,390 rpm, 51.7 hp.   **11.** 4,000 lb-ft.   **12.** 3,000 lb-ft.   **13.** (a) 45.7 lb-ft, 1,750 rpm, 15.2 hp; (b) 102.5 lb-ft, 1,280 rpm, 25 hp.   **14.** 735 lb-ft, 682 lb-ft.   **15.** 15 hp.

Chapter 10

1. (a) 759 watts; (b) 7,057 watts.   **2.** (a) 101.2 ohms; (b) 58.5 watts; (c) 28.9 watts.   **3.** (a) 4.28 per cent; (b) 1,770 watts; (c) 1,375 watts.   **4.** (a) 1,060 rpm, 37.0 per cent; (b) 1,260 rpm, 15.2 per cent.   **5.** (a) 37.9 hp; (b) 21.9 hp.   **6.** (a) 9,400 watts; (b) 2,350 watts.   **7.** 27.5 ohms.   **8.** (a) 2,300 rpm; (b) 379 watts.   **9.** 2,330 rpm, 100 hp.   **10.** 555 rpm.   **11.** 785 rpm.   **12.** 1,645 rpm.   **13.** 1.0 ohm.   **14.** 0.46 ohm.   **15.** 0.85 ohm.

Chapter 11

1. 248 watts.   **2.** (a) 1,245 watts; (b) 578 watts.   **3.** (a) 1,071 watts; (b) 571 watts.   **4.** 364 watts.   **5.** 7,325 watts.   **6.** 225 hp.   **7.** 12 kw.   **8.** (a) 84.2 per cent; (b) 80.2 per cent.   **9.** (a) 11 kw; (b) 85.3 per cent.   **10.** 89.6 per cent.   **11.** 84.3 per cent, 14.95 hp.   **12.** (a) 682 watts; (b) 86.3 per cent.   **13.** 22.2 hp.   **14.** 8 lb.   **15.** 86.5 per cent.   **16.** $224.08.   **17.** $11.09.   **18.** 39°C.

Chapter 12

1. 0.5 hp.   **2.** 13 amp.   **3.** 5.7 amp.   **4.** 5.5 kw.   **5.** 15 hp.   **6.** 40 amp.   **7.** 20 turns.   **8.** ⅓ hp.   **9.** 2.1 lb-ft, 403 oz-in.

Chapter 13

1. 4.7 volts.   **2.** 7,720 amp-turns.   **3.** 4 turns.   **4.** (a) 9,750 amp-turns per pole; (b) 435,000 maxwells; (c) 6.8 volts.   **5.** 4 turns.

INDEX

A

B

C

E

Eddy-current loss, 230, 288
Eddy currents, 228
Efficiency, conventional, 241
  directly measured, 245
  dynamo, 228
  generator, 233
  importance of, 247
  maximum, 239
  motor, 235, 245
Electric Controller and Manufacturing Company, 183
Electrodynamometer, 245
Electrographite brushes, 298
Electromotive force (emf), counter, 63
  short-circuit, 301
Element, dummy, 28
Energy, cost of, 248
  electric and mechanical, 1, 228
Equalizer connections, 31, 162, 166
Equivalent air gap, 51, 101
Excitation, dual, 54
Excitation line, 56, 113
Exciter, Rototrol, 217
External characteristics, 112, 115, 146
  comparison of, 125

F

Factor, leakage, 50
  service, 255
Faraday, Michael, 1
Fiberglass, 250
Field, 2
  compensating, 271, 289
  cross, 93, 267
  current, 218
  distortion of, 82, 93, 99, 104
  interpole, 104, 130
  magnetic, 1
  main control, 271
  pattern, 217
  pilot, 217
  resultant, 267
  self-energizing, 218
  series, 5, 8
  shunt, 5
  voltage, 218
Field resistance, 57
Field windings, summary of, 11, 108
Fields, auxiliary, 272

Flashover, commutator, 93, 107
Flat-compound generator, 120
Floating of generators, 158
Flux, armature, 302
  armature-reaction, 263
  distributions of, 63
  end, 302
  interpolar, 301
  leakage, 50, 182
  resultant, 263
  slot, 302
  useful, 51
Flux-adjustment control, 214
Flux-density distribution, 94
Food mixers, 291
Frequency, 42
Fringe sparking, 306
Frog-leg windings, 35

G

Gassing, battery, 275
General Electric Company, 169
Generated voltage, 40
Generator action, 1, 2, 40
  Lenz's law and rubber-band analysis of, 41
Generator characteristics, 110, 130, 146
Generator loading, 142
Generator operation, 140
Generator principles, 40
Generator short-circuit, 135
Generators, 223
  arc-welding, 277
  armature-reaction, 270
  automobile, 263
  build-up of, 55, 140
  compound, 119, 122, 126, 165, 269, 274
  constant-current and constant-potential, 268
  critical field resistance of, 58
  critical speed of, 58
  cumulative-compound, 269, 274
  differential-compound, 122, 279, 286
  direction of rotation of, 59, 186
  diverter-pole, 274
  efficiency of, 233
  flat-compound, 120
  floating of, 158
  interpole, 97
  load characteristic of, 143
  overcompound, 120

DATE DUE